# THE PHYSICIANS OF MYDDFAI

## CURES AND REMEDIES OF THE MEDIAEVAL WORLD

### Terry Breverton

ISBN 978-0-9572459-9-0

First published in the United Kingdom in 2012 by
Cambria Books; Carmarthenshire, Wales, United Kingdom

# ACKNOWLEDGEMENTS

I must give thanks, in no particular order, to those who helped in putting this book together:

Professor 'Dai' Thorne especially on some language problems; Lewis and Bethan Jones of Myddfai; Dr Don Williams; Dr Terry Turner; Megan and Gwynfor Lewis of Llangadog, formerly of Myddfai; Lara Bernays of Myddfai and Newport; Stella Byrne and Dylan Warren-Davies of Myddfai Herbs, Llandeilo; Hugh Davies, Myddfai Trading Company; Lesley Griffiths, Mydfai Village Hall; Dr Morfydd Owen; Dr Margaret Jones; Dr Brynley Jones, Alison Skippers, Dr Natasha de Vere, Head of Conservation and Research, National Botanic Garden of Wales; Dr Diana Luft; David Hardy, National Botanic Garden of Wales; Dr Alan Withey; Professor Bernard Knight; Dr John Launer; Richard Pryce, County Botanical Recorder for Carmarthenshire; Professor Robin Jones, Dr Brynley Jones; William Wilkins, Chris Jones of Cambria Books, Richard Taunton Oliver, Dr Don Davies, Judith Thorne, especially Dr Edward Conley and many, many others.

For any academics and book reviewers who wish to criticise the lack of full indices and lists of plants and remedies in this totally unsubsidised book, and/or the lack of the full Welsh versions of the Legend of the Lady of the Lake, Book 1 and Book 2, this would have made the book economically unviable. (One recollects that the only criticism of my 'The Book of Welsh Saints' was that it lacked an index. That 606-page book made a small loss, despite selling its print run of 1,000 copies. A full index would have added 200 pages, and transformed a small loss into a major one.) Hopefully, any later edition may have indices and be illustrated. As it stands, this totally new edition of The Physicians of Myddfai is at last available, and any errors or omissions are the fault of this author.

Cover illustration by Judith Stroud from her series of linocuts featuring remedies by the Physicans of Myddfai.

# THE PHYSICIANS OF MYDDFAI – CURES AND REMEDIES OF THE MEDIAEVAL WORLD

## 1. INTRODUCTION
1.1 A brief explanation of beliefs in the Doctrines of Signatures and Humors
1.2 The Use of Folk Medicine
1.3 The 1861 Translator and Editor

## 2. PREFACE to 1861 EDITION OF THE PHYSICIANS OF MYDDFAI BY JOHN WILLIAMS AB ITHEL
* 'THE ELEMENTS OF MAN BY TALIESIN'
* The Duties of the Mediciner of the Court of King Howel the Good – Hywel Dda
* MEDICAL MAXIMS from the Book of Iago ap Dewi

## 3. THE LEGEND OF THE LADY OF THE LAKE
– THE ORIGIN OF THE PHYSICIANS OF MYDDFAI, COLLECTED PROM VARIOUS SOURCES IN THE YEAR 1841 JOHN RHYS' EXPANSION OF THE LEGEND IN *CELTIC FOLKLORE* 1905
- THE LEGEND OF THE LADY OF THE LAKE BY EDWARD THOMAS 1805
- Rhys Gryg, a life
- The later Physicians of Myddfai
- A notable local doctor and other physicians
- The Importance of Myddfai
- Llyn y Fan Fach

## 4. BOOK 1
    – The Most Notable and Principal Ways of Healing the Human Body, by Rhiwallon the Physician and his sons Cadwgan, Gruffydd and Einion – parts 1.1-1.188

## 5. BOOK 2a
    – The Collection of Howel the Physician – parts 2.1-2.784

## 6. BOOK 2b – Information for Mediciners
* THE VIRTUES OF VARIOUS MEDICINAL HERBS – Sage, Iris, Nettle, Betony, Parley, Fennel, Rosemary, Sage, Blessed Thistle, Cleavers, Mistletoe, Oak, Vervain – parts 2.785-2.798
* EXPOSITION OF THE FOUR ELEMENTS OF MAN – Sanguineous, Choleric, Phlegmatic, Melancholic - parts 2.799-2.802
* CHARMS AND MEDICAL FEATS – parts 2.803-2.815
* LIST OF HERBS AND PLANTS WHICH EVERY PHYSICIAN OUGHT TO KNOW AND USE
* WEIGHTS AND MEASURES
* FOUR PRINCIPAL EXCITING CAUSES OF FEVER AND DISEASE
* USEFUL THINGS – to be known by every Physician and the head of every family
* THE ESSENTIALS OF A PHYSICIAN

## 7. HERBS and HAIR REMEDIES

## 8. MYDDFAI TODAY
8.1 Fenton's Tours of Wales
8.2 Myddfai past and present
8.3 The Myddfai Initiative
8.4 Myddfai Trading Company
8.5 Village SOS
8.6 The Natural Healthcare Centre
8.7 Myddfai Herbs
8.8 The National Botanic Garden of Wales

References

Other Books by Terry Breverton

# PART 1

## INTRODUCTION

In recorded history, few families have a known history of over 800 years. Even fewer have a profession that has lasted from that time, running throughout the family and pervading their small geographical area. In the sparsely-populated area of north-eastern Carmarthenshire, near the Black Mountain and where it adjoins the Brecon Beacons, we can trace doctors through to the present day, from when Wales was an independent nation.

The original doctors were mediciners to the court of Rhys Gryg, Prince of Deheubarth. Some of their original remedies, treatments and cures were assembled by the fourteenth century, and transcribed into the manuscript known as the *Red Book of Hergest*. This Middle Welsh manuscript was translated in 1861 and published as Book 1 of *The Physicians of Myddfai*, along with another book of their purported remedies. The *Red Book of Hergest* was written shortly after 1382, and is remarkable for being written in Welsh rather than Latin, as were other manuscripts all over Europe at this time.

Equally as interesting is that the physicians of the court of Rhys Gryg gave the measurements and their secrets of medical preparations. It was not until Nicholas Culpeper's *The English Physitian* (1652) and *Compleat Herball* (1653) that such preparations and remedies were revealed to the English-speaking world. Even more remarkably, the *Red Book of Hergest* gives us the origin of the knowledge of the family of court mediciners – they were the children of the '*Lady of the Lake*', Llyn-y-Fan-Fach. In the legend, dating from well before the fourteenth century, and possibly back to Celtic times, can be identified several places which can be seen today: the lake, the farm of her husband, the farm of her sons and so on.

So, why a new edition of *The Physicians of Myddfai*? The only copies available in print and on the net have often been poor facsimile copies of John Pughe's 1861 translation. Also, the book was edited by the Reverend John Williams 'ab Ithel', who unfortunately expurgated parts of the text. Thus forty remedies are omitted from Book 2 in the 1861 translation. Also, Pughe mistranslates certain words e.g. flintstone instead of iris.

Culpeper's marvellous *Compleat Herball* has been in print since its publication in 1652, recently updated and amended by this author as *Breverton's Complete Herbal: a book of remarkable plants and their uses*. Much of Culpeper's book was taken from ancient sources, as is the Myddfai compilation, but the latter is more interesting for at least six reasons.

Firstly, there is far more of an emphasis upon native British folk cures, using plants native to Britain.

Secondly, the collection dates from over 400 years before Nicholas Culpeper's works.

Thirdly, there is a wonderful contextual value. Court 'mediciners' or physicians were already common in Wales before their value was noted in the *Laws of Hywel Dda*, codified and promulgated around 930. The physicians of Myddfai practised in the court of Rhys Gryg, Rhys ap Rhys ap Gruffydd (d.1234), the grandson of '*The Lord Rhys*', and also performed in their local areas much as NHS doctors today.

Fourthly, descendants of these thirteenth century medical men are still practising today. The local area has given us many notable medical men, possibly because of the aspirations that the legend and book have promoted. The line of practising doctors was thought to have died out in the nineteenth century, but is still extant.

Fifth, the first noted medical use of such useful plants as ground ivy was by the physicians of Myddfai. Many of the remedies in both books have not been recorded by Gerard, Culpeper and other later writers, indicating their native British-Welsh provenance rather than having Arabic or Greek origins. Some, however probably owe their origins to the Roman occupation which ended around 400ce. The Romans brought several medicinal plants with them, and their villas and forts were occupied by the Romano-British nobility when the legions left.

Finally, these remedies and their social history need to be known and publicised in the wider world. Much modern research upon herbs and plants has underlined how useful they can be to modern medicine. Who knows – a cure for baldness – an instant fortune for the developer - may lie within these pages, as noted in Chapter 7.

The main elements of this book are based upon the remedies and cures of a family of Welsh medicine men, known as *Meddygon Myddfai* (the Physicians of Myddfai) who practised from the late twelfth to nineteenth centuries. Their original knowledge was said to have come from their ancestor, *The Lady of the Lake*, whose legend is included here. The remedies were collected in two separate books, and date from the twelfth to the sixteenth centuries, far predating all other British herbals, such as those of Gerard, Parkinson and Culpeper.

It is important to note that this book is in two major parts. The first is from the *Red Book of Hergest*. The second book, that of Howell the Physician, is a compilation by Iolo Morganwg, of which more later. However, the earliest Myddfai manuscript, *ms.14912* is in the British Museum and has never been published, although much of it is included in the *Red Book of Hergest* version. This author has tried to receive assistance in its translation.

There is another, smaller medical manuscript in Wales, Jesus ms.XXII which needs to be translated and published. With luck, a university or Middle Welsh expert may translate from Middle Welsh these and other unpublished medical manuscripts in the British Museum and Jesus College.

Welsh medical writings emerged in several medieval manuscripts written between the end of the 14th century and the beginning of the 16th. They contain introductory *colophons* (passages) confirming their origins in the practices of Meddygon Myddfai '*rac na bei a wypei gystal ac a wydynt hwy a wedwy*' (*lest there be none who had as good knowledge as they had after them*) – Red Book of Hergest. Mainly written in Welsh, there is also some Latin and French, signifying multilingual competence in religious and lay scriptoria across Wales.

The documents have many similarities with contemporary collections from across Europe, inferring that the Welsh tradition was part of a pan-European medical culture. Two of the manuscripts, copies of which can be found in Oxford University, are small documents, which probably means that they were used as practical handbooks for practising doctors. Another manuscript, *Hafod xvi*, is likely to have been part of a larger manuscript, thought to be written in the area of Talgarth and Llanthony.

Alan Withey relates: '*The history of medicine in Wales... is an intriguing mix of legend, folklore, religion and science, and it is not truly until the medieval period that the first records of Welsh medical practitioners can be found. Bearing this in mind, it is impossible to construct any medical history of Wales without reference to Meddygon Myddfai, a landed family from the parish of Myddfai in Carmarthenshire, possessed of medical skills, who handed down their knowledge from father to son and continued to practise until their last descendant died in 1743.*

*The Myddfai family began to appear prominently in Welsh literature from around the fourteenth century onwards, and it is significant that their records are written in the Welsh language, rather than English or the more usual Latin. The origins of this group of 'doctors' are difficult to assess since a great deal of emphasis is placed on a legend which held that they were descended from the union of a lake fairy and a mortal. In the herbal cures and remedies which they propounded, however, the intriguing mix of 'orthodox' Galenic medicine and also the more 'magical' remedies can be seen.*

*In an introduction to the first manuscript, the writers claim that their purpose in recording the information is to pass on their knowledge to future generations lest such knowledge should be lost upon their own demise.*

*The Myddfai physicians based their medical philosophy on good diet, a modest lifestyle, and simple herbal remedies, and the manuscripts contain much information directly related to the ancient writings, and on other issues such as astrology. There are, for example, calendars in Welsh, notes on the four humours and parts of the body, virtues of certain herbs and also lists of days sometimes known as 'Egyptian days' or 'Dog Days' due to a connection with ancient Arab writings and Egyptian Gods on which it was considered lucky or unlucky to be treated or let blood. Also, however, the manuscripts contain herbal cures for a range of ailments, and lists of the many diseases claimed to be treatable.*'

Around seventy clinical ailments suffered by the people of Deheubarth can be identified in the manuscripts, and there are over a thousand remedies and cures. In October 1888, Dr P. Rhys Griffiths related in *The British Medical Journal* that in Book 1: '*The materia medica consisted of about 175 plants, flowers, roots, etc., the list including foxglove, poppies, valerian, peppermint, broom, etc. The preparations were simple infusions, decoctions, pills, ointments, etc. The measure employed was a cupful or some multiple of it.*' He also noted the following conditions in Book 1 alone:

*Nervous System* - Delirium, insanity or loss of reason, irritability of mind, loss of speech, paralysis, epilepsy or falling fits, inflammation of dura mater, intoxication.

*Respiratory System* - Pneumonia, bronchitis, phthisis, pulmonary abscess, emphysema, epistaxis, quinsy, hoarseness.

*Digestive System* - Flatulence, dyspepsia, haematemesis, vomiting, reptiles in the stomach.

*Abdominal* - Adhesions of the liver, diseased liver, ascites, peritonitis, tympanites, abdominal tumour.

*Intestinal* - Constipation, haemorrhoids.

*Genito-Urinary* - Pain in the kidneys, retention of urine, strangury, gravel, calculus in the bladder, impotence, profuse menstruation, prolapsus uteri, difficult parturition.

*Skin* - Eczema, impetigo capitis, ringworm, nettle-rash, erysipelas, boils, carbuncles.

*Bone* - Exfoliation of skull, fractures of long bones, patella, os frontis, non-union of fractures, disease of knee-joints, ribs, etc.

*Fever* - Latent fever, intermittent fever, ephemeral fever, small-pox, whooping-cough.

*Eye* - Corneal opacities, catarrhal ophthalmia, blindness, pain in the eye, tinea ciliaris.

*Ear* - Deafness, deafness after fever.

*Griffiths noticed the difference with the much longer Book 2: 'In the departments of materia medica and therapeutics there are some striking changes. In the place of the 175 plants, etc., and some half-a-dozen inorganic substances, we find a list of about 800 plants, flowers, etc., many of them of great value in the present day. The number of inorganic substances is also much larger; thus, we have sulphate of copper, alum, mercury, sulphur, antimony, lead, etc.*

*These various organic and inorganic substances were employed in the manufacture of pills, infusions, decoctions, pottages, confections, potions, electuaries, baths, fomentations, plasters, and poultices... A very elaborate treatise on therapeutics is supplied. Seeds are divided into hot, cold, moist, with their degrees of first, second, and third. Careful attention was given to the medicinal virtues of the various herbs in making up a preparation for any diseased condition; and it is evident that an attempt was made to analyse the symptoms of disease before prescribing - a precaution frequently overlooked in the present day.'*

Dr. Morfydd E. Owen has researched and written much on the medical books of medieval Wales, and has related the important extant manuscripts. It is notable that these are in Welsh, not Latin or English. She is still researching and translating for publication. The first medical documents in English did not appear for at least two centuries after the Welsh writings. The London Welsh School possessed the earliest manuscript until 1840, when it went to the British Library and is known as *BL Add 14912*. It is still untranslated in full and unpublished.

Written in the second half of the fourteenth century, it was once owned by the fifteenth-century poet Dafydd Nanmor, who signed it twice. Possibly written at Llanbadarn Fawr, it was thought by the eighteenth-century antiquary Lewis Morris to be the original manuscript of *Meddygon Myddfai*. The second manuscript, known as *Hafod 16*, was in Cardiff Central Library, possibly written at Llantony Abbey. The third is *Rawlinson 467a* in the Bodleian Library, Oxford. From the Myddfai area, it was once in the collection of the great Edward Lhuyd, and dates to around 1400. Also in the Bodleian is *Jesus College 22*, written some time after

10

1400. The fifth document is *Mostyn 88*, in the National Library of Wales, written by the poet Gutyn Owain at Valle Crucis Abbey between 1487 and 1488.

Also in the National Library of Wales is the *Book of Bened Feddyg, Sotheby ms 3*, which was that doctor's handbook. It records five generations of the same Denbighshire family being doctors. As yet, most of these important manuscripts have not been fully translated from Middle Welsh, which is surprising. Cardiff University has been digitising the documents, which will make the task easier.

Four of the above manuscripts attribute at least part of the work to Rhiwallon's family of physicians, written around 1200, but based upon older remedies. Our *Book 1* is based upon extracts from Jesus College *ms 101, The Red Book of Hergest*. Our longer *Book 2* was compiled by Iolo Morganwg, and these two books formed the basis of Pughe's *The Physicians of Myddfai* in 1861.

Please note that qualified medical herbalists, with an understanding of ethno-botany and medicine, should be consulted about any of the cures in this book. It is written to be historically instructive and informative, not as a book of remedies.

## 1.1 A BRIEF DESCRIPTION OF BELIEFS IN THE DOCTRINES OF SIGNATURES AND HUMORS

### THE DOCTRINE OF SIGNATURES

This stems from the theory that God has marked everything that He created with a sign. His 'signature' thus indicated the purpose for the creation of each plant. The doctrine was followed by apothecaries and herbalists for centuries. The Swiss physician Paracelsus (1493-1541) was an advocate of the 'Doctrine of Signatures', stating that *'Nature marks each growth… according to its curative benefit.'* Paracelsus is considered to be the father of modern chemistry, and he did much in his lifetime to popularise the Doctrine of Signatures in its medical application. For example, Paracelsus observed that Christmas rose (*Helleborus niger*) bloomed in winter, and concluded that it had rejuvenative powers. He introduced the plant into the pharmacopoeia of the time and recommended it for people over fifty years old. It was later found that this plant did have an effect on arteriosclerosis. Paracelsus' ideas became part of mainstream medical thinking following the writings of Jakob Böhme (1575-1624). A German shoemaker, aged 25 Böhme had a vision in which he saw the relationship between God and man. He explained his new understanding in *De Signatura Rerum; or The Signature of All Things* (1621). Influenced by the works of Paracelsus, Böhme believed that God must have revealed Himself in the things that he created on Earth, since this was the only way that that man could have any knowledge of His true being. He wrote that: *'the greatest understanding lies in the signature, wherein man… may learn to know the essence of all essences; for by the external form of all creatures… the hidden spirit is known; for nature has given to everything its language according to its essence and form.'* The book was quickly adopted for its medical applications.

The Doctrine states that one can determine from the colour of the flowers or roots, the shape of the leaves and roots, the place of growing, or other 'signatures', what the plant's purpose was in God's plan. We can see that the liverwort, *Hepatica acutiloba*, has a three-lobed leaf that bears a resemblance to the liver, and so the herbalist named the plant after the liver, and prescribed the plant for liver ailments. The shape, colour, smell, colour and markings of plants all now indicated their usefulness in medicine. *Pulmonaria* has heart-shaped leaves spotted with silver, resembling a diseased lung, so was prescribed for consumption, and came to be called lungwort (wort is an old word for any plant). The fine hairs of quince indicated that it could cure baldness, and red roses cured nose-bleeds, as plants with a red 'signature' were used for blood disorders. The petals of the Iris were often used as a poultice for bruising because of the signature of colour, because the petals resembled the bruise they were to alleviate. Plants with yellow flowers or roots, such as Goldenrod were believed to cure conditions of jaundice, by the signature of their colour.

John Gerard states in his herbal when speaking of St. John's Wort, *'The leaves, flowers and seeds stamped, and put into a glass with oile of olive, and set in the hot sunne for certaine weeks togather and then strained from those herbes, and the like quantity of new put in, and sunned in like manner, doth make an oile of the colour of blood, which is a most precious remedy for deep wounds...'*

Here, the doctrine asks that the preparation is made before the signature evidences itself, an early type of preventative medicine. Eyebright, a plant whose flower looks like bright blue eyes, was thus used to treat eye diseases, being still used in the 1800s. The doctrine was taken up universally by medieval alchemists, apothecaries and herbalists across Europe. However, similar beliefs were held by Native Americans, Middle Eastern and Asian cultures. Folk healers in Christian and Muslim countries claimed that God, or Allah, deliberately made plants resemble the parts of the body they could cure, a concept easy to accept by commoners. Today the idea of 'like cures like' is still at the heart of much modern homeopathy.

## THE DOCTRINE OF HUMORS

Humorism, the 'theory of the four humors' was a model for the workings of the human body, emanating from Greek philosophers, although its origins are probably older. Humoral theory was central to the teachings of Hippocrates and Galen, and became the dominant medical theory in Europe. Galen accepted Hippocrates' ideas, including the accounts of Pythagoras, Empedocles and Plato that matter is composed of the four elements of fire, water, air and earth. Their qualities were hot, moist, cold and dry, respectively. They were characterized in the body as blood, yellow bile, black bile and phlegm.

This was probably the major influence upon medical practice and teaching until well into the nineteenth century. It was also proposed that each of the humors was associated with a particular season of the year, during which too much of the corresponding humor could exist in the body, for example blood was associated with spring. A good balance between the four humours was essential to retain a healthy body and mind, as any imbalance could result in disease.

In the body, these Galenic humors had elemental properties. Determining the correct balance of humors for a physician was not simple. The right mix for any one organ or person depends on the body system involved, the person's age, the season and other such factors. Treatment of imbalances would significantly involve foods or herbs thought to contain the right balance of the four natural properties for that particular medical problem. All treatments for disease were therefore aimed at restoring humoral balance.

In essence physicians took what we might call now a holistic view, often focusing only upon changes in dietary habits, exercise and herbal medicines. However, other treatments could involve more aggressive attempts to re-establish the body's balance. These may include having the body purged with laxatives and emetics, or the skin blistered with hot iron (cauterised). Patients already weakened by disease might be subjected to bloodletting, because physicians believed that their bodies contained excessive blood.

From its development in ancient Greece, humoral theory spread throughout classical Rome and the Islamic world, coming to dominate Western medical thinking throughout the Medieval and Renaissance periods. Constitutional 'imbalance' of the humors remained the primary medical framework in the seventeenth century. Members of the Royal College of Physicians practised an essentially Galenic style of medicine, with heavy reliance on the 'depletory regimen' of balancing or cleansing the humors through bleeding, cupping and blistering, purging, vomiting and sweating.

It was not displaced as the primary framework for scientific medical practice until the late 18th century, but still permeates folk medicinal practices throughout the world. Even in Victorian times, doctors took the view from the Middle Ages that bathing was more harmful for men than for women. Masculinity was associated with hot, dry humors and femininity with cold wet humors.

A benefit was that humoral theory forced physician to consider patients as a whole during diagnosis and treatment. Galen's theory of the humors became associated with a theory of temperament, giving rise to a typology of personalities - choleric, melancholic, phlegmatic and sanguine. By the Elizabethan period, it was thought that the various humors gave off vapours which ascended to the brain, such that the state of a person's humors would explain their temperament and comportment.

As stated, the aim in humoral medicine was to restore the equilibrium of bodily fluids by removing excess through purging, vomiting, bleeding, starvation, etc. Alternatively or additionally, the mediciner could replace the deficiency with medicines or certain foodstuffs. Therefore cod liver oil, 'virol' (a vitamin preparation based on malt extract), honey, garlic and a variety of infusions, cordials and tonics were used to impart goodness in the years before the National Health Service was implemented in 1956.

The humoral conceptions of illness and health that were held in South Wales can also be seen in the ideas about hot and cold and their influence on health in the early and mid-twentieth century. A 'Mrs. Scott' of 'Gwynfa Terrace, Aberffrwd' treated many conditions and ailments by the application of heat in various forms. Treatment was either carried out directly by 'hot' drinks such as brandy and water or blackcurrant tea, or indirectly by poultices, vigorous friction, a hot brick, fried salt or a hot turpentine cloth compress (a stupe). While a hot brick was best for wind around the heart it was unsuitable for wind around the kidneys, which needed a linseed poultice. Similarly, coalminers swore by the ferocious heat caused by Quack-Quack's embrocation for rheumatism (see 1.103).

Rheumatism caused miners a great deal of trouble, as they had to work to earn money – there was no paid sick leave. Thus they often 'treated' it by wearing a bright red flannel vest against their skin. The colour symbolism of red, signifying both blood and heat, was thought to bring relief. Most communities possessed a person, usually a woman, who was consulted by friends and neighbours in times of illness. A good example of this type of practitioner was Mrs. Scott. If anyone in 'Gwynfa Terrace' became ill, Mrs. Scott, famous for her linseed poultices, was called. Once diagnosed by Mrs. Scott sufferers saw no need to consult a doctor. While these unofficial practitioners were cheaper than doctors, it was also the case that their treatments were preferred. 'Mrs. Pugh Zambuck', was known throughout Bedlinog for her skill in treating boils and abscesses with poultices, and was to many patients preferable to the local doctor.

Mrs. Scott was apparently adept at treating 'inflammation' while 'Granny Marsh' was renowned for her various cure-all ointments. It was said that the only thing that 'Granny Marsh' would not treat was ulcers and would send sufferers straight to the hospital. 'Quack-Quack' was known in Bedlinog for his various tonics intended to restore vitality and vigour, as well as his special embrocation for rheumatic miners. The humoral theory is summarized here:

| Temperament | Humor | Main Organ | Element | Qualities | Complexion & Physical Type | Personality |
|---|---|---|---|---|---|---|
| Choleric (P) | Yellow bile | Spleen | Fire | Hot, Dry | Red-haired, Wiry, Thin | Violent, Vengeful, Volatile, Ambitious |
| Melancholic (A) | Black bile | Gall bladder | Earth | Cold, Dry | Thin, Pale | Introspective, Sentimental, Apathetic |
| Phlegmatic | Phlegm | Lungs | Water | Cold, Moist | Overweight | Sluggish, Lazy, Cowardly |
| Sanguine (I) | Blood | Liver | Air | Hot, Moist | Ruddy, Chubby | Amorous, Happy, Generous, Carefree, Optimistic |

# THE USE OF FOLK MEDICINE

Certain individuals specialise in forms of healing that are outside the official, orthodox system of medicine. This 'folk' sector includes a wide range of practitioners and was important in interwar South Wales. A government inquiry carried out just before the First World War found that certain types of unofficial practitioners were very prevalent in the region. Dr. D. Rocyn Jones, the Monmouthshire county medical officer, was the descendant of three generations of bonesetters and had a brother who continued the family bone-setting tradition between the wars. The inquiry of 1910 also noted that herbalists were very popular in Wales and this continued to be the case during the interwar period.

Medical herbalism was characterised by the belief that medicine should be as 'democratic' and open as possible. It was thought that ordinary people, treating themselves with simple herbal remedies, could break the monopoly of the medical establishment. Medical botany flourished in certain communities, especially where dissenting religion challenged the established church. Health and faith thus were within the power of the individual, rather than deriving from doctors or priests. Herbalists presented their skills and knowledge as a means by which ordinary people could become their own doctors and treat themselves without recourse to the monopolistic and 'poisonous' polypharmacy of orthodox medicine. '*I believe in Medical liberty*' declared Dr. John Rees Yemm.

Natural, health-giving herbal treatments were thought preferable to the unnatural methods practised by qualified doctors and were often more effective. Herbalists practising in South Wales between the wars ranged from highly educated, 'professional' practitioners to self-educated lay practitioners. Dr. John Rees Yemm is characteristic of the professional practitioners, and is mentioned elsewhere in the text as being remembered in Myddfai. Yemm became interested in herbalism through the works of Nicholas Culpeper, the English herbalist of the seventeenth century, when Yemm's father became ill.

Later studying the works of other herbalists, Yemm then began a prolonged course of professional training in herbalism. In 1921 he sat and passed the examinations of the National Association of Medical Herbalists (NAMH), and in 1926, was elected to the council of the NAMH. Yemm then took courses in physiotherapy and naturopathy in Chicago and received a doctorate in the latter from the National College of Naturopathy in Iowa. He built up an extensive practice in the Ammanford area and, at the same time, promoted the interests of organised herbalism through his editorship of the journal *Medical Herbalist*, the official organ of the NAMH.

A small group of herbalists in South Wales, and the wider movement of which it was a part, saw itself as a highly skilled profession and aspired to official recognition. Constantly criticising the state-protected monopoly of orthodox medicine the NAMH lobbied the government to grant it professional status. Yemm's obituary, when he died at Ammanford in 1958, calls him a Physio-Medical Practitioner.

It is felt that there is scope for research into the possible use of some remedies that follow in this book. Interestingly, the first noted medical use of ground ivy was by the Physicians of Myddfai. A fresh herb tea of ground ivy and honey is naturally rich in vitamin C, which explains why the mediciners found it useful combat consumption and coughs. Snuff made from ground ivy leaves was used for asthma, as well as for severe headaches and hangovers. Its leaves soaked in vinegar helped remove corns. The Celts had used an ointment made from ground ivy twigs as a salve for moderate burns. It was also considered excellent in the treatment of snake bites.

The sap from ground ivy was said to be a panacea to the Celts, believed to be a cure for ringing in the ears, congestion, diarrhoea, haemorrhoids, bladder irritation, indigestion, and eye irritation. Much later, herbalists such as John Gerard recommend ground ivy for the same reasons as the Myddfai mediciners. The ursolic and rosmarinic acids in ground ivy are used as anti-inflammatory components in modern medicine for ulcers and the Epstein Barr virus (which causes skin tumours). Ground ivy can be poisonous and should not be used by epileptics, pregnant/lactating women, or anyone suffering from kidney or liver disease.

Ground ivy was also prominent in magic and folklore. In the Scottish Highlands, ground ivy was braided with rowan and woodbine to make a lucky wreath. This was placed under the milk storage jugs, pails and churns to prevent the milk from being stolen by the *sidhe* (the people of the mounds, a race of fairies), and later to prevent witchcraft.

One modern witchcraft suggestion is to place ground ivy at the base of a yellow candle and burn it on a Tuesday in order to discover who is working negatively against you. Another Wiccan option is to burn an ivy plant to the ground in order to exorcise people who do not agree with you. As ground ivy is a persistent plant that grows under adverse conditions, it symbolizes tenacity when faced with difficulties in the pursuit of a goal.

Ground ivy is also used as a dye for fabrics. The berries produce a grey-sage green dye. The leaves produce a creamy yellow dye when blended with alum as a mordant. Boiled ground ivy produces a dark navy to nearly black dye. For nearly every plant, shrub and tree there is a magical story threading throughout history – how it acquired its name and nicknames, its medical properties, perhaps a use in spells, to make dyes etc.

Only in recent years has Western medicine stopped using a wide range of herbs, but for well over half the population of the world, herbal treatments are part of the total medical approach, for instance in China and India being used alongside the 'techno-medicine' of the West. Unfortunately, pharmacologists extract the 'active' ingredient and chemically synthesise it for treatments, and ridicule the herbalist idea that the whole plant is of value. Global testing and patents costs millions of pounds for the few multinational pharmaceutical companies, and in return they will obviously wish to safeguard their windfall profits from a useful new drug.

As new plants evolved, insects and other life forms would adapt to feeing on it, generating new species which used it as food. In turn, plants would evolve with thorns, hairs and in particular alkaloids, quinones, glycosides, essential oils etc. to repel insects. The chemicals have no physiological function for the plants, but were evolved to deal with changes in the environment. These chemicals have become useful medical tools for therapeutic purposes for mankind.

Fewer than 5% of the world's plants have been tested for their potential medical use, but 85% of pharmaceutical drugs are linked to plants. It is thought that over 80% of the world's population still relies upon herbs for everyday medical treatment. Indeed an old German proverb tells us: *'The garden is the poor man's apothecary'*.

# THE 1861 TRANSLATOR, AND EDITOR

THE TRANSLATOR

John Pughe (Ioan ab Hu Feddyg, 1814 - 1874) was a physician and litterateur, born at Ysgubor Fawr, Chwaen-wen, Anglesey. He qualified as a doctor after training at St. Thomas's Hospital, London, where he received the degree of F.R.C.S. In the 1850s there were only 850 Fellows of the Royal College of Surgeons, of whom only 12 practised in Wales, among them John Pughe. He pioneered in 1854 the operation he described on the imperforate anus. Although he made no claim to be the first to perform this operation, he believed it to be the first time 'in which the relief of this particular malformation has been successfully accomplished in this Kingdom'. He first practised at Abermo (Barmouth) but later moved to Aberdyfi where he spent most of his life. In his early days he lived at Clynnog Fawr, Caernarfonshire and was a close friend of Eben Fardd. Pughe was prominent in the public life of Aberdyfi and district, being a JP and a patron of charitable and religious causes.

His religious leanings were towards the Plymouth Brethren, for whom he preached in the small church which he established in the district. He is buried in the family vault at Cwm Maethlon burial ground. One son died but his four other sons were physicians, John Eliot Howard Pughe (d. 1880), Rheinallt Navalaw Pughe, Taliesin William Owen Pughe (d. 1893), who practised at Liverpool, and David Roberts Pughe (d. 1885), who lived in Montgomeryshire. Three were members of the Royal College of Surgeons and one a Fellow. His daughter was the artist Buddug Annwylini (Boudicca Beloved-Of-Us) Pughe (d.1939). Pughe's brother David William was also a MRCS.

The task of translating the Meddygon Myddfai took Pughe many years. Sir Benjamin and Lady Hall thought it took him too long, and this led to acrimonious exchanges, through William Rees of the Committee of the Welsh MSS Society. Sir Benjamin, afterward Lord Llanover and remembered by the eponymous clock 'Big Ben', was chairman of the committee. It was through Lady Llanover that Rees sought to influence Lord Llanover that 'leniency be shown' to Pughe for the delay. However, Lady Llanover did not wish Pughe to edit the publication, and only reluctantly allowed his name to appear on the title page. For Pughe's funeral all the places of business in the town of Aberdyfi closed and 'the almost entire cessation of the ever-sounding strokes of the mallet and chisel, the shipping with the colours half mast high ... signified ... certainly he was above the common order of men'.

## THE EDITOR

The editor of the translation was the Rev. John Williams (1811-1862), an antiquary and priest born in Llangynhafal, Denbighshire. In 1835, he graduated from Jesus College, Oxford to become the Anglican curate of Llanfor, Meirionnydd. In 1843 he became perpetual curate of Nercwys, Flintshire and in 1849 rector of Llanymawddwy, Meirionnydd. In his early writing career he used the bardic name Cynhaval, after his birthplace, but later used ab Ithel after his grandfather, William Bethell.

In 1836 he wrote *The Church of England independent of the Church of Rome in all Ages*, and in 1846 *Ecclesiastical Antiquities of the Cymry or The Ancient British Church*. Williams founded the Cambrian Archaeological Association, and edited its journal, *Archaologia Cambrensis* until 1853. Williams also organised the 1858 Llangollen Eisteddfod. It featured several Gorsedd ceremonies and was initially criticised, but became the bluepint for the National Eisteddfod. In 1856 Archdeacon Williams produced *Rules of Welsh Poetry*, and by 1860 had completed for publication *Chronicle of the Princes* and *Annales Cambriae*. A leading Welsh scholar and nationalist, he was strongly influenced by Iolo Morganwg (Edward Williams 1747–1826).

He was a main disseminator of Iolo Morganwg's 'bardo-druidism'. Willams's seminal work, the two-volume *Barddas; or, a Collection of Original Documents, Illustrative of the Theology, Wisdom and Usages of the Bardo-Druidic System of the Isle of Britain* (1862 and 1874) is the main source book for modern druidic groups. The second volume was collated and published twelve years after his death.

Williams became rector of Llanenddwyn and Llanddwywe, Meirionnydd, in 1862, and died in the same year. In his editing of *The Physicians of Myddfai*, Williams expurgated around forty remedies, which are now included in this book.

# PART 2

## PREFACE TO THE 1861 TRANSLATION
## OF THE PHYSICIANS OF MYDDFAI

### BOOK ONE – THE RED BOOK

This is taken from the original vellum manuscript, which was transferred from the Library of the Welsh Charity School, London to the British Museum. Book I is taken from the copy known as the *Red Book of Hergest*, Jesus College ms.111, Oxford. It was collated by Reverend Robert Owen, Fellow of Jesus College, with a transcript *'made by the late Mr. Saunders, from Mr. Rees of Tonn's copy; which manuscript was, moreover, copied about 1766, by William Bona of Llanpumsaint, from another belonging to Iago ap Dewi of Llanllawddog.'*

### PREFACE by the editor REV. JOHN WILLIAMS AB ITHEL 12 February 1861

Williams tells us that *Meddyginiaeth*, or medicine, numbers as one of *'the nine rural arts, known and practised by the ancient Cymry before they became possessed of cities and a sovereignty'*. Williams states as his source the 1807 *Myvyrian Archaiology* iii p,129, but some of this book is thought by some to have been embellished by Iolo Morganwg. Williams therefore places the date of medicine in Wales as *'before the time of Prydain ab Aedd Mawr, which is generally dated about a thousand years anterior to the Christian era. In that remote period the priests and teachers of the people were the GWYDDONIAID, or men of knowledge, obviously so called from their being looked upon as the chief sources and channels of wisdom in the land. It is to these men that the art of healing is attributed, which they seem to have practised mainly, if not wholly, by means of herbs. Indeed Botanology, or a knowledge of the nature and properties of plants, is enumerated as one of the three sciences, which primarily engaged their attention - the other two being Theology and Astronomy, as appears from the following Triad:-*

*"The three pillars of knowledge, with which the Gwyddoniaid were acquainted, and which they bore in memory from the beginning: the first, a knowledge of Divine things, and of such matters as appertain to the worship of God, and the homage due to goodness; the second, a knowledge of the course of the stars, their names and kinds, and the order of times; the third, a knowledge of the names and use of the herbs of the field, and of their application in practice, in medicine and in religious worship. These were preserved in the memorials of vocal song, and in the memorials of times, before there were Bards of degree and chair."* (Llanofer MS).

The original preface goes on to tell us that *'Most of the nations of antiquity pretended to derive the medical art immediately from their gods. It does not appear, however, that the Cymry went so far as to claim for it a divine origin, except in regard to its elementary principles, though the practice of it was confined to the priesthood.'* Williams then refers to the druids practising medicine, and to the *Laws of Dyfnwal Moelmud* (fl.400bce), which are first mentioned by Geoffrey of Monmouth. *'Cicero informs us that he was personally acquainted with one of the Gallic Druids, Diviacus the Aeduan, a man of quality in his country, who professed to have a thorough knowledge of the laws of nature, including, as we may well suppose the science of medicine.'* Williams then mentions that Pliny enumerated some of the plants, such as mistletoe, water pimpernel and fir moss, used in Britain for their medicinal properties. There follows the *Elements of Man* by the sixth-century British poet Taliesin, but they may be a late seventeenth-century construct by Iolo Morganwg:

> *'Man consists of eight parts:-*
> *the first is the earth which is sluggish and heavy, whence is the flesh.*
> *The second is the stones which are hard, and these are the materials of the bones.*
> *The third is water which is moist and cold, and is the substance of the blood.*
> *The fourth is salt which is briny and sharp, whence are the passions and the faculties of feeling in respect of corporeal sense and perception.*
> *The fifth is the air, or wind whence is the breath.*
> *The sixth is the sun which is clear and fair, whence is the fire, or corporeal warmth, and the light and colour.*
> *The seventh is the Holy Spirit whence are the soul and life.*
> *The eighth is Christ, that is, the intellect and wisdom, and the light of the soul and life.*
>
> *If the part of man that preponderates be of the earth he will prove unwise, sluggish and very heavy, and will be a little, short, thin dwarf, according as the preponderance may be, whether great or small.*
> *If it be of the air, the man will be light, unsteady, garrulous, and given to gossip. If of the stones, he will be hard of heart, understanding and judgment - a miser and a thief.*
> *If of the sun, he will be a man of genius, affectionate, active, docile, and poetical.*
> *If of the Holy Spirit he will be godly, amiable, and compassionate, of a just and tender judgment, and fond of the arts and sciences; and this cannot otherwise than equiponderate with Christ and divine sonship'.*

Williams also adds three disputed medical triads by Taliesin, also from the Llanofer ms:

> *'There are three intractable substantial organs: the liver; the kidney; and the heart.*
> *There are three intractable membranes: the dura mater; the peritoneum; and the urinary bladder.*
> *There are three tedious complaints: disease of the knee joint; disease of the substance of a rib, and phthysis; for when purulent matter has formed in one of these it is not known when it will get well.'*

Another translation of this latter passage is given in Lynn Hughes' Carmarthenshire Anthology: *'The three thick indispensables: liver and kidney and heart and this is the reason they are so called: it is proven, that wherever a hurt touches one of them, they cannot be cured, but death will come at once. The three thin indispensables: the membrane of the brain and the small intestine and the vesicle; and it is for the same reason that they are indispensable as the others. The three lingering wounds: the hip joint, and the marrow of a rib, and the lung; since once pus has formed in any one of those it is proven that no doctor knows when it may heal until he sees him well.'*

In 1825, Aneurin Owen began preparing an edition of the *Laws of Hywel Dda*, compiled around 930. The work appeared in 1841 under the title of *Ancient Laws and Institutes of Wales; Comprising the Laws … by Howel the Good and Anomalous Laws … with an English Translation.*

This work was remarkable for distinguishing for the first time the three versions - Venedotian, Dimetian, and Gwentian - of the original laws. Williams takes from this work the duties of the mediciner of the Royal Court: '*Of the mediciner of the household, his office, his privilege, and his duty:*

*1. The twelfth is the mediciner of the household.*

*2. He is to have his land free; his horse in attendance; and his linen clothing from the queen, and his woollen clothing from the king.*

*3. His seat in the hall within the palace is at the base of the pillar to which the screen is attached, near which the king sits.*

*4. His lodging is with the chief of the household.*

*5. His protection is, from the time the king shall command him to visit a wounded or sick person, whether the person be in the palace or out of it, until he quit him, to convey away an offender.*

*6. He is to administer medicine gratuitously to all within the palace, and to the chief of the household; and he is to have nothing from them except their bloody clothes, unless it be for one of the three dangerous wounds, as mentioned before; these are a stroke on the head unto the brain; a stroke in the body unto the bowels; and the breaking of one of the four limbs; for every one of these three dangerous wounds the mediciner is to have nine score pence and his food, or one pound without his food, and also the bloody clothes.*

*7. The mediciner is to have, when he shall apply a tent, twenty four pence.*

*8. For an application of red ointment, twelve pence.*

*9. For an application of herbs to a swelling, four legal pence.*

*10. For letting blood, four pence.*

*11. His food daily is worth one penny halfpenny.*

*12. His light every night is worth one legal penny.*

*13. The worth of a medical pan is one penny.*

*14. The mediciner is to take an indemnification from the kindred of the wounded person, in case he die from the remedy he may use, and if he do not take it, let him answer for the deed.*

*15. He is to accompany the armies.*

*16. He is never to leave the palace, but with the king's permission.*

*17. His saraad [payment due] is six kine [cattle], and six score of silver, to be augmented.*

*18. His worth is six score and six kine, to be augmented.*"

Williams adds that elsewhere we meet with the following particulars:

'*Of the three conspicuous scars this is - There are three conspicuous scars: one upon the face; another upon the foot; and another upon the hand; thirty pence on the foot; three score pence on the hand; six score pence on the face. Every unexposed scar, four pence. The cranium, four pence… For every broken bone, twenty pence: unless there be a dispute as to its diminutiveness; and if there be a dispute as to the size let the mediciner take a brass basin, and let him place his elbow upon the ground and his hand over the basin, and if its sound be heard, let four legal pence be paid; and if it be not heard, nothing is due… Four curt pennies are to be paid to a person for every bone, taken from the upper part of the cranium, which shall sound on falling into a copper basin.'*

The *Laws of Hywel Dda* (d.950) were agreed at Whitland, and the *Harleian MS 4353* (V) with emendations from *Cleopatra A XIV* (W) and these mss. date from around 1285. They note the importance of the court physician thus: *'And first they began with the Laws of a Court as they were the most important and as they pertained to the King and the Queen and the Twenty-four Officers who accompany them, namely, Chief of the Household. Priest of the Household. Steward. Judge of the Court. Falconer. Chief Huntsman. Chief Groom. Page of the Chamber. Steward of the Queen. Priest of the Queen. Bard of the Household. Silentiary. Doorkeeper of the Hall. Doorkeeper of the Chamber. Chambermaid. Groom of the Rein, Candlebearer. Butler. Mead Brewer. Server of the Court. Cook. Physician. Footholder. Groom of the Rein to the Queen... The lodging of the chief of the household is to be the largest house in the middle of the tref* [township], *because round him the lodgings of the household are to be, so that they may be ready for every emergency. In the lodging of the chief of the household, the bard of the household and the physician are to be... A court physician sits second next to the chief of the household in the hall. His land he has free, and a horse regularly from the king. Gratuitously does he prepare medicines for the household and for the men of the court; for he only receives the bloodstained clothes, unless it be one of the three mortal wounds.*

*A pound does he take without his maintenance or nine score pence together with his maintenance for the mortal wound, to wit, [first] when a person's head is broken so that the brain is seen. A bone of the upper part of the cranium is four curt pence in value if it sounds in falling into a basin; a bone of the lower part of the cranium is four legal pence in value. And [secondly] when a person shall be stabbed in his body so that his bowels are seen. And [thirdly] when one of the four pillars of a person's body is broken so that the marrow is seen; these are the two thighs and the two humeri.*

*Three pounds is the worth of each one of those three wounds...Three sârhads* [due payments] *not to be expiated if received when intoxicated: sârhad done to the priest of the household; and sârhad to the judge of the court; and sârhad to the physician of the court; because these should not be intoxicated, as they know not what time the king may have need of them... Three legal needles are: the needle of the queen's serving woman; and the needle of the physician for sewing the wounds; and the needle of the chief huntsman for sewing the torn dogs; each one of them is four legal pence in value. The needle of any other skilful woman is a legal penny in value. (Wade-Evans, A. W., Welsh Medieval Law: Being a Text of the Laws of Howel the Good Oxford 1909)*

Rhiwallon of Myddfai was assisted by his three sons, Cadwgan, Gruffydd and Einion as court physicians to Rhys Gryg (d.1234). Rhys ap Rhys ap Gruffydd was also known as Rhys Fychan, Rhys the Younger, to differentiate him from his father, and was the son of the great 'The Lord Rhys' of Dinefwr, Prince of Deheubarth. At some time in his life Rhys ap Rhys became known as Rhys Gryg (the Hoarse), possibly because of a disease of the larynx, or hoarseness caused by a wound in the throat. Rhys spent most of his life fighting, and died of wounds at Llandeilo, being buried in St David's Cathedral. Under his patronage, Rhiwallon, Cadwgan, Gruffydd and Einion made a collection of valuable medicinal recipes, treatments and cures. Although the collection bears their name, not all the prescriptions were theirs. Some had been in the *materia medica* of Wales long

26

before, and a few may be traced back to the era of of Howel the Good (c.880-950), if not to the sixth century or even to the Celtic *'ovates'* of the pre-Roman invasion.

In the fourteenth century Iorwerth ab y Cyriog of Anglesey wrote a cywydd thanking his love for a ring set with a precious stone (or possibly a field, as the Welsh is *'am gae'*). It includes the couplet: *'Meddyg, nis gwnai modd y gwnaeth / Myddfai, o chai ddyn meddfaeth. (A Physician he would not make / It heals as did Myddfai, were a man to be nourished on mead')*. Dafydd ap Gwilym (fl.1350) has been wrongly attributed with the poem. Thus by the fourteenth century, stories about a famous family of physicians in Myddfai were widespread. Also around this time, the first of several manuscript collections of the remedies and health rules of the Meddygon Myddfai were assembled. In these collections were large numbers of remedies for a wide variety of ailments, from common coughs and colds to sleeping potions. There was other 'useful' information such as lucky and unlucky days in the year.

The Myddfai physicians believed that the patient was responsible for his or her own health and emphasized moderation and good sense with sensible food, work, and sleeping habits. They made simple preparations (mostly poultices and infusions), and preferred working with *simples* (medicinal plants or the medicines associated with them). The physicians mainly used the plants growing around their locality.

The line of Myddfai physicians continued down the centuries. The last who actually practised medicine was generally accepted to be John Jones in the eighteenth century, but there are doctors even now of the line of Myddfai. In the porch of Myddfai church is a gravestone:

*HERE*
*Lieth the body of Mr. David Jones of Mothvey*
*Surgeon who was an Honest charitable & skilful man.*
*He died September 14th*
*Anno Dom 1719*
*Aged 61.*

*John Jones Surgeon*
*Eldest son of the said David Jones departed*
*this life the 25thr of November*
*1739 in the 44th year of his*
*age and also lyes Interred*
*hereunder.*

As previously noted, Book One of the *Meddygon Myddfai* is found in *Llyfr Coch Hergest* (The Red Book of Hergest) a large vellum manuscript written in Middle Welsh, shortly after 1382. It preserves a collection of Welsh prose and poetry, notably the tales of the *Mabinogion* and *Gogynfeirdd* poetry (poetry of the princes). The manuscript derives its name from the colour of its leather binding and from its association with Hergest Court between the late 15th and early 17th centuries. It is now kept at the Bodleian Library on behalf of Jesus College, Oxford, and catalogued as *MS 111*. The manuscript also contains a collection of herbal remedies associated with Rhiwallon Feddyg, the son of the Lady of the Lake, and the founder of a medical dynasty that has lasted over 800 years.

In his preface, Pughe gives some *Medical Maxims* from the *Book of Iago ab Dewi*, as follows:

*'He who goes to sleep supperless, will have no need of Rhiwallon of Myddfai.*

*A supper of apples – a breakfast of nuts.*

*A cold mouth and warm feet will live long.*

*To the fish market in the morning, to the butcher's shop in the afternoon.*

*Cold water and warm bread will make an unhealthy stomach.*

*The three qualities of water: it will produce no sickness, no debt, and no widowhood.*

*To eat eggs without salt will bring on sickness.*

*It is no insult to deprive an old man of his supper.*

*An eel in a pie, lampreys in salt.*

*An ague or fever at the fall of the leaf is always of long continuance, or else is fatal.*

*A kid a month old - a lamb three months.*

*Dry feet, moist tongue.*

*A salmon and sermon in Lent.*

*Supper will kill more than were ever cured by the Physicians of Myddfai.*

*A light dinner, a less supper, sound sleep, long life.*

*Do not wish for milk after fish.*

*To sleep much is the health of youth, the sickness of old age.*

*Long health in youth will shorten life.*

*It is more wholesome to smell warm bread than to eat it.*

*A short sickness for the body, and short frost for the earth, will heal; either of them long will destroy.*

*Whilst the urine is clear, let the physician beg.*

*Better is appetite than gluttony.*

*Enough of bread, little of drink.*

*The bread of yesterday, the meat of to-day, and the wine of last year will produce health.*

*Quench thy thirst where the washerwoman goes for water.*

*Three men that are long-lived, the ploughman of dry land, a mountain dairyman, and a fisherman of the sea.*

*The three feasts of health, milk, bread, and salt.*

*The three medicines of the Physicians of Myddfai: water, honey, and labour.*

*Moderate exercise is health.*

*Three moderations will produce long life; in food, labour, and meditation.*

*Whoso breaks not his fast in May, let him consider himself with the dead.*

*He who sees fennel and gathers it not. is not a man, but a devil.*

*If thou desire to die, eat cabbage in August.*

*Whatever quantity you eat, drink thrice.*

*God will send food to washed hands.*

*Drink water like an ox, and wine like a king.*

*One egg is economy, two is gentility, three is greediness, and the fourth is wastefulness.*

*If persons knew how good a hen is in January, none would be left on the roost.*

*The cheese of sheep, the milk of goats, and the butter of cows are the best.*
*The three victuals of health, honey, butter, and milk.*
*The three victuals of sickness, flesh meat, ale, and vinegar.*
*Take not thy coat off before Ascension Day.*
*If thou wilt become unwell, wash thy head, and go to sleep.*
*In pottage without herbs there is neither goodness, nor nourishment.*
*If thou wilt die, eat roast mutton, and sleep soon after it.*
*If thou wilt eat a bad thing, eat roast hare.*
*Mustard after food.*
*He who cleans his teeth with the point of his knife, may soon clean them with the haft.*
*A dry cough is the trumpet of death.'*

[Kenward adds a then current Salopian proverb: *'Bread a day old, cheese a year old, and ale seven years old, will make an old man sing when he is a hundred years old.'*]

Iago ab Dewi, also known as James ap David and James Davies, was a bard and distinguished translator. Born in 1644, Iago was a native of Llandysul in Ceredigion, lived for a few years in Pencader and died in 1722 at Blaengwili, Llanllawddog, Carmarthenshire. *'Iago was a diligent collector of Welsh manuscripts, both prose and poetry'* and a full description of his works and collatioins is in the *Dictionary of National Biography.*

James Kenward noted that: *'Ab Ithel [John Williams] has furnished a valuable preface, giving, in addition to these particulars, a sketch of the state of herbal medicine among the early Cymry, and an account of the fragments of medical precepts and prescriptions not comprised in the Meddygon Myddvai. He has edited the text with his usual careful scrutiny, collating in the first portion the reading of the Red Book of Hergest with that of the Tonn manuscript. The prescriptions of the Meddygon Myddvai amply reflect the superstition, while they illustrate the knowledge, of our ancestors of the Middle Ages. The collection mainly depends on a pharmacopeia of herbs and flowers, varied by animal preparations, and applied often according to days and seasons, and with cabalistic charms. The range of the diseases and ailments thus treated is very extensive, including at least as many as are said to be vanquished by the pills of Hollway, or the globules of Hahnemann. There are also many instructions for surgical operations, and remedies for sudden accidents.*

*Unquestionably many of these old recipes are valuable ... or contain suggestions of value, although a large number also ... emanate from ages which we, in our excess of light, are wont to designate dark. The old physicians practised bleeding freely and even judiciously, though they paid an excessive attention to weather and the almanack; and they had a fair knowledge of the leading drugs in modern use, though herbalism was their great principle...*

*Of temperaments the Cymric Physicians have much to say, and their account both as to classification and analysis, is, though somewhat fanciful, for the most part consistent, not only with Greek, Arab, and Gothic teachings, but with the average conclusions of modern physiology. There is a good chapter on the essentials and characteristics of a physician; and the rules laid down for his private and professional behaviour, while on the one hand they resemble the rules imposed on the Asclepiadae, on the other hand are almost identical with the courtesies, charities, and moralities, which distinguish our own medical practice....*

*Such is a fair and sufficient sample of the lore of the Physicians of Myddvai; and we may not err in concluding that - magic and sortilege excepted - it is not much less valuable than any other prescription-book in the most uncertain art of medicine. With regard to the book itself, there seems no reason for doubting that it is a true transcript of the writings of the thirteenth century, and that it embodies the British medical belief and practice of the Middle Age. Ab Ithel, in his preface, has treated it exclusively in this light, and traced the botanical practice from the Druids to Hywel Dda.*

*He does not, however, notice the fact that herbalism and magic applied to healing have been popular with all nations at all times. The Saxons in Britain had analogous rules and recipes to those of the Cymry, which they had evidently in great part derived from the Greeks, and Romans, and Goths. The Herbarium of Dioscorides, and the Herbarium of Apuleius; the "Medicina de Quadrupedibus" of Sextus Placitus, the lore of the Magi and Pythagoreans as reported by Pliny, the treatises of Avicenna, are the first repositories of a large proportion of the prescriptions, precepts, and proverbs in the British and Saxon books.'*

# PART 3

## THE LEGEND OF THE LADY OF THE LAKE

Around 409ce, after nearly four hundred years of occupation the remaining Romans left Britain. In the sixth-century circular churchyard of St Cian, Llangian, on the Llŷn Peninsula, there is a monolithic pillar with an inscription: *MELI MEDICI FILI MARTINI ICIT* (the stone of Melos, the doctor, son of Martinus). This stone, which was also used as a sundial, represents the last evidence of medical care in Roman Britain. However, the Celtic tribes of Britain had their own physicians and remedies, and the Christian Romano-British tribes carried on both British and Roman medical traditions. These were the *Dark Ages* across Europe, with barbarians over-running Italy, the Continent and England, but the *Age of the Saints* in Wales. Wales has the longest unbroken Christian heritage in the world. Despite attacks from the Irish, Danes, Norwegians, Scots and the Germanic tribes which over-ran England, Wales resisted the pagans and remained independent until the murder of its last king, Llywelyn II in 1282. Not until the end of Owain Glyndŵr's War against the usurper Henry IV in 1415 was Wales completely conquered.

During this time Wales had its own British language, unique culture, the most humane laws in the known world, and its own medical traditions. Princes, nobles and kings each had their court mediciners, who also treated commoners. Many of the treatments were gathered in manuscripts over the centuries, but Wales was invaded upon dozens of occasions, with the consequent burning of scriptoria, libraries, monasteries, castles, great houses, courts, cathedrals and churches. Little remained except oral traditions and a very few surviving manuscripts. War across Wales did not end from the leaving of the Romans until the end of the Civil War in the mid-seventeenth century. There is a paucity of written materials in Wales, virtually unknown across the rest of Europe, which makes the *Physicians of Myddfai* manuscripts especial.

Three years after the 1861 edition of the *Meddygon Myddfai*, there appeared the Reverend Thomas Oswald Cockayne's collection: *Leechdoms, Wortcunning, and Starcraft of Early England*. His book illustrates Saxon practice, alongside Myddfai's British-Welsh practice, with both being mainly derived from Avicenna and Greek sources, and used as the basis for numerous herbals from medieval times onwards. Cockayne tells us tales of elves and dwarves, but has nothing comparable with Myddfai's 'The Legend of the Lady of Llyn y Fan Fach.' (Llyn means lake, and y fan fach means the small hill, with ban [hill] and bach [small] being mutated to fan and fach. Thus it is the lake of the small hill). The legend was written down by W. Rees, of Llandovery, from the oral recitation of several aged people, and is prefixed to the Myddfai book. A young farmer is herding cattle on the Carmarthenshire Bannau (bans, or hills), and sees a beautiful nymph sitting on the calm surface of the lake, with and falls immediately in love.

As proof of his love, the farmer offers her the bread and cheese he had brought for his mid-day meal. She tells him that his 'bara' (bread) has been baked too long and is hard, and that it is not easy to catch her. The farmer rushes home and consults with his 'mam'. The next day, he comes with an offering of bread of which has not been baked enough, and she rejects both him and the unbaked bread.

On his third attempt, the bread is just right, and she shares it with him, then dives into the cold lake to tell he father that she wishes to marry. Seemingly to test the farmer's affections, her father takes on one arm this daughter and on the other her identical sister. The father and daughters rise to the surface of Llyn y Fan Fach, and the father is willing to accept the farmer as his daughter's fiancé, if he can tell which daughter is his true love.

He is unsure, but his love pushes her foot slightly forward and he recognizes her sandal, claiming her for his bride. The father gives her to the young farmer, with the promise of as many sheep, goats, horses and cattle as she can count without drawing breath. The only condition is that both the wife and dowry will be taken away if the farmer gives her *'three causeless blows.'* The bridegroom agrees, and his fiancée calls a large herd of livestock from the lake by ingeniously counting in fives, and they are married.

All prospers, and the couple have three handsome boys, Cadwgna, Gruffydd and Einion, running a prosperous farm. However, the *'three causeless blows'* cannot be avoided, as seen in the following story. The farmer's wife returns to the lake with all the livestock, even taking a young black calf which has just been slaughtered for veal. The dead calf returns to life, comes down from his hook and proceeds with the other cattle and livestock *'yn iach adre'* (quite well home.) The 'Lady of the Lake', however, then sometimes left her father and sisters, to come to see her sons.

She met them on a mountain side or in a wooded glade (Pant y Meddygon), but never entered their house or invited them to her own. Before her final leave-taking, she gave them a mysterious present, a bag which would console them for the loss of their mother and give them fortune and fame in the world. The bag contained medical prescriptions, and the farmer's sons became the *'Meddygon Myddfai'*, the Physicians of Myddfai.

The tale first appeared in print in 1821 in *The Cambro-Briton*, where Siencyn ab Tydvil of Trehomer wrote *The Legend of Meddygon Myddvai*. An almost exact copy appeared in Louis Stuart Costello's *The Falls, Lakes and Mountains of North Wales* in 1845; and in Wirt Sykes' *British Goblins* in 1880. William Rees was an antiquarian, printer and publisher of Tonn, Llandovery (Llanymddyfri) who compiled the fullest account, published in 1861 as part of *Meddygon Myddvai*. The family mansion at Tonn burnt down in 1916.

The story tells of a young man tending cattle upon the Black Mountain, which is known to have occurred from pre-Norman times until the nineteenth century, when sheep took over. We know that the story is of pre-Norman origin, from the archaic terms used for cattle, also referencing the white bull from the court of the king. It is similar to other legends across Wales and Western Europe, and some believe that it may give reference to a royal crannog existing in the lake. The only definite crannog in Wales was destroyed in 916. Aethelflaeda of Mercia's army invaded Brycheiniog, taking the king's wife and forty-three prisoners from the royal crannog which still exists on Llyn Safaddon (Llangors Lake in

32

Breconshire). It had been a court from 860, and presumably the lady captured was the wife or mother of Tewdwr ab Elise of Brycheiniog.

The legend may even exist from early Celtic times when lakes, rivers and springs were especially venerated, along with Mother Earth. Many Celtic Christian churches in Wales, dating from the sixth century or earlier, are pre-Christian sites with circular graveyards, all with a nearby water source. Many Celtic burial chambers were also built over underground streams.

Until around 1820, many people used to visit the lake on the morning of the first Sunday in August. In 1881 the Warden of Llandovery College said that an old woman from Myddfai remembered seeing *'thousands and thousands'* of people visiting the lake when she was young. She heard that old men said that at that time a *'commotion'* occurred in the lake, when its water *'boiled'*, heralding the approach of the Lady of the Lake and her cattle. The story of the Lady of the Lake is found in the *Red Book of Hergest*, dating from just before 1400, but compiled from much earlier sources.

# THE LEGEND OF LLYN-Y-FAN-FACH,
## OR THE ORIGIN OF
## THE MEDDYGON MYDDFAI

## COLLECTED FROM VARIOUS SOURCES* IN THE YEAR 1841**

*Pughe relates.* * The notes were written down by Mr. William Rees, the publisher and antiquarian of Tonn 'near' Llandovery, from the oral recitations of the late Mr. John Evans, Tiler, Myddfai (died 1843); Mr. David Williams, Mason, about 90 years old of Morfa (a cottage between Rhyblid and Alltycarw Farms), Myddfai; and Mrs. Elizabeth Morgan, of Henllys Lodge, near Llandovery, a native of Myddfai.

** Mr. Rees begs us to acknowledge his obligations to J. Joseph, Esq. F.S.A. Brecon for recalling several particulars and incidents of the Legend from amongst the old inhabitants of Llanddeusant.

When the eventful struggle made by the Princes of South Wales to preserve the independence of their country was drawing to its close in the twelfth century, a widow lived at Blaensawdde near Llanddeusant, Carmarthenshire. She was the survivor of a farmer who had fallen in those disastrous times of war. The widow had an only son to bring up, and Providence smiled upon her. Despite her forlorn condition, her livestock had so increased over the course of time, that she had not enough pasture for them upon her farm. Thus she sent a portion of her cattle to graze on the adjoining Black Mountain [*Mynydd Ddu*], and their most favourite place was near the small lake called Llyn y Fan Fach, on the north-western side of the Carmarthenshire Vans. [*Bannau, or hills*]

Her son grew up to manhood, and was generally sent by his mother to look after the cattle grazing on the Black Mountain. One day in his wanderings along the margin of Llyn y Fan Fach, to his great astonishment, he saw a lady sitting on the unruffled surface of the waters. She was one of the most beautiful creatures that mortal eyes had ever seen. Her hair flowed gracefully in ringlets over her shoulders, the tresses of which she arranged with a comb, while the glassy surface of her watery couch served for the purpose of a mirror, reflecting back her own image. Suddenly she noticed the young man standing on the brink of the lake, with his eyes riveted on her, and unconsciously offering to her the provision of barley bread and cheese with which he had been provided when he left his home.

Bewildered by a feeling of love and admiration for the object before him, he continued to hold out his hand towards the lady, who imperceptibly glided near to him, but gently refused the offer of his provisions. He attempted to touch her, but she eluded his grasp, saying:

| *Cras dy fara!* | *Hard-baked is thy bread!* |
|---|---|
| *Nid hawdd fy nala.* | *'Tis not easy to catch me.* |

She then immediately dived under the waters, and disappeared, leaving the love-stricken youth to return home, a prey to disappointment. He deeply regretted that he had been unable to make further acquaintance with her, in comparison with whom all of the fair maidens of Llanddeusant and Myddfai were as nothing.

On his return home the young man told his mother of his extraordinary vision. She advised him to take some unbaked dough the next time in his pocket. She thought that there must have been some spell connected with the hard-baked bread, or 'bara cras', which had prevented him from catching the lady. The next morning, before the sun had gilded with its rays the peaks of the Vans, the young man was again at the lake. This time it was not for the purpose of looking after his mother's cattle, for he was seeking for the same enchanting vision that he had witnessed the day before. However, in vain did he anxiously strain his eyes and glance over the surface of the lake, as only the ripples occasioned by a stiff breeze met his view. A cloud hung heavily on the summit of the Van, which imparted an additional gloom to his already distracted mind.

Hours passed on, the wind was hushed, and the clouds which had enveloped the mountain vanished into thin air, before the powerful beams of the sun. Now the young man was startled by seeing some of his mother's cattle on the precipitous side of the slopes, nearly on the opposite side of the lake. His duty impelled him to attempt to rescue them from their perilous position. He began to hasten away towards them, when, to his inexpressible delight, the object of his search again appeared to him as before, and seemed even more beautiful than when he first saw her. His hand was again held out to her, full of unbaked bread, which he offered with an urgent offer of his heart also, and vows of eternal attachment. All was refused by her, as she responded:

| *Llaith dy fara!* | *Unbaked is thy bread!* |
| *Ti ni fynna.* | *I will not have thee.* |

However, the smile that played upon her features, as the lady vanished beneath the waters, raised within the young man a hope that forbade him to despair by her refusal of him. The recollection of this cheered him on his way home. His aged mother was told of his ill-success, and she suggested that his bread should next time be just slightly baked, as this was most likely to please the mysterious lady, of whom he had become enamoured.

Impelled by an irresistible feeling, the youth left his mother's house early next morning, and with rapid steps he passed over the mountain. He was soon near the margin of the lake, and with all the impatience of an ardent lover, he waited with a feverish anxiety for the re-appearance of the mysterious lady. The sheep and goats browsed on the precipitous sides of the Van. The cattle strayed amongst the rocks and large stones, some of which were occasionally loosened from their beds and suddenly rolled down into the lake. Rain and sunshine alike came and passed away, but all were unheeded by the youth, so wrapped up was he in looking for the appearance of the lady.

The freshness of the early morning had disappeared before the sultry rays of the noon-day sun, which in its turn was fast verging towards the west, as the evening was dying away and making room for the shades of night. His hopes had well nigh gone of seeing once more the Lady of the Lake. The young man cast a sad and last farewell look over the waters, and, to his astonishment saw several cows walking along its surface. The sight of these animals caused hope to revive, that they would be followed by another object far more pleasing. Nor was he disappointed, for the maiden re-appeared, and to his enraptured sight, looked even lovelier than ever. She approached the land, and he rushed to meet her in the water. A smile encouraged him to seize her hand. She did not refuse the moderately baked bread he offered her; and after some persuasion she consented to become his bride. Her condition was that they should only live together until she received from him three blows, without any cause

| *Tri ergyd diachos.* | *Three causeless blows.* |
|---|---|

And if he ever should happen to strike her three such blows, she would leave him forever. To such conditions he readily consented, and would have consented to any other stipulation, had it been proposed. The young farmer was only intent upon securing such a lovely creature for his wife. Thus the Lady of the Lake engaged to become the young man's wife, and having loosed her hand for a moment, she darted away and dived into the lake. His chagrin and grief were such that he became determined to cast himself headlong into the deepest water. He wished to end his life, in the element that had contained in its unfathomed depths, the only one for whom he cared to live on earth. As he was on the point of committing this rash act, there emerged out of the lake *two* most beautiful ladies accompanied by a hoary-headed man of noble bearing and extraordinary stature, but having otherwise all the force and strength of youth.

This man addressed the almost bewildered youth, in accents calculated to soothe his troubled mind, saying that as he proposed to marry one of his daughters, he consented to the union. The only provision was that the young man could distinguish which of the two ladies before him was the object of his affections. This was no easy task as the maidens were such perfect counterparts of each other. It seemed quite impossible for him to choose his bride, and if perhaps he chose the wrong one, all would be forever lost.

While the young man narrowly scanned the two ladies, he could not perceive the least difference between the two, and was almost giving up the task in despair, when one of them thrust her foot a slight degree forward. The motion, simple as it was, did not escape the observation of the youth. He discovered a trifling variation in the mode with which their sandals were tied, and this at once put an end to the dilemma. On previous occasions, he had been so taken up with the general appearance of the Lady of the Lake, that he had also noticed the beauty of her feet and ankles, and on now recognizing the peculiarity of her shoe-tie, he boldly took hold of her hand.

'*Thou hast chosen rightly*', said her father, '*be to her a kind and faithful husband, and I will give her, as a dowry, as many sheep, cattle, goats, and horses, as she can count of each, without heaving or drawing in her breath. But remember that if you prove unkind to her at any time, and strike her three times without a cause, she shall return to me and shall bring all her stock back with her.*'

Such was the verbal marriage settlement, to which the young man gladly assented. His bride was asked to count the number of sheep she was to have. She immediately adopted the mode of counting by *fives* thus: - '*Un, dau, tri, pedwar, pump'* (One, two, three, four, five) – *'Un, dau, tri, pedwar, pump'* (One, two, three, four, five); as many times as possible in rapid succession, until her breath was exhausted. The same process of reckoning was used to determine the number of goats, cattle, and horses respectively. In an instant the full number of each came out of the lake, when called upon by her father. The young couple were then married, by what ceremony was not stated, and afterwards went to reside at a farm called Esgair Llaethdy, somewhat more than a mile from the village of Myddfai, where they lived in prosperity and happiness for several years. They became the parents of three sons, who were beautiful children.

Once upon a time there was a christening in the neighbourhood, to which the parents were specially invited. When the day arrived, the wife appeared very reluctant to attend the christening, alleging that the distance was too great for her to walk. Her husband told her to fetch one of the horses which were grazing in an adjoining field. *'I will'* said she, *'if you will bring me my gloves which I left in our house.'* Her husband went to the house and returned with the gloves, and finding that she had not gone for the horse, jocularly slapped her shoulder with one of them, saying *'Dos! Dos!'* (Go! Go!). She now reminded him of the understanding upon which she consented to marry him. He was not to strike her without a cause, and she warned him to be more cautious in the future.

On another occasion they were together at a wedding. In the midst of the mirth and hilarity of the assembled guests, who had gathered together from all the surrounding countryside, she burst into tears and sobbed most piteously. Her husband touched her on her shoulder and enquired the cause of her weeping. She said *'Now people are entering into trouble, and your troubles are likely to commence as you have the second time struck me without a cause.'*

Years passed on, and their children had grown up, and were particularly clever young men. In the midst of so many worldly blessings, at home the husband almost forgot that there remained only one causeless blow to be given, which would destroy the whole of his prosperity. Still he was watchful less any trivial occurrence should take place, which his wife must regard as a breach of their marriage contract. She told him, as her affection for him was unabated, to be careful that he would not, through some inadvertence give the last and only blow. By an unalterable destiny, over which she had no control, this would separate them for ever.

However, it so happened that one day they were together at a funeral, where, in the midst of the mourning and grief at the house of the deceased, she appeared in the highest and gayest spirits, and indulged in immoderate fits of laughter. This so shocked her husband that he touched her, saying *'Hush! Hush! Don't laugh.'* She said that she laughed *'because people when they die go out of trouble.'* Rising up, she went out of the house saying, *'the last blow has been struck, our marriage contract is broken, and at an end! Farewell!'* Then she started off towards Esgair Llaethdy, where she called her cattle and other stock together, each by name.

The cattle she called thus*:-

| | |
|---|---|
| *Mu wlfrech, Moelfrech,* | *Brindled cow, white speckled,* |
| *Mu olfrech, Gwynfrech,* | *Spotted cow, bold freckled,* |
| *Pedair cae tonn-frech,* | *The four field sward mottled.* |
| *Yr hen wynebwen* | *The old white-faced,* |
| *A'r las Geigen,* | *And the grey Geingen,* |
| *Gyda'r Tarw Gwyn* | *With the White Bull,* |
| *O lys y Brenin;* | *From the court of the King;* |
| *A'r llo du bach,* | *And the little black calf* |
| *Sydd ar y bach,* | *Though suspended on the hook,* |
| *Dere dithau, yn iach adre!* | *Come thou also, quite well home!* |

[* According to Fransis Payne (*'Yr Aradur Cymraeg', Cardiff 1950*) this 'run' of cattle names is unique in Welsh folk-tales. He suggested that the names can be identified with the names of primitive breeds of cattle.]

The cattle all immediately obeyed the summons of their mistress. The *'little black calf'* although it had been slaughtered, became alive again and walked off with the rest of the stock at the command of the Lady. This happened in the spring of the year, and there were four oxen ploughing in one of the fields, and to these she cried,

| | |
|---|---|
| *Pedwar eidion glas* | *The four grey oxen,* |
| *Sydd ar y maes,* | *That are on the field,* |
| *Deuwch chwithau* | *Come you also.* |
| *Yn iach adre!* | *Quite well home!* |

All of the livestock went away with the Lady across Myddfai Mountain, towards the lake from whence they came, a distance of above six miles. They disappeared beneath its waters, leaving no trace behind except a well marked furrow, which was made by the plough the oxen drew after them into the lake, and which remains to this day as a testimony to the truth of this story.

What became of the frightened ploughman - whether he was left on the field when the oxen set off, or whether he followed them to the lake has not been handed down by tradition. Neither has the fate of the disconsolate and half-ruined husband been kept in memory. But of the sons it is stated that they often wandered about the lake and its vicinity, hoping that their mother might be permitted to visit the face of the earth once more, as they had been told of her mysterious origin, her first appearance to their father, and the untoward circumstances which so unhappily deprived them of her maternal care.

In one of their rambles, at a place near Dôl Howel, at the Mountain Gate, still called 'Llidiad y Meddygon' (The Physician's Gate), the mother appeared suddenly, and accosted her eldest son, whose name was Rhiwallon. She told him that his mission on earth was to be a benefactor to mankind, by relieving them from pain and misery, through healing all manner of their diseases. For this purpose she furnished him with a bag full of medical prescriptions and instructions for the preservation of health. She told him that by strict attention to these, he and his family would become for many generations the most skilful physicians in the country.

Then, promising to meet him when her counsel was most needed, she vanished. But on several occasions she met her sons near the banks of the lake, and once she even accompanied them on their return home as far as a place still called 'Pant-y-Meddygon' (The Dingle of the Physicians). Here she pointed out to them the various plants and herbs which grew in the dingle. She revealed to them their medicinal qualities or virtues, and the knowledge she imparted to them, together with their unrivalled skill soon caused them to attain such celebrity that no-one ever possessed before them. And in order that their knowledge should not be lost, they wisely committed the same to writing, for the benefit of mankind throughout all ages.

And so ends the story of the Physicians of Myddfai, which has been handed down from one generation to another, thus: -

| | |
|---|---|
| *Yr hên wr llwyd o'r cornel,* | *The old grey man in the corner,* |
| *Gan ei dad a glywodd chwedel,* | *Of his father heard a story,* |
| *A chan ei dad fe glywodd yntau* | *Which from his father he had heard,* |
| *Ac ar ei ôl mi gofiais innau.* | *And after them I have remembered.* |

As stated in the Introduction of the present Work, Rhiwallon and his sons became Physicians to Rhys Gryg, Lord of Llandovery (Llanymddyfri) and Dyneyor (Dinefwr) castles, '*who gave them rank, lands, and privileges at Myddfai for their maintenance in the practice of their art and science, and the healing and benefit of those who should seek their help*', thus affording to those who could not afford to pay, the best medical advice and treatment, gratuitously. Such a truly royal foundation could not fail to produce corresponding effects. Thus the fame of the Physicians of Myddfai was soon established over the whole country, and continued for centuries among their descendants.

Of the above lands bestowed upon the Meddygon, there are two farms in Myddfai parish still called Llwyn Ifan Feddyg, (the Grove of Evan the Physician); and Llwyn Meredydd Feddyg (the Grove of Meredith the Physician.) Esgair Llaethdy, mentioned in the foregoing Legend, was formerly in the possession of the above descendants, and so was Tŷ Newydd, near Myddfai, which was purchased by Mr. Holford, of Cilgwyn, from the Rev. Charles Lloyd, Vicar of Llandefalle, Breconshire, who married a daughter of one of the Meddygon. Lloyd had the living of Llandefalle from a Mr. Vaughan, who presented him to the same out of gratitude, because Mr. Lloyd's wife's father had cured him of a disease in the eye. As Mr. Lloyd succeeded to the above living in 1748, and died in 1800, it is probable that the skilful oculist was John Jones, who is mentioned in the following inscription on a tombstone at present fixed against the west end of Myddfai Church.

*HERE*
*Lieth the body of Mr. David Jones, of Mothvey, Surgeon,*
*who was an honest, charitable, and skilful man.*
*He died September 14th, Anno Dom 1719, aged 61.*
*John Jones, Surgeon.*
*Eldest son of the said David Jones, departed this life*
*the 25th of November, 1739, in the 44th year*
*of his Age, and also lyes interred hereunder.*

These appear to have been the last of the Physicians who practised at Myddfai. The above John Jones resided for some time at Llandovery, and was a very eminent surgeon. One of his descendants named John Lewis lived at Cwmbran, Myddfai, at which place his great grandson Mr. John Jones, now resides [*this is in 1861*]. Dr. Morgan Owen, Bishop of Llandaff, who died at Glasallt, parish of Myddfai, in 1645, was a descendant of the Meddygon, and an inheritor of much of their landed property in that parish, the bulk of which he bequeathed to his nephew, Morgan Owen, who died in 1667, and was succeeded by his son, Henry Owen; and at the decease of the last of whose descendants, Robert Lewis, Esq. the estates became through the will of one of the family, the property of the late D.A.S. Davies, Esq. M.P. for Carmarthenshire.

Bishop Owen bequeathed to another nephew, Morgan ap Rees, son of Rees ap John, a descendant of the Meddygon, the farm of Rhyblid, and some other property. Morgan ap Rees' son, Samuel Rice, resided at Loughor, in Gower, Glamorganshire, and had a son, Morgan Rice, who was a merchant in London, and became Lord of the Manor of Tooting Graveney, and High Sheriff in the year, 1772, and Deputy Lieutenant of the County of Surrey, 1776. He resided at Hill House, which he built. At his death the whole of his property passed to his only child, John Rice, Esq. whose eldest son, the Rev. John Morgan Rice, inherited the greater portion of his estates.

The head of the family is now [*in 1861*] the Rev. Horatio Morgan Rice, Rector of South Hill, with Callington, Cornwall, and J.P. for the County, who inherited with other property, a small estate at Loughor. The above Morgan Rice had landed property in Llanmadock and Llangenith, as well as Loughor, in Gower, but whether he had any connexion with Howel the Physician, (ap Rhys ap Llywelyn ap Philip the Physician, and lineal descendant from Einion ap Rhiwallon) who resided at Cilgwryd in Gower is not known.

Amongst other families who claim descent from the Physicians were the Bowens of Cwmydw, Myddfai; and Jones of Dollgarreg and Penrhock, in the same parish; the latter of whom are represented by Charles Bishop, of Dollgareg, Esq. Clerk of the Peace for Carmarthenshire, and Thomas Bishop, of Brecon, Esq. Rees Williams of Myddfai is recorded as one of the Meddygon. His great grandson was the late Rice Williams, M.D. of Aberystwyth, who died May 16th, 1842, aged 86, and appears to have been the last, although not the least eminent, of the Physicians descended from the mysterious Lady of Llyn-y-Van. [John

Rhys, in *Celtic Folklore* (1905) states *'This is not quite correct, as I believe that Dr. C. Rice William, who lives at Aberystwyth, is one of the Meddygon.* ]

The last few paragraphs are taken from the 1861 edition, and an update upon the present physicians of Myddfai appears later in this book. Of the places associated with the legend and its descendants:

Llwyn Ifan Feddyg, (the Grove of Evan the Physician), is sometimes spelt Llwynifanfeddyg, and was a farm, but is now unoccupied.

Llwyn Meredydd Feddyg (the Grove of Meredith the Physician) is now Llwyn Meredydd Farm, the home of the Jones family, descendants of the physicians.

Tŷ Newydd, near the above, was formerly known as Tŷ Issa or Tŷ Isha.

Esgair Llaethdy is six miles from Llyn-y-Fan-Fach, run as a farm by the Morgan family.

Cwmbran is still a farm in Myddfai, run by the Williams family.

Glasallt, parish of Myddfai, is now a care home.

The farm of Rhyblid – Rhyblid Fach is now a holiday cottage near Myddfai;

Cwmydw or Cwm-Ydw or Cwm Ydw, Myddfai is a dairy farm;

There is a 'Ffynnon Meddygon', Physicians' Well, now just a trickle signposted on a footpath past Sarnau, walking towards Mynydd Myddfai.

Pant y Meddygon, Pant Feddygon was partly wooded but has been affected by grazing and the Forestry Commission.

Dôl Hywel is now the site of the Usk Reservoir.

Blaensawdde, or the upper end of the river Sawdde – is situated about three quarters of a mile S. E. from the village of Llanddeusant. It gives its name to one of the hamlets of the parish. The Sawdde has its source in Llyn-y-Fan-Fach, which is nearly two miles from Blaensawdde house.

## JOHN RHYS' EXPANSION OF THE LEGEND IN *CELTIC FOLKLORE* 1905

'This brings the legend of the Lady of the Fan Lake into connexion with a widely-spread family. There is another connexion between it and modern times, as will be seen from the following statement kindly made to me by the Rev. A. G. Edwards, Warden of the Welsh College at Llandovery, since then appointed Bishop of St. Asaph: *'An old woman from Myddfai, who is now, that is to say in January 1881, about eighty years of age, tells me that she remembers "thousands and thousands of people visiting the Lake of the Little Fan on the first Sunday or Monday in August, and when she was young she often heard old men declare that at that time a commotion took place in the lake, and that its waters boiled, which was taken to herald the approach of the Lake Lady and her Oxen."* The custom of going up to the lake on the first Sunday in August was a very well known one in years gone by, as I have learned from a good many people, and it is corroborated by Mr. Joseph Joseph of Brecon, who kindly writes as follows, in reply to some queries of mine: *'On the first Sunday in the month of August, Llyn y Fan Fach is supposed to be boiling (berwi). I have seen scores of people going up to see it (not boiling though) on that day. I do not remember that any of them expected to see the Lady of the Lake.'* As to the boiling of the lake I have nothing to say, and I am not sure that there is anything in the following statement made as an explanation of the yearly visit to the lake by an old fisherwoman from Llandovery: *'The best time for eels is in August, when the north-*

*east wind blows on the lake, and makes huge waves in it. The eels can then be seen floating on the waves.'*

Last summer I went myself to the village of Myddfai, to see if I could pick up any variants of the legend, but I was hardly successful; for though several of the farmers I questioned could repeat bits of the legend, including the Lake Lady's call to her cattle as she went away, I got nothing new, except that one of them said that the youth, when he first saw the Lake Lady at a distance, thought she was a goose - he did not even rise to the conception of a swan - but that by degrees he approached her, and discovered that she was a lady in white, and that in due time they were married, and so on. My friend, the Warden of Llandovery College, seems, however, to have found a bit of a version which may have been still more unlike the one recorded by Mr. Rees of Tonn: it was from an old man at Myddfai last year, from whom he was, nevertheless, only able to extract the statement *'that the Lake Lady got somehow entangled in a farmer's "gambo," and that ever after his farm was very fertile.'* A 'gambo,' I ought to explain, is a kind of a cart without sides, used in South Wales: both the name and the thing seem to have come from England.

Myddfai parish was, in former times, celebrated for its fair maidens, but whether they were descendants of the Lady of the Lake or otherwise cannot be determined. An old pennill records the reputation of their beauty thus:-

| | |
|---|---|
| *Mae eira gwyn* | *There is white snow* |
| *Ar ben y bryn,* | *On the mountain's brow,* |
| *A'r glasgoed yn y Ferdre,* | *And greenwood at the Verdre,* |
| *Mae bedw mân* | *Young birch so good* |
| *Ynghoed Cwm-brân,* | *In Cwm-brân wood,* |
| *A merched glân yn Myddfe.* | *And lovely girls in Myddfe.* |

[*Y Ferdre* is a farm in the parish of Llandingat-Without, which borders Myddfai]. Among other legends about lake fairies, there are, in the third chapter of Mr. Sikes' *British Goblins*, two versions of this story: the first of them differs but slightly from Mr. Rees', in that the farmer used to go near the lake to see some lambs he had bought at a fair, and that whenever he did so three beautiful damsels appeared to him from the lake. They always eluded his attempts to catch them: they ran away into the lake, saying, *Cras dy fara*, &c. But one day a piece of moist bread came floating ashore, which he ate, and the next day he had a chat with the Lake Maidens. He proposed marriage to one of them, to which she consented, provided he could distinguish her from her sisters the day after. The story then, so far as I can make out from the brief version which Mr. Sikes gives of it, went on like that of Mr. Rees.

The former gives another version, with much more interesting variations, which omit all reference, how ever, to the Physicians of Myddfai, and relate how a young farmer had heard of the Lake Maiden rowing up and down the lake in a golden boat with a golden scull. He went to the lake on New Year's Eve, saw her, was fascinated by her, and left in despair at her vanishing out of sight, although he cried out to her to stay and be his wife. She faintly replied, and went her way, after he had gazed at her long yellow hair and pale melancholy face. He continued to visit the lake, and grew thin and negligent of his person, owing to his longing. But a wise man, who lived on the mountain, advised him to tempt her with gifts of bread and cheese, which he undertook to do on Midsummer Eve, when he dropped into the lake a large cheese and a loaf of bread. This he did repeatedly, until at last his hopes were fulfilled on New Year's Eve. This time he had gone to the lake clad in his best suit, and at midnight dropped seven white loaves and his biggest and finest cheese into the lake. The Lake Lady by-and-by came in her skiff to where he was, and gracefully stepped ashore. The scene need not be further described: Mr. Sikes gives a picture of it, and the story then proceeds as in the other version.' [*John Rhys gives several other legends of the Lady of the Lake from around Wales.*]

## THE LEGEND OF THE LADY OF THE LAKE BY EDWARD THOMAS

The '*quintessentially English*' poet Edward Thomas was killed in World War I in 1917, but called himself '*five-eighths Welsh*' and named his children Mervyn, Myfanwy and Bronwen. Thomas wrote *Beautiful Wales* in 1905, and in it gives a wonderful version of the legend: 'On the next day I was near the lake, Llyn-y-Fan Fach, and high up among hills, which had in many places outgrown their grassy garments, and showed bare cliffs, senates of great boulders, and streams of sliding fragments of stone like burnt paper. The delicate mountain sheep were panting in the heat, or following the shifting oasis of a shadow that sometimes moved across the hill; a horse stood nervously still, envying the shadow which he cast upon the ground. The world, for hours, was a hot, long road, with myself at one end and the lake at the other, when gradually I descended into a gentle land again.

Far off, church bells were celebrating the peace and beauty of the morning as I turned into a lane of which more than twenty yards were seldom visible at one time; and I lost sight of everything else. Tall hedgerow elms and orchard trees held blue fragments of the sky among their leaves and hid the rest. Here and there was a cottage among the trees, and it seemed less the work of human hands than the cordon and espalier trees, apple and pear, and the fan-shaped cherry on the wall, with glowing bark. July, which had made the purple plum and the crimson bryony berry, had made it also, I thought. The lane was perhaps long enough to occupy an hour of the most slow-paced tranquil human life. Even if you talked with every ancient man that leaned on his spade, and listened to every young linnet that was learning to sing in the hazels, you could not spend more than two hours in passing along it. Yet, more than once, as I was pausing to count the white clusters of nuts or to remind myself that here was the first pale-blue flower of succory, I knew that I took up eternity with both hands, and though I laid it down again, the lane was a most potent, magic thing, when I could thus make time as nothing while I meandered over many centuries, consulting many memories that are as amulets.

And even as I walked, the whole of time was but a quiet, sculptured corridor, without a voice, except when the tall grasses bowed and powdered the nettles with seed at my feet. For the time I could not admit the existence of strident or unhappy or unfortunate things. I exulted in the knowledge of how cheaply purchased are these pleasures, exulted and was yet humiliated to think how rare and lonely they are, nevertheless.

The wave on which one is lifted clear of the foam and sound of things will never build itself again. And yet, at the lane's end, as I looked back at the long clear bramble curves, I will confess that there was a joy (though it put forth its hands to an unseen grief) in knowing that down that very lane

I could never go again, and was thankful that it did not come rashly and suddenly upon the white highroad, and that there is no such tiling known to the spirit as a beginning and an end. For not without cool shadow and fragrance was the white highroad. Then, after some miles up a hot and silent hill, I came to the lake under the chin of a high summit, and it was cool...

At the end of the twelfth century, when Owen Gwynedd in the north and Lord Rhys in the south made little of English kings, a farmer's widow lived with one son at Blaensawdde, near the lake. She sent her cattle on to the Black Mountain under the care of her son. And the cattle liked Llyn-y-Fan because the great stones on its shore gave them shade, and because the golden stony shallows were safe and sweet, and no water was finer than that in the little quiet wells of the Sawdde brook.

Watching his cattle there one day, the youth saw a lovely girl, with long, yellow hair and pale, melancholy face, seated on the surface of the lake and looking down into the mirror of the water, for she was combing her hair. Some say that she was rowing with golden sculls up and down the lake in a golden boat, so ample was her hair. The young man was moved by her loveliness to hold out to her his own barley-bread and cheese, which was all that he had with him. And she came near, but she would not accept the food; when he tried to touch her, she slid away, saying – "*O thou of the crimped bread, 'Tis not easy to catch me*"; and so disappeared, as a lily when the waves are rising.

The youth told his adventure to his mother, who advised him to take unbaked dough for the girl, instead of his crisp barley bread. The next morning he was at the lake before dawn, and saw cold ripples on the water and a cloud on the highest of the hills. But as the light overcame the cloud and began to warm the ripples, he saw some of his cattle in danger on the steep side of the lake, where the rains run almost perpendicularly down to the margin and cut weals of naked red earth in the mountain-side. And as he was running round to the cattle, he saw the girl upon the water, and again held out his hand to offer his unbaked dough. Again she refused, and said: "*O thou of the moist bread, I will not have thee.*" Then, with smiles, she disappeared. The youth told his second adventure to his mother, and she advised him to take slightly baked bread. The Welsh have a proverb: "*Better is cookery than kingship*"; and she being skilled with the oven, baked him the bread.

The next morning he was again at the lake. The cold ripples turned to gold and then to silver, and the cloud left the mountain; and he saw the wind making grey O's and V's on the water, until it was almost evening, and behind him the oak trees in the Sawdde valley gleamed where his homeward way would be, when he saw several cows walking on the water, and then the girl moving towards him. He ran forward into the water; he held out the bread, and she took it, and promised to marry him on the condition that he should not give her three causeless blows; if he did, she would disappear. Suddenly she left him, and he would have cast himself in with despair, if she had not returned with another as beautiful and in the same way, together with a majestic, tall, and hoary man, who promised to bestow the girl upon him if he could distinguish her.

So the two girls stood before him; and the youth, casting down his eyes in thought and perplexity, saw one thrust her little foot forward, and he noticed how her sandals were tied, because he had before studied the beauty of her ankles and feet; and he chose rightly. The old man promised that they should have as many cattle, horses, sheep, and goats as she could count of each without drawing breath. The girl counted quickly, 1, 2, 3, 4, 5, 1, 2, 3, 4, 5, and so on, and all the beasts came up from the lake; and the young man went with the girl and married her, and lived at Esgair Llaethdy beyond Blaensawdde, and there she bore him three sons.

But one day, when they were to go together to a christening, she was reluctant, saying that it was too far to walk; and he bade her take a horse. She asked for her gloves, and when he returned with them, he found her still delaying, and flicked her shoulder with one and said pettingly, "*Go, go.*" And she reminded him that he had given her a causeless blow. On another day, at a wedding, she gave way to tears, and he tapped her shoulder to admonish her. And she reminded him that he had given her two causeless blows. Many years later, at a funeral, she laughed, and again he tapped her shoulder. And she turned, and called her cattle and horses and sheep and goats by name - the brindled cow, the white speckled, the mottled, the white-faced cows; "*And the grey Geingen / With the white bull / From the court of the king; / And the little black calf / Though suspended on the hook. / Come thou also quite well home*"; and the four grey oxen ploughing in the fields. They followed her to the lake, and behind them grew the furrow made by the plough which the four oxen still drew, and they all entered the lake.

Her sons desired to see her, and she appeared again to her son Rhiwallon, and told him that he was to be a healer of men, and gave him prescriptions, and promised that if he needed her, she would come again. So she often met them near the lake, and once walked with them towards Myddfai, as far as Pant-y-Meddygon, where she showed them herbs and their virtues. And they became famous and good physicians. They were physicians to Rhys Gryg of South Wales; and the last of their descendants who practised at Myddfai was buried in 1739 at Myddfai church.'

## RHYS GRYG – A LIFE

It was to Rhys Gryg's court that the physicians of Myddfai were attached, receiving freehold lands around Myddfai in exchange for their services. The life and times of Rhys Gryg are years of constant fighting, against and with his brothers, father, nephews and Norman invaders. We know he was fighting from 1189 until his death in battle in 1233, at least 44 years of conflict. His father Rhys ap Gruffudd, the Lord Rhys, had overcome the power of the Norman French-speaking lords and reinstated the kingdom of Deheubarth, becoming one of the most admired leaders in the history of Wales.

Dinefŵr is first mentioned in the chronicles in 1163 when Rhys submitted to Henry II at Pencader and was granted Cantref Mawr and land at Dinefŵr. He went on to control an area which covered most of south west Wales, all ruled from his power-base at Dinefŵr Castle outside Llandeilo. Given that Norman control had been imposed and rigorously upheld since 1093 this was a great achievement though he sometimes had the tacit support of the crown.

Rhys Gryg, or Grug, means Rhys the Hoarse, or Rhys the Stammerer. He is also called Rhys Fychan, or Rhys the Younger, as his father was The Lord Rhys. He is called both Rhys Gryg and Rhys Fychan is the panegyric addressed to him by Llywarch ap Llywelyn (*Pridydd y Moch*). Llywarch (fl. 1173-1220) was his contemporary, and was the most prominent court-poet of Gwynedd: '*Proud croak voice, with cruel dented sword / Passionate in anger, harsh in battle / Warmongering, blade-thrusting lion / Bloody spear always at the slant.*' Rhys was the fourth son of Rhys ap Gruffydd, by Gwenllian, daughter of Madog ap Maredudd, King of Powys, who died in 1160.

Rhys married Ellyw ferch Sir Thomas ap Gwgon, who probably died in childbirth. By her he had the sons Rhys 'Mechyll', Iorwerth, Ieuan, Gruffydd, Caradog and Meurig; and the daughters Arddun, Angharad, Ellyw, Gwenllian, Ionet and one unnamed daughter, who may have died with her mother. Rhys also married Joan de Clare, who was born around 1170 in Tonbridge Castle, Kent. Her name is also given as Mathilde, and she was the daughter of Richard de Clare, the third Earl of Hertford. Their children were Hywel, Llywelyn 'Ddiriad' and Philip. His third marriage was to Gwenllian ferch Elidr, and Maredudd was their son.

The Lord Rhys intended Gruffydd, the elder brother of Rhys Gryg, to be his main heir, and in 1189 Gruffydd married Matilda de Braose, having two sons Rhys and Owain. In Rhys ap Gruffydd's old age his sons feuded as to who would succeed him. Welsh laws meant that the kingdom had to be shared equally between all sons, legitimate or illegitimate, which would destroy the power of Deheubarth. Rhys Gryg formed an alliance with his brother Gruffydd ap Rhys against another brother, Maelgwn. In 1189 the Lord Rhys was persuaded to imprison Maelgwn, and he was given into Gruffydd ap Rhys's keeping at Dynefwr Castle. Gruffydd then handed Maelgwn over to his father in law, William de Braose.

In 1192 the Lord Rhys secured Maelgwn's release, but by now Maelgwn and Gruffydd were bitter enemies. In 1194 Maelgwn and another brother Hywel defeated and imprisoned the Lord Rhys, though their father was later released by Hywel. In 1195 the two joined with another brother, Maredudd, in a conspiracy against their father the Lord Rhys and captured Dinefwr Castle. However, the Lord Rhys captured Rhys Gryg and Hywel, and they were imprisoned in Ystrad Meurig Castle.

The Lord Rhys died in 1197. Gruffydd was recognised as his successor, after an interview with the Justiciar of Wales, Archbishop Hubert. Now Maelgwn used troops supplied by Prince Gwenwynywyn ab Owain of Powys to attack Aberystwyth, taking the town and the castle. Gruffydd was taken prisoner, and handed over to Gwenwynwyn, who transferred him to the English who imprisoned him in Corfe Castle. In 1198 Gwenwynwyn threatened the English holdings at Painscastle and Elfael, and Gruffydd was released from captivity to try to mediate in the dispute. His efforts failed, and in the ensuing battle Gwenwynwyn was defeated.

Gruffydd kept his new liberty and by the end of the year had captured all of Ceredigion from Maelgwn except for the castles of Cardigan and Ystrad Meurig. In 1199 he took Cilgerran Castle. Maelgwn now made an agreement with King John, selling him Cardigan Castle in exchange for the possession of the remainder of Ceredigion. In July 1201, Maredudd ap Rhys, one of the Lord Rhys's illegitimate sons was killed in battle in the commote of Carnwallon by the followers of William de Londres II. The English garrison of Cydweli Castle (built by the Lord Rhys in 1190) was involved in the battle. The commotes and castles of Cydweli and Carnwallon passed into Norman hands again.

By 1201, Rhys Gryg's brothers Gruffydd Fychan and Maelgwn had taken possession of most of Deheubarth, only for Gruffydd to die in that year, being buried in Strata Florida Abbey. Rhys Gryg only reappears in 1204, making an alliance with Gruffydd's sons, Rhys and Owain. He drove Maelgwn out of Ystrad Tywi and shared the lands with his nephews, with Rhys Gryg obtaining the larger portion, Cantref Mawr. However, by 1211 he had fallen out with his nephews, who were supporters of Llywelyn the Great (Llywelyn ab Iorwerth).

In support of King John, Rhys Gryg attacked and captured Llandovery from his nephews, in an alliance with English troops. John then forced Llywelyn to give up all his conquests outside the core homeland of Gwynedd. Now, Rhys joined with Maelgwn to eject his nephews from the rest of their lands. However John built a castle at Aberystwyth, and perceiving the threat to Deheubarth, Rhys and Maelgwn changed sides, attacked the castle and burnt it. In 1212 Rhys attacked and burnt Swansea Castle.

The sons of Gruffydd ap Rhys, Rhys and Owain, had now made peace with John and joined his forces. In 1213 an English army led by Falkes de Breauté (Viscount of Cardiff and Warden of the Marches) was despatched to strip Rhys Gryg of his lands and give them to his nephews. *Brut y Tywysogion, The Chronicle of the Princes*, gives us this entry for 1213: '*And after Rhys Gryg had been summoned to answer to the king's command, he said in answer that he would not share a single acre with Rhys Ieuanc* [This is his nephew, Rhys the Young, the brother of Owain].

*And Rhys Ieuanc was enraged. And he gathered a mighty host from Brycheiniog and came by force to Ystrad Tywi, and he encamped in the place called Trallwng Elgan on the Thursday after the eighth day from the Feast of St Hilary. And on the following day, Friday, there came to him Owain, his brother, and Falkes, seneschal of Cardiff, and their hosts. And on the following day they made for the territory of Rhys Gryg and they arrayed their troops and placed Rhys Ieanc and his troop in the van and Falkes and his troop in the centre and Owain and his troop in the rear. And it was not long till Rhys Gryg and his host met with them.*

*And in the battle with the first troop Rhys Gryg and his men were defeated, and he retreated in flight, after some of his men had been slain and others had been captured. And then Rhys Ieuanc went with the intention of laying siege to the castle at Dinefwr. But nevertheless Rhys Gryg forestalled him and fortified the castle with men and arms. And having burnt Llandeilo he retreated thence. But nevertheless Rhys Ieuanc made for the castle.*

*And on the following day he placed engines and contrivances to lay siege to the castle, and made ladders against the walls for his men to climb over the walls. And thus he gained possession of the whole castle except for one tower. And in that the garrison undertook to fight and put up a defence with missiles and other engines; and outside there were archers and crossbow-men and sappers and knights besieging them. And thus they were forced before afternoon to surrender the castle.*

*And they gave three hostages against surrendering the castle unless they received help by noon the following day, on condition that they should have their raiment and their arms and their members safe. And so it was done. And after the castle had been taken Rhys Gryg and his wife and sons and his war-band fled to Maelgwn, his brother, after the castle of Llandovery had been fortified with men and arms and food and engines and other necessities. And a second time Rhys Ieuanc went to Brycheiniog. And then he gathered a mighty host of Welsh and French and made for Llandovery. And before they encamped, the garrison surrendered the castle to him on condition that they should have their lives and their members safe.'*

Rhys Gryg had been defeated at Llandeilo, being forced to flee with his wife and children to Ceredigion and the protection of Maelgwn at Aberystwyth Castle. Later that year, Rhys Gryg was captured and placed in Carmarthen gaol. In 1215 the sons of Gruffydd ap Rhys turned against John, making an alliance with their uncle Maelgwn. The English now released Rhys Gryg, in the hope that he would start a civil war but instead Rhys joined forces with his former enemy Llywelyn the Great.

Rhys, Maelgwn and their nephews joined Llywelyn in the capture of many castles in South Wales in December 1215. In 1215, Rhys Gryg burned and destroyed both Cydweli and Carnwallon (Carnwyllion) castles. Also in that year, Rhys Gryg and Rhys Ieuanc, as allies of Llywelyn ab Iorwerth, attacked Swansea and then captured Oystermouth (an English corruption of Ystum Llwynarth) Castle.

At the parliament held by Llywelyn at Aberdyfi in 1216, Rhys Gryg was given the greater parts of Cantref Mawr and Cantref Bychan and the commotes of Cydweli and Carnwyllion by Llywelyn. From Dinefwr Castle, he now ruled around a third of the old kingdom of Deheubarth. However, in 1220 Rhys Gryg was forced to restore the commotes of Cydweli and Carnwallon to the de Londres family.

In the war of 1231 Rhys joined with his brother Maelgwn's son, Maelgwn Fychan, to burn Cardigan and then and then capture its castle for Llywelyn. In 1234 he joined with Maelgwn Fychan again to attack Carmarthen. He had laid a three-month siege to the castle, and was supervising the building of a temporary bridge across the Tywi. A naval force came up with the tide to demolish the bridge, and he was struck by a missile. He was carried up the Tywi valley to Dinefŵr, but his wounds were too severe, even for the Physicians of Myddfai.

Rhys Gryg died at his home of Dinefŵr Castle shortly afterwards. After a life of constant warfare, Rhys was buried in St David's Cathedral, where his effigy may be seen today. His son Maredudd, Lord of Dryslwyn, succeeded him. Upon Rhys Gryg's death in 1233 internecine fighting started afresh and continued for several generations with the crown intervening from time to time to demand homage and to provide occasional military support. This situation was not resolved until Edward I conquered Wales in 1283.

Court mediciners existed well before their documentation in the tenth-cnetury Laws of Hywel Dda. The first duties of mediciners were to their lord, and it is not surprising that Rhys Gryg's physicians had many remedies for wounds. Rhiwallon or one of his sons would have accompanied Rhys Gryg upon his endless campaigning – fighting against his father, brothers, Normans and Welsh, and also battling for his father, brothers, Normans and Welsh – for at least forty-four years.

In the *Hendregadredd* ms. there is an elegy for Rhys Gryg, attributed to Hopcyn ap Thomos ab Einion, around 1380. In English, it reads:

> *'Many freely-flowing tears course down*
> *About the fortress-tomb of Rhys,*
> *Ruler of Dinefwr, a man of splendid children,*
> *Lion of battle, and its privileged king.*
>
> *Privileged Rhys, a powerful king,*
> *Battle-companion, one who feeds ravens*
> *The chosen hawk among mighty hawks,*
> *We are lost because of the dragon who has departed.*
>
> *I am lost in my grief, enslaved to lamentation,*
> *We are lost without the chieftain, a red-speared lion,*
> *Rhys, son of Rhys, despoiler of Rhos,*
> *Has met his end in a stone tomb at St David's.*
>
> *Near St David's I saw Rhys the attacker of Rhos,*
> *The chieftain, lion of Haverford,*
> *Heroic prince, in a battle of ten thousand men,*
> *Handsome, iron-clad prince.*
>
> *Rhys of the splendid court, captor of Rhos,*
> *Ruler of a host while he lived,*
> *Proud, of stammering speech, and gapped sword,*
> *Deep his wrath, ferocious in battle.*
>
> *Attacker in battle, lion with dripping blade*
> *Was Rhys, red-speared, prompt to anger on the slope*
> *A stammering prince, lord of shining [drinking] horns,*
> *His hand was a safeguard to his armies.'*

Among Rhys Grug's possessions was Cantref Bychan, consisting of the commotes of Hirfryn, Perfedd and Is-cennen. The commote of Perfedd was made up of the maenors (manors) of Myddfai, Llanddeusant, Gwynfe and Fabon. It seems that either Rhys Gryg or his father had placed some of their court officials in Myddfai as free tenants, one of them being Rhiwallon, the mediciner (doctor) to the king's court. A survey of 1317 seems to confirm this, stating that ten free tenants of the maenor of Myddfai had to supply the Lordship of Llandovery with a doctor. This implies that there was a tradition for a doctor from the free tenants of this particular parish, which carried on even after the Normans partially conquered the land.

# THE LATER PHYSICIANS OF MYDDFAI

*'During the thirteenth century this place was much frequented by physicians, among whom was Rhiwallon who, in conjunction with his three sons, while residing here, distinguished himself by a manuscript treatise on the practice of physic, which is preserved among the Welsh manuscripts in the library of the Welsh charity school in London. Tradition affirms that his descendants continued to follow the practice of medicine in the parish till within the memory of persons living at the beginning of this century.' A Topographical Dictionary of Wales* - Samuel Lewis, 1849.

## THE 2011 MEETING

A meeting to celebrate the tradition of the Physicians of Myddfai, its continuation and influence, was held in the New Village Hall at Myddfai upon 2 July 2011. The hall had been opened on the previous Thursday by Prince Charles, who has a home in nearby Llwynywermod. Many had come from some distance, from England, Scotland and the United States. The audience consisted of local people, doctors from the area and individuals interested in the tradition of the distinguished physicians. Eminent speakers included Professor Sioned Davies, Head of Welsh at Cardiff University, who outlined the *Legend of Llyn Y Fan Fach*. Dr Morfydd Owen of Aberystwyth described the historical evidence that exists about the Physicians, material from ancient books and manuscripts. Dr Owen stated that the physicians were not herbalists, but doctors practising to a high standard and receiving high fees. The third speaker was Professor Terry Turner from Cardiff, who created the exhibition about the physicians at the National Botanic Garden at Llanarthne. He described a range of remedies that the physicians employed.

Dr Brynley Jones of Llanwrda outlined how the area around Myddfai had continued to produce high quality doctors. He concentrated on Sir John Williams (1840-1926) from Gwynfe, the greatest medical benefactor to Wales. John Williams played the pivotal role in the creation of the Welsh National Library in Aberystwyth. Dr Donald Williams, Swansea developed this theme by describing the career of Ifor Lewis (1895-1982) who was born in Llanddeusant, an eminent doctor and an important surgical pioneer. He told the meeting about two doctors from Llangadog who, until fairly recently, were consultants at Barts, the world famous hospital in London. Mr Gareth Rees was a cardiac surgeon and Mr Glyn Evans an obstetrician, and both were in the audience. He concluded that the village of Myddfai had continued to produce exceptional doctors. Also present were Dr John Davies of Guildford, Dr Heti Davies of Edinburgh and Professor Robin Jones from Seattle. All three were brought up in the village.

Robin Jones is the son of Llwyn Meredydd Feddyg, a local farm that has strong links with the physicians, and his family are direct descendants of the hereditary physicians. Dr Jones is now a professor of Oncology in Seattle, a world-leading centre for cancer studies.

# THE JONES OF MYDDFAI LINE OF PHYSICIANS

Fenton, when he came to Myddfai in 1809 recorded that the family of Jones who lived at Tŷ Issa were descendants of the Meddygon Myddfai. Margaret Jones of Tŷ Issa (later called Tŷ Newydd, or Tynewydd, after rebuilding) is buried in Myddfai churchyard. Her brothers were James Jones, vicar of Myddfai (1673-1684), and Daniel Jones who lived at Garregfechan, Llanwrda. Daniel Jones had two sons who were surgeons, including William Jones (1687-1756) of Carregfechan and Brunant. Daniel is also buried at Myddfai. James Jones was the son of '*John of Mothvey*', and matriculated from Jesus College, Oxford in 1664/5 aged 17. In the 1684 return we find that Myddfai church possessed a Welsh and an English bible as well as two Welsh common prayer books. James Jones, the then vicar, also had charge of another parish but provided for the parish church in Myddfai to have a curate in his absence.

The son and grandson of Revered James Jones were the surgeons David (d.1719) and John Jones (d.1739), both commemorated in the church porch. There is also a record in the parish register for Llandingat that John Jones, 'Doctor of this town', was buried at Myddfai upon 17 November 1739. His death is also noted in the diary of the great preacher Howel Harris, upon 16 December 1739: '*I hear of a Persecutor at Llanymddyfri* [Llandovery] *Jn. Jones the Surgeon that died miserably and was for having me and others pray for him then, poor soul, the Lord might have left me to be so…*' It seems that John Jones was one of the leaders of the opposition to Harris preaching in Llandovery.

Esgair Llaethdy, mentioned in the legend, was formerly in the possession of descendants of the physicians, and so was Tŷ Newydd, near Myddfai, which was purchased by Mr. Holford, of Cilgwyn, from the Rev. Charles Lloyd, vicar of Llandefalle, Breconshire. Lloyd married a daughter of one of the '*meddygon*', and had the living of Llandefalle from a Mr. Vaughan, who presented him with it out of gratitude, because Mr. Lloyd's wife's father had cured him of a disease in the eye. As Mr. Lloyd succeeded to the above living in 1748, and died in 1800, it seems likely that the oculist was John Jones, who is mentioned with his father David in the inscription on a tombstone in the porch of Myddfai Church. John Jones (d.1739) was at one time thought to be the last descendant of the Meddygon Myddfai, but later that title passed to Rice Williams (d.1842). It has now passed to Robin Jones.

There was a folk tale that the Jones of Myddfai had a record of eleven generations of seven sons in each, with the seventh son becoming a doctor. Probably the practice of medicine was carried out by just one or two families in the village. Some believe that David Samuel (Dafydd Ddu Feddyg), the ship's surgeon who witnessed and described the death of Captain Cook in 1779, was also descended from the Physicians of Myddfai. Families with doctors who claimed descent from the Physicians of Myddfai included the Williams of Aberystwyth; the Jones family of Dolgarreg and Penrhock, Myddfai; the Powell family of Carreg Cennen, Trapp; and the Bowens of Cwmydw, Myddfai. Dolgarreg manor house still stands and was the family seat of the Williams and the Bishops. According to Celtic Folklore (1901), *'the Jones of Dollgarreg and Penrhock… are represented by Charles Bishop, of Dollgarreg, Esq., Clerk of the Peace for Carmarthenshire; and Thomas Bishop, Esq., of Brecon.'* Charles Bishop was Harrow-educated, and was a descendant of John Rhys Bishop of Dolgarreg. The *Cambrian Quarterly* announced the death of John Rhys Bishop in 1832. In 1816 he had featured in a most unusual court case. This was the divorce of John Rees Bishop of Dolgarreg from his wife Gwenllian by *'reason of divers acts of fornication and adultery committed by the said J.R. Bishop'*. There was also the issue of alimony to be allotted Gwenllian Bishop, out of the estate of her husband. The citation and warrant for the appearance of J.R. Bishop at the consistory court in St. Peters Church, Carmarthen was attached to the Church door at Myddfai, but to make doubly sure a copy was delivered personally to Mr Bishop by the court apparitor. It seems he stayed at Dollgarreg while Gwenllian went to nearby Penrhock to live. More upon the Jones line of physicians follows in the Bowens of Cwm Ydw Entry below.

THE WILLIAMS OF ABERYSTWYTH LINE OF PHYSICIANS

There is much more information available upon this line, but this author is no trained genealogist, and lacks both the skills and time to format family trees. Daniel Williams of nearby Llwynywermod (1686-1765) married Elizabeth Morgan, and their son Rice Williams was a surgeon at Queen's Square, London. However, his practice may not have been a success, as upon his death the *London Gazette* 8 July 1788 reported: *'Pursuant to a Decree of the High Court of Chancery, made in a Cause Williams against Williams, the Creditors of Rice Williams, late of Queen's-square, in the Parish of St. Margaret, Westminster, in the County of Middlesex, Surgeon, deceased, are, on or before the 25th Day of January next, to come in and prove their respective Debts before Peter Holford, Esq; one of the Masters of the said Court, at his Chambers in Symond's-inn, Chancery-lane, London, or in Default thereof they will be peremptorily excluded the Benefit of the said Decree.'*

In the Great Sessions Gaol Files for 1785, we read of the trial and conviction of Edward Mason for manslaughter, where Dr. Rice Williams gave evidence: *'…That deponent then saw Edward Mason giving the deceased a blow with a piece of wood used by miners and by them called an overlay, when the deceased was carried off on a sledge in appearance dead, the deceased having previously struck the said Edward Mason two several times... Rice Williams of Aberystwith in the county of Cardigan surgeon on his oath saith that he was applied to go on the tenth day of November last to one Lewis Rowland of the parish of Llanbadarnvawr who had been dangerously beat & bruised in a fray between him & other miners at Ystimtean minework, That on his coming to his house deponent found Lewis Rowland in a state of insensibility, and on examining him he found a depression of the skull on the back part of the head, whereupon deponent thought it necessary to trepan said Lewis Rowland which deponent did the following morning, saith that on his taking out part of the bone he found it no only depressed but fractured which deponent thinks must have been done by a heavy blunt instrument.'* It is difficult to find a genealogy for this Dr. Rice Williams, with Rice being the Anglicised form of Rhys. It is not known at present whether this Rice Williams of Aberystwyth is the same person as Rice Williams of London.

Richard Taunton Oliver informs me of Rees Williams of Myddfai (1650-1739)... *'He seems to have been rather a famous (locally) doctor in his time and a man who was by no means hidebound by convention. In the Genealogical Room of the New York Public Library (History of Carmarthenshire) there is a reference to his getting into trouble for climbing over a high-backed pew during the sermon, in Myddvai church, to wake up a local squire, who was snoring and preventing him from "hearing the Word of God!' Rees Williams of Myddfai was recorded as one of the Meddygon, and his great-grandson Dr. Rice Williams was for many years thought to be the last of the line of the physicians of Myddfai'.* Richard Oliver has kindly supplied his family tree from Rees Williams of Myddfai, who died in 1727. Rees married Katherine, their son William Williams married Joyce, and their son was Lewis Williams, an innkeeper who died in Llandovery in 1763. Lewis Williams married Mary Price around 1749, and their daughter Anne Williams (b.1761) married Charles Williams of Llanfair-ar-y-Bryn, Llandovery on 11 December 1784.

One of their sons was William Williams, FRCS, born in March 1797 at Llandovery, and dying at Penbryn House, Marine Terrace, Aberystwyth on 2 March 1880. Dr. William Williams married Jane Oliver on 9 February 1852 at Llanbadarn Fawr. William Williams practised medicine all his life, appearing in Aberystwyth in 1821 when he married Jane Oliver, and having Charles Rice Williams. They moved to Worcester and then back to Aberystwyth. This son of Dr. William Williams, Dr. Charles Rice Williams of Aberystwyth died in 1890.

The brother of Dr William Williams was also a doctor, Richard Williams. According to *The Aberystwyth Guide* of 1816, Richard Williams lived and practised in Great Darkgate Street, Aberystwyth with his brother, William Williams and both are described as Surgeons. In *The Aberystwyth Guide* of 1816, Richard wrote *'A descriptive analysis of the Chalybeate Spring at Aberystwyth'*. In the same Guide, and in a later 1817 Llandrindod well-water analysis, Richard Williams is described as Surgeon, and Honorary Member of the Physical Society of Guy's Hospital, London. It seems that Richard Williams was born around 1797, and it would appear that he had written his essay on the Aberystwyth chalybeate spring at the age of eighteen, and the book on Llandrindod whilst only nineteen years old. It was not until 10 June 1819, according to the Official List 1815-1840 of the Society of Apothecaries, that Richard Williams was admitted L.S.A.

It hardly seems possible that he could have written his book while still a student or apprentice, and furthermore, he described himself as 'Surgeon' in 1816. It is known that by 1823, and possibly earlier, Richard Williams was taking an active interest in the affairs of the dispensary established two years previously, because in the copy of the Register of the Aberystwyth Dispensary, 1821, there is a *'Report from the 18th February 1822 to 18th February 1823'* signed as follows:- 'I certify this to be correct, Richard Williams.' In 1826 Richard married Susannah Edleston. A letter from Sir Astley Cooper (1768-1841), one of the most distinguished London surgeons of the day, supported Williams' efforts. Written about 1821, it reads *'My dear Sir, I have so high an opinion of your merits and of your desire to do all that can be done in your profession that if my name can be of any service to ye advancement of your institution I beg you will make what use you think proper of it. Yours very truly, Astley Cooper.'*

In the 1966 National Library of Wales Journal, we read that '*RICHARD WILLIAMS, Surgeon, of Great Darkgate Street, Aberystwyth, wrote an Essay bearing the title 'Observations on Parturition amongst the Poor In the Upper District of Cardiganshire', and the manuscript was recently deposited in the National Library of Wales. (N.L.W. 12165D). As relatively few essays of this type exist in Wales it might well be that its publication would be a matter of considerable interest as a sociological as well as a medical document. In this essay Richard Williams is highly critical of the people of the 'Upper District of Cardiganshire' as patients and apparently as persons. The probable date of the manuscript, judging by the watermark of the paper, is about 1837, and the author refers to various current social customs in the County which had survived from previous generations. Some of the customs, such as bidding, received his approval; whilst others, such as bundling, came under his severe censure.*'

When Dr. Richard Williams died a letter was sent to his son, Edleston, from the Shrewsbury specialist in attendance, expressing '*regret that all our efforts failed to preserve so valuable a life*'. There was an announcement in *The Lancet* that Dr. Richard Williams died on 25 December 1855, and the obituary in Medical Times and Gazette, 12 January 1856 reads: '*WILLIAMS:-Recently at Aberystwyth, Richard Williams, Esq. The deceased gentleman held a position of great eminence in the country, and his loss will be deeply felt by a very large circle. Much sympathy has been evinced by the surrounding resident nobility and gentry; and more especially the indigent poor will lament his decease, to whose necessities and distresses he was ever ready to respond. Mr. Williams was the originator of the Aberystwyth Infirmary and the Cardiganshire General Hospital, and also the Medical Attendant upon the inmates of the Aberystwyth House of Correction. He had a large practice among the nobility and the leading clergy and gentry of Aberystwyth and the surrounding district: and was a magistrate for the county, and Coroner for the upper district. He died in his 59th year after a short illness, brought on by exposure to all weathers in the discharge of his duties. The Carnarvon Herald expresses the hope, "that the Infirmary will be carried on as a monument to his memory". L.S.A. 1819; Physician to the Aberystwyth Infirmary; Honorary Member to the Physical Society of Guy's Hospital. Author of "An Analysis of the Medicinal Waters of Llandrindod." 1817.*' With the reference to Richard being 59 when he died, his birth seems to have been around the same time as that of his brother William Willams, which is confusing at present.

There is a historical review of the Aberystwyth Infirmary in the *Programme and Souvenir of a Bazaar* which was held for three days in September 1920. The review refers to the original 1821 Report of the first year of the activities of the Dispensary, and it is headed, '*Public Dispensary under the Patronage of a Charitable Public: Established March 1st 1821*'. After the names of the lay members of the committee appear the names of the physicians, W. Bonsall M.D. and Rice Williams M.D.; and surgeons, Mr. Rathill, Mr. Edwards and Mr. Evans; and '*an extra medical officer, who will give advice to the sick poor in his neighbourhood, John Rogers M.D., Hafod.*' Dr. Rice Williams lived in Bridge Street, Aberystwyth, and in 1810 established the Marine Baths on the Terrace. This is probably a son of Lewis Williams, the Llandovery innkeeper, and thus the uncle of the doctors William and Richard Williams.

In 1813 Rice Willams became the Coroner. By 1824, according to the *Guide to Aberystwyth* for that year, Dr. Rice Williams of Bridge Street and Mr. Richard Williams (his nephew) of Great Darkgate Street, were among the members of the

Aberystwyth Infirmary's Medical Staff. At the same time, the Guide indicated there were two dispensaries in the town both apparently in Great Darkgate Street. One was in a room in the Britannia, which belonged to Dr. William Bonsall, and the other was housed in one of the rooms of the Hearts of Oak.

The *Guide to Aberystwyth* of 1858 seems to note Williams' baths again: '*About the centre of the Terrace, at No. 14, is another establishment, called the Old Warm Bath House, which is fitted up with every regard to comfort and cleanliness, and where every civility and attention is shown. Warm, tepid, and shower baths are provided on the shortest notice.*' Rice Williams claimed that he was the last of the Physicians of Myddfai, a great-grandson of Rees Williams of Myddfai, and died 16 May 1842 at the age of 86 or 87. His birth was registered in Llandovery in 1755. Perhaps, Williams claimed descent from the Physicians of Myddfai to promote his therapeutic bathing establishment in Aberystwyth. He married Jane Cole, one of the Lloyds of Ffos-y-bleiddiaid.

Richard Oliver also tells me that '*Doctor Rice Williams of Aberystwyth (1755-1842), great-grandson of the above Rees Williams, seems to have been a strenuous and colourful person. There are many stories about him, which were still extant when my mother (Jane Jacobs) was a girl. She was once talking about him to an old market-woman, who remembered him in the following terms: "Yes, indeed, he was a devil among the girls, God Bless him!"... I have seen a picture of him (it was destroyed in the bombing of the late war, World War II), and he looked it. The picture shows him in middle age with the powdered hair of the period, shirt frill, lace cuffs and tight-fitting coat. He had a merry eye and a ruddy complexion. There was a black ribbon over one eye, which he had lost either (1) in a duel or (2) as an after result of small pox.*

*As the picture shows him with a perfectly clear skin, I prefer to believe (1). He was a friend of the Duke of Newcastle, and the duel is supposed to have been between them as the result of a quarrel while both were pretty well stewed to the ears. This may be apocryphal, but in the Bridge Street house in Aberystwyth there were two chairs with the Newcastle arms emblazoned on them, supposed to be a present to him from that nobleman, after they became friends again.*'...

*There was another house belonging to him (or his nephew) called Penbryn House, which stood almost on the beach. It was pulled down towards the end of the 19th century to make room for the Parade (esplanade) when Aberystwyth became a popular watering-place, but there was a brass plate on its site "Here stood Penbryn House". I have seen this (about 1902).*

*Incidentally I have a strong resemblance to him, and once went to a fancy dress ball as my Great Grandfather's Uncle, with the costume (including the ribbon) of the picture. The resemblance was startling. Dr. Rice was reputed to be a "three bottle man", and was said to have used the whip from his gig on two ferrymen, who at first refused to take him across the estuary of the river Ystwyth, in a rough sea, to a patient; this at the age of eighty. Most of the above was in an issue of the local paper, about half a century ago, which featured the lady of the Lake story as "A Welsh Fairy Tale". I remember reading this as a boy. I believe that in his youth he served as a surgeon on a privateer in one of the French wars.*'

Actually, Penbryn House was the name of the Dr Rice's bath house, located where the northerly shelter on the promenade now stands, and removed in 1892. Aberystwythguide.co.uk/history gives details of the bath's facilities, including bed chambers, a vapour bath, a shower bath, marine baths and a cold plunging bath.

The line of Rice Williams seemed to have ended with his spinster daughter Anna Maria Williams (d. 1864 or 1865, who left the family home in Aberystwyth to another branch of the family. Rice Williams was the third-great-grand-uncle of Richard Oliver. Rice Williams' sister Anne Williams is the third-great-grandmother of Richard Oliver. Rice and Anne, plus at least five others, were the children of Lewis Williams, a Llandovery publican, who married Mary Price c. 1749.

Lewis Williams would thus be a grandson of the said Rees of Myddfai. So there would be just one generation in the gap. Anne Williams is said to have married a 'cousin' called Charles Williams. If he was also a great-grandson of Myddfai's Rhys Williams, then he and Anne would be second cousins. Rees Williams of Myddfai died in 1727 and his will lists a wife named Katherine and sons named as William, Rowland and David. (This seems to be a different Rees Williams to the one mentioned above who died in 1739). There is also a grandson named Thomas Popkins or Hopkins, so he must have had a daughter also.

This Rees seems to have been a farmer, judging from the livestock he bequeathed, but he could have had medical ancestors. As for medical descendants, Anne and Charles produced Richard Oliver's second great-grandfather William Williams who studied medicine under his uncle Rice in Aberystwyth. William Williams practised as a surgeon all his life, as did his son Charles Rice Williams.

The article *Aberystwyth – A Fashionable Watering Place*, in *The Lancet* 19 March 1881, was co-authored by a C. Rice Williams MD, a great-nephew of Rice Williams, of the Meddygon Myddfai: *'To those requiring the warm or tepid bath, the marine baths at the northern extremity of the Terrace afford the requisite accommodation. These baths are built on a rocky foundation projecting into the sea, called Bryn Diodde, and are defended from the force of the sea by a strong wall. The baths were erected by the late Dr. Rice Williams, a practitioner of old standing in the town, on scientific principles suggested by an eminent engineer, and carried into effect by the public-spirited proprietor without regard to the outlay in accomplishing his scheme. The baths are underlaid by iron pipes extending into the sea, conveying from a pure and rocky source the saline water without any admixture of sand or gravel.*

*The water is pumped by horse power into a cistern, and carried by a conductor thence into a boiler, capable of containing eight hundred gallons, fresh every tide. From the boiler are various pipes leading to the different baths, which baths are six feet long and two and a half wide, lined with Dutch tile, as being less porous and more easily cleansed than marble from the impurities to which they are liable.*

*Each bath occupies one end of a neat room, with a fire place; and there are two cocks attached to every bath, one conducting hot, the other cold water, which bathers can turn and temper to any degree at their own pleasure. A shower bath which is recommended by the faculty to bathers of delicate constitution, as less liable to create cramps than when they use the ordinary cold bath. In an upper apartment is a vapour bath. This building likewise contains bedchambers, intended by the projector for the accommodation of invalids, whose state of health might render it dangerous to remove them after bathing.'* ...

*'Frederick bathed on several days, though he does not say whether in the sea or in the Bath House, built by Dr. Rice Williams on a rocky outcrop near Penbryndioddef in 1810. Mr. Williams, an eminent medical practitioner in Aberystwyth, had been a pupil of Sir Astley P. Cooper, a leading London surgeon, and was also an honorary member of the Physical Society of*

*Guy's Hospital. Sir Astley, whose second wife was Catherine Inglis Jones of Derry Ormond, became consultant surgeon to the Aberystwyth Dispensary, founded in 1821.*

*In his diary for 8 January 1819, Frederick recorded: 'Wrote Mr Williams of Post Office, Aberystwyth about his son's book, viz: Analysis of ye Llandrindod Waters'; this book had been published in London in 1817. (Journal of the Cardiganshire Antiquarian Society: Vol 10 1984-1987 Holidays at Aberystwyth, 1798-1823: from the diary of Captain Frederick Jones). A former secretary of Aberystwyth's Freemasonic Lodge, Williams was its Grandmaster in 1880-1881. John Rhys, writing Celtic Folklore in 1881, mentions this C. Rice Williams as being descended from the physicians of Myddfai. Dr Rice Williams was the Poor Law Medical Officer for Aberystwyth 1887-1890. Born in Aberystwyth in 1822, he died on 26 February 1890 at Marine Terrace, Aberystwyth.'*

This C. Rice Williams must have practised in Aberystwyth. Dr C. Rice Williams has a memorial in Llanbadarn churchyard, and there is an amusing account of an incident on his working life: *'William Joseph Davies may be buried at Llanbadarn; many attended his funeral at that place and watched his coffin lowered into the grave. William was born at Tanycastell Farm, Llanfarian, and seems to have been a man of some promise for he obtained a Master's degree at Oxford and became a Church of England clergyman. He lived with his wife and three sons at Llanbadarn but when his wife died he moved, with his sons, to The Cupola, a common lodging house at Penyranchor, Trefechan, and seems to have lost his interest in life.*

*Davies was a big, tall and strong man, but his eccentric behaviour soon earned him the nickname Cracky Bill. He was often in trouble as a result of his drinking but took some pleasure in conducting his own defence before the magistrates, many of which were reported in the newspapers. On one occasion he was pressed by the Clerk of the Court to answer a direct question. Davies rounded on the man and replied "No. I won't answer any of your questions, because you bully me. You have no right to speak, Sir, your duty is to advise the Magistrate and not to talk. You think to have your own way here, but you shan't."*

*When told by the Magistrate to be quiet, Davies politely asked if he was entitled to expenses for attending the Court. Davies was also involved in a war of attrition with the Board of Guardians of the Aberystwyth Workhouse and threatened to assault the Master as well as accusing some Guardians of failing in their duties. Perhaps as a result of his lifestyle Davies fell ill and was treated by a highly respected local physician, Dr Rice Williams.*

*After his death many attended his funeral at Llanbadarn but soon rumours began to spread around Trefechan that Davies had made a deal with the Doctor whereby he received free medical treatment while alive, and the Doctor would then take his skeleton after his death, and that the coffin only contained large stones. The presence of a large skeleton in the doctor's surgery only served to confirm the rumours in the minds of many people. Like many of his contemporaries who died poor Davies had no memorial headstone; only a simple wooden cross, marked with the letters W.D, marked his grave.'* (A.W. Gilbey and Penglais School History Society Llanbadarn Churchyard website.)

Richard Oliver is looking for details of his great-great-grandmother Jane Oliver. She was born in or near Aberystwyth about 1803, and married Dr. William Williams in Llanbadarn Fawr in 1821. He said that *'owing to a quirk of fate her surname has come down to me instead of her husband's.'* The two sons of the marriage were Charles Rice Williams (surgeon) and William Oliver Williams (1829-1901, a noted artist, who is represented in the Tate Gallery).

There was also a Doctor Rice Williams working at the National Agriculture Advisory Service in Aberystwyth in 1960, who although probably a scientist rather than a medical doctor, may have been descended from Charles Rice Williams. The Williams of Aberystwyth family weaves a tangled web beyond this author's powers to untangle.

THE POWELLS OF CARREG CENNEN LINE OF PHYSICIANS

The *Welsh Medical Gazette* of Winter 1971 draws our attention to two later doctors than Rice Williams or Charles Rice Williams. Joan Jones, niece of John Jones, the *'last physician of Myddfai'* married John Rees. Their daughter, Anne Rees, married Lewis Hopkins of nearby Llangadog. Their son was Edward Hopkins (b. 1875), and their daughter Mary Hopkins married Thomas Powell of Llangyfelach, going to live at Carreg Cennen. Edward Hopkins became a surgeon-major in the army and served with Lord Roberts, taking part in the Kabul to Khandahar march in the Afghan War. He was on the First Infantry Brigade staff and also served in the Indian Mutiny, Egypt 1884-86 and Umbeyla. Upon retirement as a Brigade-Surgeon Lieutenant-Colonel, Edward Hopkins worked freely for local people around Carreg Cennen who in 1908 presented him with a large portrait of himself. The painting still hangs in Carreg Cennen House.

John Edward Powell died in 1970, aged 95. He was descended in the female line from his great-grandmother Joan Jones mentioned above, and was the nephew of Edward Hopkins. He qualified from Guy's Hospital and entered the Royal Navy Medical Service. In 1900 he served on HMS Centurion the flagship on the China Station, under Admiral Lord Jellicoe, and treated Lord Jellicoe when he was hit in the Boxer Rebellion. Leaving the navy in 1903, Powell joined the army, and commanded a field ambulance in France throughout World War I. Lieutenant-Colonel John Edward Powell served with the Royal Army Medical Corps, and was awarded the DSO in the London Gazette of 22 June 1917.

Leaving the army in 1923, he served as a GP in Llandovery until 1931. Dealing with many monoglot Welsh speakers, Powell regained fluency in his childhood Welsh. In 1931 John Powell inherited Carreg Cennen House and retired from practice, later moving to Tenby. A treasured possession was the 1861 edition of *The Physicians of Myddfai*.

William Wilkins' mother's father was John Edward Powell, and much of her interest in plants came from gathering wild plants and herbs during the War. She was directed by the WRVS which to search for useful wild plants, and grew, gathered and dried plants for medical purposes[+]. Her interest was passed on to William, who became a highly successful artist. However, William has also contributed massively to Welsh heritage. He has been involved in the restoration of Llanelly House, one of the greatest landcaped gardens in Europe at the Hafod Estate, the restoration of the gardens at Aberglasney, and inspired the foundation of the National Botanic Garden on the Middleton Hall Estate at Llanarthne. Wilkins has done more for Wales than any other person in this author's lifetime. The latter three projects would be cherished in any country in the world.

* In World War I, the British Government paid a shilling per pound for garlic, which was used with sphagnum moss to help the healing of war wounds. The juice and pulp of garlic have antiseptic properties.


## THE BOWENS OF CWM YDW LINE OF PHYSICIANS

Living at Llwyn Meredydd Feddyg are Lewis and Bethan Jones. Lewis farmed here until recently. His son is Dr Robin Jones, presently working in Seattle as Professor of Oncology in a world-leading cancer research initiative. One of the recognised families in Myddfai which was descended from the physicians were the Bowen family of Cwm Ydw, a farm in Myddfai. Professor Jones's great-great grandmother Ann Morgan, born in 1832, was a direct descendant of the Bowen family of Cwm Ydw. It thus appears that the physicians of Myddfai survive from around 1190 (or possibly earlier) to the present day, over 800 years. Owen Bowen (1695-1761) of Cwm Ydw had a son William (1734-1813), and his great-grand-daughter Ann Morgan (1832-1868) married Thomas Jones (1826-1918) of Llwyn Meredydd Feddyg, Myddfai. Lewis Jones is the grandson of Thomas Jones and Anne Morgan (1828-1866).

Lewis Jones was born at Cwm Ydw, and has farmed at Llwyn Meredydd Feddyg, opposite Tŷ Newydd, for most of his life. Lewis says that the unique heritage of collecting plants as remedies has come down from the eighth century to the present day. He remembers his father making a remedy for a lady who had jaundice. He took off the bark and used the yellow sap, boiling it to make a juice to drink. The tradition may stem from treating like with like, e.g. yellow jaundice with yellow juice.

Elderflower wine was a 'great favourite' as a remedy for colds, and elderflower wine was kept in storage for winter. Elderberry wine was used for influenza, and both were to be taken last thing at night. An older villager said that everyone should raise their hat to the elder tree (this was in the 1930s when everyone wore hats), as it was to be especially valued. Sloe wine was the best medicine for diarrhoea, and the strongest wine was rhubarb. Lewis remembered that during the war there was no petrol, so farmers used potato wine to run their Fordson tractors and work the land.

Young nettle shoots (not from bushy plants) are still used to make nettle tea, to 'purify the blood', and for arthritis and rheumatism. The young shoots are also placed in cawl or broth as few minutes before serving. (This author has had nettle soup in Galway, and it is delicious.) Nettles, when small, were also used in omelettes and in flavouring ginger beer. Nettles were boiled and the liquid drunk for better heart circulation. The bitter wormwood was recommended for stomach ache or a 'bad stomach', with boiling water being poured on the leaves and left to infuse for a while. Prince Charles' nearby home is called Llwynywermod, Grove of the Wormwood.

Lewis and Bethan reminisced about eating a lot of watercress which grew around the well at the beginning of a stream. It was especially favoured in sandwiches, but the water is not as clean now, probably because of the use of chemical fertilizers upon fields. Holly was used to beat chilblains until they were red and bleeding, and then one walked barefoot in the snow to cool the feet down. Lewis recalls that his mother had a condition in her eye, and a local lady recommended the juice of crushed snails, similar to a recipe of the Physicians of Myddfai.

Raw egg and sherry was a favourite tonic if one was run down. Goose fat was always retained, and rubbed into a bad chest. A flannel vest was then worn over it to stop chest colds. Sometimes brown paper was placed over the goose fat, probably to stop it rubbing off on clothing. People really believed that the 'quench water' from the village smithy could cure warts. Bacon was also bandaged over a wart to remove it, or they were treated with the milky sap from the stems of dandelions. There were also plant cures for sheep, cattle, chickens, horses etc.

Lewis states that ringworm can exist in wooden partitions for years, so everyone had their own secret recipe. One local lady was known to be able to cure ringworm with her remedy, but she died in her 80s and the recipe was lost. Lewis and Bethan remember eating cuckoo cheese, *caws y gwcw*. This seems to be an unrecorded name for *bara can y gwcw* (white cuckoo bread), which is common wood sorrel. Wood sorrel, Oxalis acetosella, has been eaten by humans for millennia, its slight sourness giving it a refreshing taste. Algonquin Indians consider it an aphrodisiac, for those who are interested. Cherokees took it for mouth sores and sore throats, and the Kiowa chewed it to alleviate thirst on long trips.

The Morgans of Esgairllaethdy were convinced that the water from the nearby Physicians' Well, Ffynnon Meddygon, was good mineral water. Villagers remember crowds of local people going to Llyn-y-Fan Fach every August upon horseback. Older villagers also remember the esteemed herbalist, Dr Yemm of Ammanford in the 1940s. He was said to be able to cure yellow jaundice and diabetes, by recommending not only plant remedies but changes in lifestyle. Yemm would only charge if people could afford it, but *'went to his grave with all his knowledge'*. Yemm's daughter was also thought to have become a doctor.

Dr. John Rees Yemm of Ammanford was widely respected until his death in 1958. Arguing against the sectional interests of the medical establishment, he presented his herbal skills and knowledge as a means by which ordinary people could become their own doctors and treat themselves without recourse to the 'poisonous' and 'evil' polypharmacy of orthodox medicine. Yemm delared: *'I believe in medical liberty.'* To him, natural, health-giving herbal treatments were preferable to the unnatural methods practised by qualified doctors and were, in any case, more effective.

Yemm first became interested in herbalism through the works of Nicholas Culpeper, an English herbalist of the seventeenth century, when his father became ill. Acquainting himself with the works of other notable herbalists, Yemm embarked upon a prolonged course of professional training in herbalism. In 1921 he sat and passed the examinations of the National Association of Medical Herbalists (NAMH), and in 1926, was elected to the council of the NAMH. Dr. Yemm then took courses in physiotherapy and naturopathy in Chicago and received a doctorate in the latter from the National College of Naturopathy in Iowa. He built up an extensive practice in the Ammanford area and, at the same time, promoted the interests of organised herbalism through his editorship of the journal *Medical Herbalist*, the official organ of the NAMH. A group of herbalists in south Wales, and the wider movement of which it was a part, saw itself as a highly skilled profession and aspired to official recognition. Constantly criticising the state-protected monopoly of orthodox medicine, the NAMH lobbied the government to grant it professional status. A fund was started to build a college where herbalists could be trained and professional qualifications conferred. At this time, J. F. Bridgman of Neath was still receiving a great deal of work as a urine-caster, Dr. Yemm claimed to be skilled in '*Osteopathy, Chiropractic, Eclecticism, Bio-chemic, Hydrotherapy, Physio-Medicalism, scientific herbalism.*'

## A NOTABLE LOCAL DOCTOR AND MORE MYDDFAI PHYSICIANS

Just under seven miles from Myddfai, at Bailey Farm, Gwynfe, Carmarthenshire, John Williams was born in 1840, the son of David Williams, Congregational minister. John Williams' father died when he was only two, so he was brought up by his mother Eleanor, who now ran the farm. Educated locally, John Willams entered the Normal College, Swansea with the intention of joining the ministry, but left to study medicine at Glasgow University, 1857-58. He was then apprenticed to two Swansea doctors, and went on to the University College Hospital, London. Williams was a superb student, gaining his MRCS, MB and MD in addition to winning a gold medal for pathology, before establishing a general practice in Swansea. Here he began collecting books of Welsh and Celtic interest which would form the basis of the collections of the National Library of Wales. In 1872, he married Mary Elizabeth Anne Hughes, and returned to London.

He took up the post of House Surgeon at the University College Hospital, the beginning of a successful career as a medical practitioner and teacher. In 1886 he was made Court Physician, attending Queen Victoria, and was raised to the baronetcy by her in 1894. He was given a KCVO in 1902 and a GCVO in 1911. He also dedicated his energies toward the establishment of a Welsh Hospital in South Africa during the Boer War, and toward the campaign for the eradication of tuberculosis in Wales. In 1894, Williams was made a baronet, and he received honorary doctorates from the Universities of Glasgow, Edinburgh, Aberdeen and Wales.

The special contribution of Sir John Williams to the progress of medicine was his immediate application of Lister's discoveries on antiseptics to the practice of obstetrics, and then, as an operating gynaecologist to the surgery of the abdomen, made possible by these new methods. It was Williams who first combined in one person, the practice of obstetrics and the skill of an operating gynaecologist.

Williams was a skilful operator, both in plastic and abdominal work. Williams' success in ovariotomy which was the chief factor in obtaining for obstetricians the right to operate at the hospitals of other medical schools, a right now universally recognised, to the great advantage of gynaecology. 1903 saw Williams return to Wales once again, settling at Llansteffan, Carmarthenshire, in order to be closer to, and more involved with Welsh culture during his retirement. He had become involved with the Welsh Library Committee of the University of Wales, Aberystwyth, which was calling for the establishment of a national museum and library for Wales.

In 1898, Williams had purchased the *Peniarth* collection of manuscripts, with the aim of donating it to the National Library of Wales, if that institution was established at Aberystwyth. It was, and Williams donated the *Peniarth* and *Llansteffan* manuscripts, along with his own library of 25,000 books, to the institution on its opening in 1909. He was made first President of the National Library of Wales, a position to which he was re-elected upon many occasions. He was also made President of the University of Wales, Aberystwyth in 1913.

Sir John was suggested as a possible Jack the Ripper suspect in 2005 by Tony Williams (an actual relative) in his book *Uncle Jack*. His theory is that Williams, in an attempt to find a cure for his wife's apparent infertility, stalked Whitechapel looking for women of a similar age whom he may have been familiar with from his clinic in Whitechapel (where he was an obstetrician), killed them, and removed their uteri which he took back to the hospital to study. Williams goes on to suggest that Mary Kelly was John Williams' lover.

Why did Williams believe that his illustrious ancestor was Jack the Ripper? In amongst Sir John's belongings in the collection of the National Library were a knife and three slides containing *'animal matter'*. In addition, there is a letter where Sir John indicates that he will be in Whitechapel on the 6th of September 1888. There is also a notebook listing patients in which Sir John has noted that he has performed an abortion on a 'Mary Ann Nichols' in 1885.

However, there is very little to suggest that he was Jack the Ripper. Jennifer Pegg demonstrated in two articles that the version of the notebook entry published in Uncle Jack to show that Sir John Williams had met Ripper victim Mary Ann Nichols had been altered for print and did not match the original document. The entry in the original document, housed in the National Library of Wales, was written in different handwriting from that found in the rest of the book. She further demonstrated that much of the other research in the book arguing for a link between Sir John Williams and the Ripper crimes was flawed. Sir John Williams, 1st Baronet, GCVO, KCVO, MD, FRCP died on 24 May 1926 at Aberystwyth, bequeathing his beloved Library of Wales, which he effectively founded, a large sum of money.

Notably, Dr. Donald Williams is a descendant of Sir John Williams. Donald has studied how the story of the physicians has lasted over the centuries to the present day. He was born at Glanceidrich Farm, Bethlehem, in sight of Mynydd Myddfai, and he recalled that the story of the Lady of the Lake and the Physicians of Myddfai was part of his boyhood culture. He also recalled the other famous line of Welsh medical men, the *'bone-setters of Anglesey'*, a line which carried through from Tudor times to Hugh Owen Thomas (1834-91) and Sir Robert Jones (1857-1933). Hugh invented the *'Thomas splint'*, revolutionising the treatment of fractures of the thighbone. His nephew Sir Robert Jones was *'the father of modern orthopaedic surgery'* and established the world-renowned orthopaedic hospital at Gobowen on the Welsh border. [This author's mother and aunt briefly worked there during wartime, as does a cousin today].

64

Donald Williams had a distinguished career as a physician and consultant psychiatrist and has recounted eminent Welsh physicians practising across the globe. Two boys in school with him at Llandovery, Gareth Rees and Glyn Evans became consultants at St. Bart's, the leading London teaching hospital. Gareth Rees of Llangadog, near Myddfai, was a noted consultant cardiac surgeon, and Glyn Evans came from a farm outside Llangadog. Evans was a consultant obstetrician and gynaecologist, and was awarded the MBE in 1975 for his services at the scene of the Moorgate Train disaster.

Donald arranged for Glyn and Gareth to give a talk at their old school in 2009, and he noted that as well as Sir John Williams, Glyn and Gareth, there had been another local man, Ifor Lewis (1892-1982) of medical renown. Ivor Lewis was born in Llanddeusant and brought up at Carnau Gwynion, Gwynfe, near the Black Mountain. In 1938 Lewis was the first British surgeon to perform a successful pulmonary embolectomy, an emergency operation to remove a fatal blood clot from the lungs. Don then decided to arrange a meeting in Myddfai in 2011, and even more local doctors emerged from this tiny, under-populated area.

Apart from Professor Robin Jones, mentioned above, Don discovered Dr. Eurfyl Richards, born in 1934 in Myddfai post office. Eurfyl Richards' father, uncle and grandfather had been the village blacksmiths, and his mother had been the village postmistress. Eurfyl opted to become a GP, practising in Worcester, but unfortunately died recently. Attending the 2011 Myddfai meeting along with Professor Robin Jones was Dr. John Davies, the son of Myddfai's vicar, who became a GP in Guildford. Dr. Heti Davies of Llandeilo was the daughter of the headmaster of Myddfai School, becoming a consultant psychiatrist in Edinburgh. Also attending the 2011 meeting were the doctors and consultants Anna Davies of Llangadog, Terry Davies of Cwmllynfell, Siôn Edwards of Cilycwm, Llandovery, Olwen Harries of Llangadog, Gareth Rees of Llangadog, Glyn Evans of Llangadog, Gordon Thomas of Llandovery, and Donald Williams of Bethlehem, among others.

THE IMPORTANCE OF MYDDFAI

Michael Porter has researched extensively into the need for 'clusters of excellence' to achieve success in industry or services. There has been for centuries a cluster of medical expertise in the form of herbalists, physicians and researchers from the small area surrounding Myddfai. One of the major problems in Welsh rural areas has been that farms and smallholdings are only sufficient to raise a single family. There has been a tradition of large families, with the farm being left to one child, rather than breaking it up. Often the parents stay on the farm, so there may be three or even four generations living in a farmhouse and perhaps farm cottage. This has often led to major resentment from the children who have not been left the 'family business'. (The same principle applies to the local blacksmith, baker and so on.) However, around Myddfai, these non-farming children have always had another option. They have seen their peers' uncles, grandfathers etc., becoming respected doctors from humble beginnings.

Unlike in other parts of the country, there is an expectation that children can 'break out' and improve themselves in an occupation thought unattainable elsewhere. There is a similar resonance in the mining valleys where children were encouraged to become teachers, and avoid the terrible working conditions down the pit. Equally, seamen in many Welsh ports encouraged their children to get an education and avoid a hazardous and uncomfortable life at sea. Myddfai and its environs have had an integral aura for children and adolescents. They grew up knowing about plants and herbs, and being attended by local people, and seeing local people rise to eminence as physicians.

The herbalist Lara Bernays was brought up in Myddfai, which formed her view of the world, as it did with many other medical practitioners from the local area, but there is more that can be learned from what is happening here. Villagers and people living nearby are committed to keeping local culture alive, even if they are incomers to the area. This sense of pride in one's '*bro*' (locality or community) is essential for rural areas to survive. Without a community spirit, there is nothing – in the memorable words of Yeats – '*Things fall apart; the centre cannot hold*'. People have to work together for a community to survive and thrive, respecting the past and building upon it. Too many pretty parts of Wales are now full of second homes and holiday homes. The nature of Cymrucism has lasted for two millennia and we must strive hard to keep it.

LLYN-Y-FAN-FACH

The Western Mail 27 September 2011 reported that: '*A remote Carmarthenshire lake shrouded in Welsh legend has been named as one of the 1,000 must-see sights across the globe by an influential travel bible.*

*Llyn y Fan Fach, 12km southeast of Llandovery in the Brecon Beacons, is the only spot in Wales to make the list, which was put together by Lonely Planet. The travel guide describes the Mid Wales beauty spot as "enchanting" and recounts the tale of The Lady of the Lake. "This isolated drop of blue, beneath a cirque of raw Welsh hills, is enchanting – and enchanted," Lonely Planet's 1,000 Ultimate Sights tells readers. "The story goes that in the 13th century a farmer grazing cattle on the nearby slopes spotted the most beautiful woman he'd ever seen. "She was a fairy maiden, who agreed to marry him on one proviso – he must not hit her more than twice. "In time, the inevitable happened – three strikes, and the otherworldly wife disappeared back into the lake, taking her magic cows with her."*

*The valley, the guide adds, is rich in medicinal herbs and bog plants, suggesting this may be the mistreated fairy maiden's healing legacy. The lake is featured in the top 10 most unusual lakes category, which is one of 100 top 10 lists in the book. Broadcaster and conservationist Iolo Williams, said he could understand why the site had made the list. "It's a fantastic place," he said. "The walk up to it, following the river up, and the river's got dippers and grey wagtails. You go up to the lake and you climb up the ridge and you can see all the peaks of the Brecon Beacons. It's a magical place. If you enjoy walking, if you enjoy scenery, it's a beautiful place. For people like me, the added bonus is red kites are quite common in the area."*

Fortunately, the area lies within the Brecon Beacons National Park, and is not subjected to the inefficient blight of wind-powered intermittent energy stations, referred to in marketing-speak as windfarms (one wonders why there are no nuclear, gas, water or coal farms). Wales has five times the density of these environmental disasters as does England, as the wind obviously stops at Offa's Dyke. Plaid Cymru is still fervently proselytising for more wind turbines, pylons, substations and roads and should rename itself Plaid Gwynt, The Party of Wind. China is building a coal-powered power station every week, so how despoiling Wales can halt climate change is anyone's guess.

Wales already has three times the electrical energy that it needs, with its latest power station at Pembroke snaking all its power over massive pylons across Wales into England. The new nuclear reactor at Wylfa will supply at 75% load factor 2.8 million homes, whereas Wales has a population of only 3 million. This means that Wales will have over six times its energy needs, with nearly all of it going to England. The new Pembroke station has about the same capability, and there is yet another proposed station in Pembroke, which will then make up to 9 times Welsh energy needs. Wales has only one industry, tourism, and the Party of Wind seems determined to ruin it. The Cambrian Mountains, the spine of the tiny country of Wales, have been often proposed as a National Park, but are plastered with wind turbines, with hundreds more on their way. The Cotswolds, the Chilterns, the Shropshire Hills are treated as sacrosanct landscapes, but the far more ecologically diverse and attractive hills of Wales are thought expendable. For those in denial, please read about Milanković Wobbles in my 2012 book on inventions.

Llyn y Fan Fach lies about 2 miles to the east of Llyn y Fan Fawr, being of similar origin and size but was dammed in the 1930's. Llyn y Fan Fawr (lake of the big peak or hill) is a natural lake, lying at the foot of Fan Brycheiniog, the highest peak of the Black Mountain range within the Brecon Beacons National Park. The lake is enclosed within a rock hollow formed as a result of glacial action during the Ice Ages, and is drained by a stream known as Nant y Llyn whose waters flow into the River Tawe, exiting into the sea at Abertawe (Swansea). The surface of Llyn y Fan Fawr lies almost 2,000 feet above sea level.

## PART 4

## BOOK ONE – THE RED BOOK

Professor Morfydd E. Owen (now Davies) has described the roles of medieval court mediciners such as Rhiwallon and his sons. The court mediciners, or meddygon llys, were respected members of the court who not only looked after the noble's household, but also cared for subjects living outside the court in their community. Their first role was to deal with whatever injuries arose from battle wounds or skirmishes. Rhiwallon and his sons were given freehold lands and rights in perpetuity for such services, acting almost like today's local health service. They also provided advice on what the king should eat, and administered medicines for a wide range of ailments, including herbal treatments, surgery and blood letting. Payment for these services followed a strict tariff where the damaged part of the body was ranked: '... *the value of the tongue is the value of all the limbs... if a man's ear be cut off, but he still has the ability to hear, the value of such abscission is two cows and two ounces of silver, if it be completely closed (i.e. deaf) six cows and six ounces of silver... the value of a finger is two cows and twenty pence... the genital organs are equated with one half of the limbs... if anyone be struck on the head and bone fragments are shed from the upper part of the skull four legal pence should be paid for every fragment of bone which shall sound in a brass basin; but if from a lower part (of the) skull, four legal pence should be paid for every fragment of bone which shall sound in a brass cup...'*

In Books One and Two – If the footnoted asterisk* is followed by italics, that note is explained by this editor. If not in italics, the text follows John Pughe's translation. Equally, anything in square brackets is by this editor, but notes in normal brackets are by Pughe. In Book One, the Welsh is in the form of Middle Welsh, and there were no headings for each remedy. Translation is far more difficult for Book One, and Pughe's headings for the English translation have generally been used.

Book Two is in modern Welsh, and the Welsh headings have been retranslated into English. The numbering system has been kept intact from Pughe's original translation. Where this author disagrees with Pughe's translation, it is asterisked and footnoted after the remedy. Any remedies expurgated by Rev. John Williams are now included, along with the original Welsh in case of any mistranslation by this author.

# THE PHYSICIANS OF MYDDFAI

From the original manuscript transferred from the Library of the Welsh Charity School, London to the British Museum. Book I is taken from the copy known as the *Red Book*, in Jesus College Oxford. This was collated by Reverend Robert Owen, Fellow of Jesus College, with a transcript *'made by the late Mr. Saunders, from Mr. Rees of Tonn's copy; which manuscript was, moreover, copied about 1766, by William Bona of Llanpumsaint, from another belonging to Iago ap Dewi of Llanllawddog.*'*
*[Iago's *Maxims* are listed in the earlier Preface]

[The Jesus XXII manuscript's colophon, or introduction, has been translated by Dr. Morfydd Owen as: 'This book was put together from the various books of the physicians and mediciners, such books as have been proved to be correct, namely the books of Rhiwallon, the doctor, and his sons, namely Cadwgan, Gruffudd, and Einion.']


## INTRODUCTION

Here by the help of God, the almighty Lord, are shown the most notable and essential remedies for healing man's body. And those who caused them to be written down in this manner were Rhiwallon the Doctor, and his sons, Cadwgan, Gruffydd and Einion. They were the ablest and most eminent of the physicians of their time, of the time of Rhys Gryg* their lord, and the lord of Dinefwr, the nobleman who safeguarded their status and privilege, completely and honourably, as was their due. The reason why they thus caused the rules of their art to be committed to be written down was, lest there be no one who knew the should be found after them so endowed with the requisite knowledge after their days [were over].

*Pughe footnotes:* *Rhys Gryg, 'arwr Dinefwr' [hero of Dinefwr] was the son of Rhys ap Gruffydd, Prince of South Wales. He married the daughter of the Earl of Clare, A.D. 1219, died at Llandeilo Fawr in 1233 [1234], and was buried in the Cathedral of St David's, where his monumental effigy still remains in a good state of preservation. Rhys Gryg was a distinguished warrior, and fought with various success in the wars which were carried on in Wales, almost without intermission, during his life. Several odes are preserved in the first volume of the *Myvyrian Archaiology*, which were addressed to him by the poets, Llywarch ab Llywelyn, Philip Brydydd, and Dewi Mynyw, the two latter of whom also wrote elegies about him. *Rhys Gryg (the Hoarse) was Rhys ap Rhys ap Gruffydd, also known as Rhys Fychan (the small, to distinguish him from his father Rhys ap Gruffydd. Rhys ap Gruffydd was known as 'The Lord Rhys', and was the major Welsh leader of his lifetime, ruling Deheubarth from Dinefwr Castle. Rhys Gryg died of wounds at Llandeilo after a forty years of warfare, fighting for Llywelyn the Great in 1234. He had been gravely wounded while besieging Carmarthen.*

71

## THE HEAD

2. The head is the first and the most important portion of man's body, which God formed, for within it are the five corporeal senses.

## THE ORIGIN OF DISEASES IN THE HEAD

3. Diseases originate in three places in the head: one is the pericranium*; the second is the cranium; and the third is the dura mater.

*The pericranium is the outer membrane, or scalp, that covers the external surface of the skull. The cranium is the upper portion of the skull, which protects the brain. The dura mater is the tough fibrous membrane covering the brain and the spinal cord, and also lining the inner surface of the skull.*

## PRESERVATION OF THE CRANIUM AND SCALP

4. By an incision in the scalp, extending to the cranium, and giving exit to the venom, the cranium is healed. By phlebotomy [bleeding] and cauterization [cutting and/or burning] the scalp is preserved.

## DURA MATER - TREATMENT

5. Expose the dura mater*, by opening the scalp. Take two parts of wood betony**, and a third part of violet***, together with salt butter. Pound them together. Apply the mixture to the wound, and the poison will be removed from the dura mater. It will extract any existing inflammation and infection.

*To trepan, or cut through bone to expose the brain, has been practised since Neolithic times. Trepanning, or trephination, involves drilling or scraping away the bone to relieve pressure; **Stachys officinalis, Bishop's Wort; ***Viola odorata, Sweet Violet. Pughe mistakenly translates 'traean' here as 'three parts' instead of 'a third part'.*

## THE DURATION OF TREATMENT

6. This should last from when the scalp is laid open until the end of the ninth day, with the above damp covering remaining on the bone. This remedy should be followed in the case of an old head wound.

## A WOUND ON THE HEAD – TREATMENT and PHYSICIAN'S FEE

7. For a new blow or fresh wound on the head, the sooner it is opened up the better, less there should be extravasated blood* upon the dura mater, and in case it should become congealed or compacted [i.e. setting up inflammation]. When the bone is removed and the dura mater is exposed, take violet and fresh butter, and beat them together. If violet is not available, take the white of eggs and linseed**, beating them together. Or fresh butter and linseed, beaten together, can be used. Apply to the wound until the pain is assuaged and it forms a scar. Then an ointment should be prepared of herbs, butter, and tallow or wax. Apply until it is cured. A pound is the physician's fee for this treatment as regards the deed of mercy, without sustenance. The fee is nine score (pence)*** with victuals.

*Pughe adds:* 'The same fee is ordered in the Venedotian Code of Hywel Dda:- "The compensation for the medicaments is this. For each, (a stroke on the head unto the brain; a stroke in the body unto the bowels; and the breaking of one of the four limbs,) the person wounded is to receive three pounds from the one who shall have so wounded him; the amount likewise due from the person who shall wound him, for his medical treatment is a pound, without food; or nine score pence, with his food, and the bloody clothes." - Ancient Laws and Institutes of Wales, v. i. p.313'

*Blood or lymphatic fluid which is forced and congealed by pressure into surrounding tissues; **Linseed is the seed of flax; ***180 pence is fifteen shillings, the equivalent to 75 pence today.*

## CAUTERY* FOR A PAIN IN THE EYE

8. A cautery, applied to the hollow of the eyebrow, and another in the nape of the neck, is beneficial for rheum** of the head.

*To cauterise would have been to use some sort of branding iron, as a cautery involved burning. However, it can also mean to cut using a hot or cold instrument. The original Middle Welsh is llosc, in modern Welsh llosg, meaning to burn or scald; **Rheum is thin, watery mucus naturally discharged from the eyes, nose or mouth during sleep. It may form a thin crust in the corners of the eye. A heavy build-up of rheum, with pus, can indicate conjunctivitis.*

## TREATMENT FOR A WATERY EYE

9. For a red watery eye (ophthalmia tarsi cum epiphora) insert a seaton* under the jaw, and apply the cautery in the nape of the neck, and this is beneficial for rheum of the head.

*A seaton is a thick hair or bristle, but the Welsh 'dodi magyl dan y dvy en' is a translation of bagyl. Bagl is a crutch and baglu is to trap, so I am unsure if Pughe's translation is correct. A 'seton' was one or more threads or horsehairs, or a strip of linen introduced beneath the skin by a knife or needle, to provide drainage or to produce or prolong inflammation. It is now a term medically a thread of gauze or other suture material, threaded through tissue, and used to keep a wound open.*

## REMEDY FOR DISEASED EYELIDS

10. For a dry scurfy condition of the eye. Take the juice of the strawberry, a hen's fat and May butter*. Pound them well together, and keep in a horn (container).** When going to bed, anoint about your eye and eyelids well, and they will be cured.

*'May butter' was thought to be most nutritious, particularly for children. In 1584 the physician Thomas Cogan wrote: 'It is to be made chiefly in May, or in the heat of the year, by setting Butter new made without salt, so much as you wish in a platter, open to the Sun in faire weather for certain days, until it be sufficiently clarified, and altered in colour, which will be in twelve or fourteen days, if it be faire Sun shining.' In Cogan's day, butter was used for treating growing pains and for constipation. Being left in sunlight would have made it rancid, and thus more purgative. Perhaps butter also gave a sufficiently increased amount of vitamin D to enhance its reputation as a valuable food for children;*
***Stoppered animal horns were used to preserve ointments and powders. For instance, until the 18th century, a soldier's personal gunpowder was kept in his 'powder-horn'.*

## TREATMENT FOR PNEUMONIA

11. There are three kinds of lung disease: simple pneumonia; white pneumonia [bronchitis]; and black pneumonia [phthisis]*. Black pneumonia is marked by pain below the mammae [breasts], under the armpit, and in the top of the shoulders, with acute redness of the cheeks. These diseases are they treated as following. Let the patient take, for three successive days, the following herbs: hemlock, agrimony, herb Robert and asarabacca. Then let him undergo a three day's course

of aperients [laxatives]. When the disease is thus removed from the bronchial tubes, an emetic should be given to the patient daily until the end of nine days. Afterwards let a medicine be prepared, by infusing the following herbs in wheat ale or red wine: madder, sharp dock, anise, agrimony**, daisy, round birthwort, meadow sweet, yellow goat's beard, heath, water avens, woodruff, crake berry, the corn cockle, caraway, and such other herbs as will seem beneficial by the physician.

Thus is the 'blessed confection' prepared: take May butter, a she-goat's suet or a doe's fat, shepherd's needle***, and as many as may be desired of such herbs as may be suitable for the purpose. A wounded lung is the physician's third difficulty, for he cannot control it, but must wait for the will or God. By means of the herbs just mentioned, a medicine may be prepared for anyone who has a pulmonary abscess (emphysema.) The physician should let out the matter and support the patient, as in the case of a wounded lung, until he is recovered. However, most usually, the patient will have died within eleven years (alternatively one year.)

*Pneumonia is inflammation of the lungs, caused by a virus or bacteria. Bronchitis is bronchial inflammation, or inflammatory catarrh, not a form of pneumonia, but affecting the air passages to the lungs. Bronchopneumonia affects both these passages and the lungs – this author suffered this as a child. Black pneumonia was also called pulmonary consumption, and was accompanied by emaciation, debility, cough, acute fever and pus-discharging (purulent) expectoration. It is possibly the disease known as White Death, the name which was also given to pulmonary tuberculosis; **Pughe seems to make a mistake of translation here, as the two agrimony plants are translated from initially 'trydon' and then 'y tryw', with an acute accent on the v, meaning 'tryw'. The original Welsh would not have given two different words in the same list for one meaning, so the plants could be hemp agrimony and agrimony. Y Tryw, or Llysiau'r Drwy (flowers of tryw) is generally recognised as Agrimonia eupatoria. One therefore wonders whether 'trydon' could be an old word for hemp agrimony, i.e. Eupatorium cannabinum; ***The list of herbs will be familiar to readers of Culpeper and Gerard. See 'Breverton's Complete Herbal' for more information: Hemlock- Conium maculatum; Agrimony- Agrimonia Eupatoria (see above); Herb Robert- Geranium Robertianum; Asarabacca- Asarum Europaeum, European Wild Ginger; Madder- Rubia tinctoria; Sharp Dock- Rumex conglomeratus; Anise- Pimpinella anisum; Daisy- Bellis perennis – the Welsh is Llygad y Dydd, Eye of the Day; Round Birthwort- Aristolochia rotunda, Mercury Goosefoot; Meadowsweet- Filipendula ulmaria; Yellow Goat's Beard- Tragopogon pratensis, Noon Flower, Meadow Salsify; Heath- This is one of the species of Erica, but Calluna vulgaris, Common Heather was once included in that family. The Welsh word is grug, which is now translated as heather; Water Avens- Geum rivale; Woodruff- Galium Odoratum, Sweet Woodruff; Crakeberry- Empetrum nigrum, Crowberry or Black-berried Heath; Corn Cockle- Agrostemma githago; Caraway- Carum carvi; Shepherd's Needle- Scandix pecten-veneris, Venus' Comb.

## FEVERS

12. There are four kinds of fevers, deriving their origin from the summer, namely latent fever*, intermittent fever**, ephemeral fever*** and inflammatory fever****. The fifth fever is typhus*****, and this kind proceeds from the brain. A latent fever is relieved by an emetic, a cordial and by cauteries. It originates from the over-generation of tough humor in the stomach, from which results distaste for food and lassitude during summer. Mugwort, madder, meadow sweet,

74

milfoil, hemp, red cabbage and tutsan - all these seven herbs enter into the composition of the medicine required.

Whoever obtains them all, will not languish long from a wounded lung, nor need fear for his life. Any of the following herbs may be added to the mixture: butcher's broom, agrimony, tutsan, dwarf elder, amphibious persicaria, centaury, round birth wort, field scabious, peppermint, daisy, knap weed, roots of the red nettle, crake berry, St. John's wort, privet, wood betony, the roots of yellow goat's beard, heath, water avens, woodruff, leaves of the earth nut, agrimony, wormwood, bastard balm, small burdock and orpine.\*\*\*\*\*\*

*\*Latent Fever- Caelianus Aurelianus, in the 5th century CE described phthisis as 'latent fever that begins towards evening and vanishes again at the break of day, is accompanied with violent coughing which expels thin purulent sputum...'; \*\*Intermittent Fever-* 'Intermitting fevers, or agues, are those which, during the time that the patient may be said to be ill, have evident intervals or remissions of the symptoms.' (Buchan 1785); *\*\*\*Ephemeral Fever- An 'ephemora' was a* fever which runs its course of the cold, hot, and sweating stages in twelve hours; *\*\*\*\*Inflammatory Fever- 'Inflammation' was 'a* disease characterized by heat, pain, redness, attended with more or less of tumefaction (swelling) and fever' (Hooper 1829); *\*\*\*\*\*Typhus- '*a contagious continued fever lasting from two to three weeks, attended with great prostration and cerebral disorder, and marked by a copious eruption of red spots upon the body. Also called jail fever, famine fever, putrid fever, spotted fever, etc.' (Webster); *\*\*\*\*\*\* 'Trydon' and 'tryw' are again both translated and repeated as agrimony by Pughe, as in the Treatment for Pneumonia entry immediately above. There is a similar treatment of tutsan, being entirely different words in the Welsh manuscript.*

*The following herbs are not listed in the previous entry: Mugwort- Artemisia vulgaris; Milfoil- It is uncertain at present whether 'y filwydd' is Yarrow, Achillea millefolium or one of the Water Milfoil species, but is probably the former, as the common medicinal herb yarrow is not mentioned elsewhere in the text; Hemp- Cannabis sativa; Red Cabbage- Brassica oleracea var. capitata f. rubra. This was first described in England in 1570, and lasts longer than white cabbage, so does not have to be preserved in dishes such as sauerkraut to last the winter; Tutsan- Hypericum androsaemum, but there may be another plant named, but not tutsan, noted as well; Butcher's Broom- Ruscus aculeatus; Dwarf Elder- Sambucus ebulus, Dane's Blood; Amphibious Persicaria- Persicaria amphibia, Willow Grass, Amphibious Bistort; Centaury- Erythraea centaurium; Field Scabious- Knautia arventis; Peppermint- Mentha piperita; Knapweed- One of the knapweeds, probably Common Knapweed, Centauria nigra; Red Nettle- Also called the Dead Red Nettle, Red Dead Nettle, Purple Archangel, Lamium purpureum; St. John's Wort- Hypericum perforatum; Privet- Ligustrum vulgare; Earth Nut- The author believes this to be the Pig Nut, Conopodium majus, also known as Earth Chestnut and Ground Nut. My mother and her sisters used to dig them out and eat them in Montgomeryshire, Wales, in the 1920s; Wormwood- Artemisia absinthum; Bastard Balm- Melittis melissophylum; Small Burdock- Arctium minus; Orpine- Sedum telephium*

## TREATMENT FOR INTERMITTENT FEVERS [AGUES WITH PERIODS OF REMISSION]

13. Take dandelion and fumitory\*, infused in water, the first thing in the morning. Then about noon take wormwood infused in water likewise, drinking it as often as ten times, the draught being rendered tepid. Let bread, made with pounded wheat also be taken, or oaten cakes, goat's whey, the flesh of a young fowl, and

husky porridge**. Abstain from milk, indeed from every kind of milk diet. If the ague does not then terminate, the patient must be put in a bath, when the paroxysm comes on, and an emetic given him while in the bath, as it will then act more powerfully.

*Dandelion- Taraxacum officinale: Fumitory- Fumaria officinalis; **With the oats not completely dehusked.*

## COOLING DRINKS

14. The three best cooling drinks are: apple juice; goat's whey*; and spring water.

*The liquid remaining after milk has been curdled or strained. This might also be translated as goat's milk.*

## ANOTHER TREATMENT FOR INTERMITTENT FEVERS

15. Take mugwort, dwarf elder, tutsan, amphibious persicaria, pimpernel, butcher's broom, elder bark and mallow. Boil them together as well as possible in a pot, or cauldron. Then take water and herbs, and add them to the bath. The following is a good medicine for this class of diseases. Take moss, ground ivy, or elder, if obtainable, (if not obtainable, caraway.) Boil these two vegetable substances well together. Then take mallow, fennel, pimpernel, butcher's broom, borage, and the young leaves of the earth nut, and bruise them as well as possible, putting them on the fire with the two herbs before mentioned, boiling them well.

This being done, let elder bark be taken from that portion of the tree which is in the ground. Scrape and wash it thoroughly, and bruise well in a mortar.* Then take the liquor prepared from the aforementioned herbs, and mix the elder bark assiduously between both hands. Set it to drain into a vessel to acidify, fermenting it with goat's whey, or cow's whey. Let a good cupful be drunk every morning as long as it lasts. Take a portion of raw honey, apple or wood sorrel** subsequently in order to remove the taste from the mouth, after the drink. This liquor is beneficial to every man who requires to purge his body.

*The mortar and pestle were sometimes called the Apothecary Grinder, and is the trademark of the Tŷ Talcen Myddfai Charity. Mortars and pestles were traditionally used in pharmacies to crush various ingredients for a prescription, especially in the days before safe storage of medicines, pills and remedies. Mortar derives from the Latin mortarium, meaning receptacle for pounding, and pestle from the Latin pistillum, meaning pounder. They are mentioned in the oldest preserved medical literature, the Ebers Papyrus of around 1550 BCE, and in the Old Testament, being used throughout history; **Elder- Sambucus nigra; Mallow- Malva officinalis or Malva sylvestris; Ground Ivy - Glechoma hederaceae, Gill-over-the-ground; Fennel- Foeniculum vulgare; Pimpernel- Anagallis arvensis, Scarlet Pimpernel, Poor Man's Weatherglass; Borage- Borago officinalis, Starflower; Wood Sorrel- Oxalis acetosella*

## CAUSES OF HAEMORRHOIDS AND SURGICAL TREATMENT; ANOTHER MEDICAL METHOD; FORBIDDEN FOOD

16. There are two kinds of haemorrhoids, humoral haemorrhoids and inflamed haemorrhoids. The latter is produced by summer heat, and the former by summer moisture, when either condition prevails. It is in this manner that haemorrhoids come. Four veins proceed from the liver to the anus. Therefore, it may be cured as follows. Secure three of these veins by means of a ligature, and let the fourth be left free. The cautery* also should be applied to the ankles, and about the

knees and hams. Thus the blood will be habitually diverted to the lower extremities, when the cauteries shall have discharged all the humor from the vein.

The second plan or treatment is as follows. Take mallow, and boil it in wheat ale, or in spring water. Then take the bark which grows in the earth on the elder, bruise it well in a mortar. Mix it, crude as it is, with the above-mentioned decoction. Administer it quickly to the patient, so it acts upon his bowels. Let him afterwards be forbidden beef, cheese, leeks, large fish, salmon, eels, ducks, garlic and all kinds of milk diet, except for whey made with warm cows' milk.

*Here cautery must mean a cut rather than a burn.*

## FOUR TYPES OF ABDOMINAL COMPLAINTS – EMETIC TREATMENT OF PERITONITIS – TREATMENT FOR AN INTERNAL ABDOMINAL TUMOUR

17. There are four kinds of abdominal complaints: ascites*, peritonitis**, abdominal tumour, and tympanitis***. Ascites cannot be cured. Tympanitis also is a disease from which there is no escape, though it is not soon fatal. Peritonitis is treated by means of an emetic, the blue confection**** and a medicine. These are the herbs required for the medicine: sweet gale*****, bay leaves, pimpernel, male speedwell, river startip, borage, moss, liverwort, the young leaves of the earth nut, and the mallow. The above-mentioned emetic should be thus prepared. Take stinking hellebore dug fresh from the ground, from the root, washing it well and slicing it thin. Bruise it in a mortar, as well as can be done. Throw the refuse away after the juice has been expressed. The juice should then be put in a pan on the fire and boiled until nearly solid. Keep it by you as long as you wish, making small pills of it when you administer it to the sick. An abdominal tumour is cured by means of cauteries, issues, a cordial, and an emetic.

*Ascites – 'A collection of serous fluid in the abdomen. Ascites proper is dropsy of the peritoneum; and is characterized by increased size of the abdomen, by fluctuation, and general signs of dropsy. It is rarely a primary disease; but is always dangerous. Dropsy of the lower belly.' (Dunglison 1874); **Peritonitis – 'Inflammation of the peritoneum (membrane lining the abdominal cavity). Characterized by violent pain in the abdomen, increased by the slightest pressure, often by simple weight of bed clothes. It frequently occurs in parturient state and begins on the second or third day after delivery. At times, a malignant epidemic, and perhaps contagious, variety has made its appearance, and destroyed numbers of females. This has been described under the name puerperal fever, metroperitonitis and low fever of child bed.' (Dunglison 1874); ***Tympanitis now refers to inflammation of the inner ear, not abdomen. However, historically Tympanites, or Tympanitic Abdomen featured distension of the abdominal wall, as in peritonitis, caused by the accumulation of gas or air in the intestine or peritoneal cavity. If the patient was tapped, the sound was like that of a drum, hence its name; **** The 'blue confection' reads as glas-gyfleith in the original text. 'Glas' can actually mean blue, green, grey or silver in context as an adjective, although generally blue. The soft-mutated 'cyfleith' seems to be the modern 'cyflaith', toffee. However, this seems to be a 'violet confection'. A 17th century 'violet confection' reads: 'Take a quantity of blew [blue] violets, clip off the whites, and pound them well in a stone mortar. Take as much fair running water as will sufficiently moisten them and mix with the violets. Strain them all. To every ½ pint of liquid put one pound of the best sugar.Set it on the fire, putting the sugar in as it melts, still stirring it. Let it boyle [boil] but once or twice at most. Then take it from the fire and keep it for your use. This is a dainty sirrup* *[syrup] of violets'. Violets had many uses in herbal medicine. In Book 2:150 Pughe again refers to 'glas-gyfleith' and gives a recipe for 'blue confection of the stone'; \*\*\*\*\*Sweet Gale- Myrica Gale, Bog Myrtle; Pimpernel- Probably Anagallis arvensis, Scarlet Pimpernel, Poor Man's Weatherglass; Bay- Laurus nobilis, Bay Laurel, Sweet Bay Tree; Male Speedwell- Veronica officinalis, Gipsywort; River Startip- I am unsure of this plant. The Old Welsh is 'griessyn', with a footnote indicating 'gwessyn'; Liverwort- Hepatica nobilis or possibly a species of the plant division Marchantiophyta. In Grieve's Herbal of 1931, English Liverwort is Peltigera canina, Dog Lichen; Stinking Hellebore- Helleborus foetida, known charmingly as Dungwort*

## ANAL WARTS

18. Certain warts will often form about the anus. The best way to remove them is to dig them out with cold iron, afterwards cauterizing* their seat, and anointing the area with honey.

*Burning to destroy infection.*

## THREATMENT FOR THREE KINDS OF URINARY DISORDERS

19. There are three kinds of painful urinary disorders. Strangury* is cured by means of an emetic, a cordial, cauteries and a dry (hot air) bath. A hard vesical calculus [bladder stone] is thus extracted by operation. Take a staff and place it in the bend of the knee. Then fix both arms within the knees, doubling them up over the staff, and secure both wrists with a fillet, over the nape of the neck. The patient is placed on his back, his stomach up, with some support under both thighs, and the calculus cut for on the left side of the urethra. Let him be subsequently put in a water bath that same day, also early the day following, and after this he should be put in the kyffeith**.

Then he should be removed to his bed, and laid there on his back, his wound being cleaned, and dressed with flax and salt butter. He should be kept at the same temperature, until it is known whether he will escape the effects of the operation. He should be kept without food or drink for a day and a night previous to the operation, and should have a bath. If the disease is gravel [kidney stones], make a medicine of the following herbs, macerated in strong clear wheat ale, namely water pimpernel, tutsan, meadow sweet, St. John's wort, ground ivy, agrimony, milfoil, birch, common burnet, columbine, motherwort, laurel, gromwel, betony, borage, dandelion, little field madder, amphibious persicaria, liverwort.***

*Strangury is a slow and painful discharge of urine, due to spasm of the urethra and bladder; **Cyffaith (cyffeithiau is the plural) means confection or concoction. Cyffeith means preserve, or can also mean a pit used for tanning leather. The meaning is unclear; ***Water Pimpernel - Samolus valerandi (also parviflorus and floribundus), Brookweed; Birch - Betula pendula, Silver Birch; Common Burnet - Sanguisorba officinalis, Great Burnet; Columbine - Aquilegia vulgaris, Granny's Nightcap; Motherwort - Leonorus cardiaca, Throw-wort; Laurel - One assumes this is the Bay Laurel noted above; Gromwel- Lithospermum officinale, European Stoneseed; Little Field Madder - probably Sherardia arvensis, Blue Field Madder, Spurwort.*

## TREATMENT FOR STERILITY

20. A sterile woman may have a potion prepared for her by means of the following herbs, namely: St. John's wort, yew, agrimony, amphibious persicaria, creeping cinque foil, mountain club moss, orpine and pimpernel*, taking an emetic in addition.

*Yew- Taxus baccata; Creeping Cinquefoil- Creeping Tormentil, Potentilla repens; Mountain Club-moss- Lycopodium selago

## TREATMENT FOR PROFUSE MENSTRUATION

21. A woman who is subject to profuse menstruation, should take the reddish bastard balm, small burdock, orpine, stinking goose foot*, pimpernel, water avens, with the ashes of a hart's horns, that has been killed with his antlers on. Boil them, as well as possible in red wine, straining the liquor carefully. Drink the liquor daily, until it is finished, all the while abstaining from stimulating food. Being restrained by the above means, the blood will be habitually diverted to the thighs and ankles.

*Reddish Bastard-Balm- Melittis melissophyllum, known as Bastard Balm; Stinking Goosefoot- Chenopodium vulvaria, Notchweed

## REMEDY FOR QUINSY

22. The roots or the com bell flower*, will break the quinsy, being digested in cold water, drunk and retained in the mouth.

*This was thought to be Campanula hybrida, but seemed to be Campanula rapunculus, Rampion Bellflower. However, could also be Lady's Looking Glass or Venus' Looking Glass, Legousia hybrida, also known as Corn Bellflower. Alternatively it could be speedwell, Veronica arvensis. The Welsh for corn bell-flower, Campanula hybrida is Drych Gwener, but the Middle Welsh original is drycheigyavc.

## EXFOLIATION OF DEAD BONE FROM THE SKULL

23. Dandelion digested in cold water, and drunk, will promote the exfoliation of the skull in aged men.

## ISSUES AND SEATONS

24. The juice of the roots of viper's garlic* and shepherd's needle will form an issue**. The juice of the leaves will form a seaton***.

*Viper's Garlic was Allium viperinum. Today we know it as Rocambole, Serpent or Hardneck Garlic, Allium sativum var. ophioscorodon; **The Middle Welsh baessa is translated by Pughe as issues, but is not mentioned in GPC. Baes is baize, and baesned is bassinet, but neither seems applicable here. An 'issue' is a suppurating lesion allowing the discharge of blood, pus or other harmful matter. It follows that the juice of the roots promote this discharge, part of the healing process;***The Middle Welsh is magyl, from bagyl, and the meaning is not given in the Geiriadur Prifysgol Cymru. A 'seton' was material such as thread, wire, or gauze, and formerly horsehair, passed through subcutaneous tissues or through a cyst in order to form a sinus or fistula. The meaning of Pughe's translation of 'seaton' is still unclear. However, 'seaton or seton (from the medieval Latin for bristle, and also silk) is a thread or tape drawn through the skin next to a wound or sore to keep open an issue, to stop it entirely healing *over.' This definition from Ellis seems to say that the juice will stop wounds from repairing, possibly to allow harmful matter to discharge.*

## ISSUES AND WORMS

25. The root of mugwort, boiled in wine, will also form an issue. The leaves treated in the same manner will destroy worms.

## AN IMPOSTUME

26. Obtain comfrey root, dock root, valerian root**, butter, old lard and sulphur. Pound them together (in a mortar), and express through a cloth. This is useful for an impostume [*an old word for abscess*].

    *Comfrey- Symphytum officinale; Valerian- Valeriana officinalis*

## MILK, YOUNG PORK, AND MUTTON

27. From the time of calving up to fifteen days, a cow's milk will be warming. From then until she is in calf, as long as she remains in profit, the milk will be warming. The flesh of a sow under a year old, and sheep flesh, is watery. For a man whose flesh is flabby in consequence of disease, such meat is not proper.

## WHOLESOME MEATS AND FISH

28. The most wholesome wild beast's flesh is venison. The most wholesome domestic animal's flesh is pork. The most wholesome wild fowl's flesh is partridge. The most wholesome domestic bird's flesh is that of the hen. The most wholesome sea fish is the flatfish. The most wholesome fresh water fish are bass and trout.*

*John Pughe adds four proverbs here: 'The best hunted flesh is venison. The best animal meat is mutton. The best sea fish are the flounders. The best fresh water fish is trout.'*

## FOR ECZEMA OR HUMID TETTER*

29. Use a mixture of derwhyden wlŷb **, honey of ivy***, fox marrow and white rosin.

    *\*Any of various skin diseases, such as eczema, psoriasis, shingles, ringworm or herpes, characterized by eruptions of pustules, red patches and itching; \*\* Pughe here omits a translation of derwhyden wlŷb, which may mean oak tree liquid, but I cannot find a translation of derwhyden; \*\*\*Hedera helis, Common Ivy*

## FOR TOOTHACHE

30. Take the inner bark of ivy and the leaves of honeysuckle. Bruise them well together in a mortar. Express them through a linen cloth into both nostrils, with the patient lying on his back, and this will relieve him.

## FOR DEAFNESS – DROPS AND A CAUTERY

31. Take a ram's urine, eel's bile and the juice of the ash tree. Express these into the ear, and around the tooth. The actual cautery should also be applied behind the ear and angle of the jaw, a nut being inserted inside. This is a good plan.

## FOR A VIPER'S BITE. A STRANGE PROPOSAL FOR EXTRACTING THE VENOM BY MEANS OF FOWLS

32. If the patient is a male, let a living cock be procured, and let cock's anal extremity be applied to the wound, and so held. This is a good plan. If the patient is a woman, let a living hen be procured and applied in the same way. This will extract the venom.

## FOR A CRUSTED SCALP, OR IMPETIGO CAPITIS

33. Take goat's dung, barley meal and red wine. Boil together into a poultice, and apply to the affected part. This is the remedy, when the sore is not opened by the forcible removal of the crust.

## TREATMENT BY COUNTER-IRRITATION FOR HEADACHE, AND PAIN OF JOINTS

34. Take cakes of pounded wheat, and grind into fine meal. Then take wood sorrel, dandelion, betony* and red wine, bruising them well together in a mortar. Then mix them throughly together on the fire, freely adding ox tallow and salt. Let this plaster, spread on a thick cloth, then be applied onto the shaven scalp. This will induce the breaking forth of boils, thereby extracting the venom, and relieving the patient.

*This is the same Welsh word 'yr danhogen' as wood betony above. Betony, Stacchys Officinalis, is commonly known as Purple Betnoy, Bishopwort, Lousewort, Wild Hop and Wood betony. The name betony is said to derive from the Celtic 'bew' (head) and 'ton' (good), an indication of its use for headaches. The word stachys comes from the Greek, meaning 'an ear of grain' and refers to the fact that the inflorescence is often a spike.

## REMEDY FOR THE BITE OF A SPIDER

35. The bite of the spider will not be found venomous, except from the Feast of the Nativity of the Virgin Mary*, to that of her Purification. By applying bruised yellow bedstraw**, the venom will be extracted.

*The traditional date of the Feast of the Nativity of the Blessed Virgin Mary, September 8, falls exactly nine months after the Feast of the Immaculate Conception of Mary. The Feast of the Purification is the same as that of the Presentation of Jesus at the Temple, Candlemass, February 2. Thus it was believed that British spiders were not venomous for around 5 months. It may come as a surprise to many that native British spiders can bite and cause pain and swelling, sometimes needing hospital treatment. Medically documented cases have occurred featuring the following spiders: False Widow, Tube Web, Walnut-orb Weaver, Cellar, Black Lace, Mouse, Woodlouse, Rustic Wolf, Black Sac, Stone, Cross or Garden, Bruennichi's Argiope, Lace Weaver and even the tiny Money Spider; **Galium verum, Lady's Bedstraw. The name Lady's Bedstraw commemorated the Virgin Mary.

## TREATMENT FOR WORMS WHILE FASTING

36. Take elder bark, walnut bark, white thorn bark and bittersweet*, and boil them together in water. Let a cupful be drunk while daily fasting, and let the patient abstain from food until it is almost evening. This should be repeated nine times**.

*White Thorn- Crataegus monogyna, or Common Hawthorn; Bittersweet is Solanum dulcamara, or Woody Nightshade; **Three was a sacred number to Celts and Druids. Three times three therefore features many times in the cures, possibly denoting an ancient, pre-Christian source.*

## FOR A PUNCTURED WOUND

37. Take the dung of a bull* and apply. It will be healed.

*Pughe notes here that 'warm dung' is specified in the Book of Harri Sion of Pontypool.*

## SEVERAL PLANS OF TREATMENT FOR A CARBUNCLE

38. Take St. John's wort, and apply it to the carbuncle, when it is first observed. Another plan is to take the flower of knapweed or the leaves, pounding with the yolk of an egg and fine salt. Apply, and this will disperse it. Another remedy is to take selfheal, bruise it with rancid lard, and apply. Another remedy is to take the roots of purple dead nettle*, the roots of mugwort, and speedwell. Boil well together in goat's milk whey, adding butter to the scum formed, and drink it day and night.

*Selfheal- Prunella vulgaris; Purple Dead Nettle- Lamium purpurium, Purple Archangel*

## FOR TREATMENT OF THE CARBUNCLE WHEN THE SLOUGH HAS BEEN REMOVED

39. This is also useful for a burn (cauterization) in a like circumstance. Take wild chamomile*, bake it well and powder it. Anoint the wound regularly, sprinkling the powdered herbs upon it. This will produce a good and fair cicatrix**. We judge that every kind of wound is benefited by milk whey.

*Chamomile- Anthemis nobilis, Camomile; **A cicatrix is a scar resulting from the forming and contracting of fibrous tissue in a wound.*

## TO RESTRAIN AN ACTIVE HAEMORRHAGE

40. Take meadowsweet, infuse in cold water, and drink. This will stop it, by the help of God.

## FOR HOARSENESS

41. Take water avens, and St. John's wort. Boil in pure milk, mixing in butter when it is boiling. Boil a portion of the mixture briskly every morning and drink.

## FOR TOOTHACHE: SEVERAL REMEDIES

42. Take betony and lay it under the head, in an unbleached linen cloth, and it will cure it. Another method is to take self-heal, put it in a dock leaf under the tooth, or on a hot stone, and place it hot in a cloth under the painful tooth. Another is to take round birthwort, bruise it well, and apply it to the patient's tooth for a night. Another is to take thorn apple* and apply it well.

*Datura stramonium, Hell's Bells, Devil's Weed*

82

## FOR INFLAMMATION OF THE MAMMAE [BREASTS]
43. Take round birthwort and lard, apply them to the mammae, and they will cure the inflammation.

## REMEDY FOR INTESTINAL WORMS
44. Take wine and natron*, mix together, and drink every morning while fasting.
*Natron was historically harvested as a salt mixture from dry lake beds in Egypt, and used for millennia as a cleaning product. Blended with oil, it was an early form of soap, and softens water while removing oil and grease. Undiluted, it was used as a mouthwash and cleanser for the teeth. The Egyptians used it in the mummification process as it acts as a drying agent. It is a mixture of sodium carbonate decahydrate and sodium bicarbonate (Baking Soda). When exposed to moisture, it creates a hostile environment for bacteria by raising alkalinity, so would have made the intestine a more hostile environment for intestinal worms.

## A REMEDY FOR THE BITE OF A VIPER
45. Take round birthwort, knapweed, and field scabious. Mix with water and drink.

## OPPROBRIUM MEDICI*
The Physician's three master difficulties are: a wounded lung, a wounded mammary gland and a wounded knee joint.
   Pughe here adds a Triad from the Venedotian Code of Welsh Laws: 'The three imminent dangers to a man are: a stroke on the ear, unto the brain; a stroke in the body, unto the bowels; and the breaking of one of the four limbs of the body.'
   *Literally, 'the shame of physicians'. Two entries appear to have been amalgamated here.

## FOR RING WORM
46. For ring worm, (favus*). Take white rosin**, warm it, and when soft apply it to the part. This will cure it.
   *Favus is a fungal skin infection of the scalp with thick yellow crusts over the hair follicles;
**Common, or yellow rosin (Colophony) is the resin left over after the distillation of turpentine, and when strongly agitated with water was called resina alba, white rosin.

## SEVEN THINGS INJURIOUS TO THE EYES
47. There are seven things hostile to the eye: weeping, watching, feasting, drunkenness, impurity, a dry film, and smoke.

## THREE BONES WHICH WILL NOT UNITE WHEN FRACTURED
48. There are three bones in a man's body, which when broken, will never knit, and not one of them exists when a man is born: a tooth, the knee pan [patella], and the fontenelle (os frontis) of the cranium.

## TO INDUCE SLEEP
49. Poppy heads bruised [broken up] in wine, will cause a man to sleep well.*
*Pughe notes: 'This is practically identical with Sydenham's "Liquid Laudanum"**, so that our Meddygon may be said to have anticipated the discovery of that preparation.'; ** Thomas Sydenham (1624-1689) was one of the first physicians to describe Scarlet Fever, as well as what came to be known as Sydenham's Chorea. He invented 'Sydenham's Liquid Laudanum', derived from opium, to be sold in apothecaries' shops as a painkiller. In 1676 he published the seminal work, 'Medical Observations Concerning the

*History and Cure of Acute Diseases'*, in which he promoted his brand of opium tincture, advocating its use for a range of medical conditions. According to the Paris Codex it was prepared as follows: 'opium, 2 ounces; saffron, 1 ounce; bruised cinnamon and bruised cloves, each 1 drachm; sherry wine, 1 pint. Mix and macerate for 15 days and filter. Twenty drops are equal to one grain of opium.'

## FOR IMPOTENCY

50. Take some birch, digest in water, and drink.*

*The original is in Middle Welsh, and reads: 'Rac lluydyas eghi. Kymryt y uedlvyn, ae tharav ar dwfyr ae yuet ar y vnyt.' Each v has an acute accent, which cannot be found among usual typefaces. Birch, or bedwen, was then uedlvyn. Similarly, impotence is now analluedd, not the Middle Welsh lluydyas. Lluydya means 'a call to arms' which may well mean standing to attention in this context of impotency. 'Yuet ar y vnyt' means to drink it standing up. Thus the partial translation should be: 'A Call to Arms: Take some birch, ingest in water and drink it while standing up.'*

## TREATMENT FOR INTERMITTENT FEVER

51. Take mugwort, purple dead nettle, and round birthwort, as much as you like of each. Bruise them well in stale goat's milk whey, and boil afterwards. Let the patient drink some every morning, and it will cure him.

## FOR TOOTHACHE - A STRANGE REMEDY AND A STRANGER PATHOLOGY

52. Take a candle of sheep's suet*, some eryngo** seed being mixed with it, and burn it as near the tooth as possible, some cold water being held under the candle. The worms destroying the tooth will drop into the water, in order to escape from the heat of the candle.

*Candles used to be made from animal fat; **Eryngo is Sea Holly, Eryngium maritimum.*

## A TUMOUR OF THE ABDOMEN – A POULTICE

53. For a tumour of the abdomen. Take sheep's suet, oatmeal, foxglove*, and pimpernel, making a poultice of them, and apply it to the abdomen. If it contains matter, this will bring it to a head.

*Digitalis purpurea*

## TUMOUR OF THE ABDOMEN AGAIN

Take fresh goat's milk whey, mix ramsons* with it, and drink it for three days, and the swelling will disappear.

*Ramsons is a common folk name for the familiar Wild Garlic of deciduous woodlands, Allium ursinum. Goat's milk and garlic would not be a particularly pleasant drink.* The concept that a cure should be foul tasting to be effective has been a belief across many cultures. People of all ages resorted to a great variety of domestic treatments in their efforts to prevent sickness or cure illness. Ron Berry (1920-1927) of Blaenycwm in the Rhondda Valley remembered in *'History is Where You Live'* (1998) the large range of materia medica used to fight sickness, kept at home: *'We fought against sickness with goose grease, hot salt in socks, poultices, warmed flannels, Sloan's liniment, zinc ointment, vinegar and brown paper, the squeezed juice of Mind Your Own*

84

*Business* [Soleirolia soleirolii, also known as Baby's Tears and Mother of Thousands] *grown in a tin on the windowsill for earache, senna pods, wintergreen oil, liquid paraffin, Epsom salts, bi-carb., Vaseline, cloves, elderflower tea, Syrup of Figs, olive oil, borax powder, eucalyptus oil.'*

## A ROUGH BUT READY TREATMENT FOR FALLING FITS
54. Burn a goat's horn, directing the smoke upon the patient, and in consequence of the smell he will arise. Before he has risen from the ground, apply dog's gall* upon his head, and that disease will not attack him any more.

*This is now usually called bile. In humans it is a bitter, alkaline, brownish-yellow or greenish-yellow fluid that is secreted by the liver, stored in the gallbladder, and discharged into the duodenum. Bile aids in the emulsification, digestion, and absorption of fats.*

## FOR INTERMITTENTS OR AGUES
55. For all sorts of agues, write inside three apples, on three separate days. In the first apple draw a diagram of a Maltese Cross, followed by *'o nagla pater'*. In the second apple draw a diagram of a Maltese Cross, followed by *'o nagla filius'*. In the third apple draw a diagram of a Maltese Cross, followed by *'o nagla spiritus sanctus.'* * On the third day the patient will recover.

*The spell invokes the Father, the Son and the Holy Spirit on successive days.*

## A STRANGE MODE OF PROGNOSTICATION
If you would know how it will happen to a man who sickens, whether he will live or die of his disease, take the herb called violet*. Bruise it, and bind a portion to both legs, and if the patient will live he will sleep. If he cannot sleep, he will die.

*Viola odorata*

## TO PREVENT INTOXICATION
56. If you would not be drunk, drink in the morning the juice of hemp agrimony, as much as will fill an egg-shell.

## TO PREVENT WEARINESS
If you would not be weary on a journey, drink in the morning an egg-shell full of the juice of mugwort and garlic. You will neither be hurt nor tired, whatever distance you may walk that day.

## TO REMOVE DRUNKENNESS
57. It you would remove a man's drunkenness, let him eat bruised saffron* with spring water.

*Crocus sativus*

## HOW TO BE MERRY
58. If you would be at all times merry, eat saffron in meat or drink, and you will never be sad. However, beware of eating over much, lest you should die of excessive joy.

## TO CURB ENVY

59. If you would never be in an envious mood, drink as much as would fill an egg shell of the juice of the herb called wild clary*. You will not fall into an evil temper after drinking it. If you would be always in good health, drink a spoonful of the juice of the herb mallows**, and you will always be healthy.

*Salvia verbenica, Clary Sage, Christ's Eye; ** Malva sylvestris, the Common, or Blue Mallow*

## TO PRESERVE CHASTITY

60. If you would always be chaste, eat daily some of the herb called hart's tongue*, and you will never assent to suggestions of impurity.

*Asplenium scolopendrium, the Hart's Tongue Fern*

## TREATMENT FOR PROLAPSUS UTERI

61. For prolapsus of the womb (i.e. an extrusion), the best remedy is to take wheaten flour. Knead it with the yolks of nine eggs* and honey. Work into it the breast fur of two hares. Then bake it under ashes, and make a potion of it. Drink this until the organ returns to its place.

*Pughe writes: 'Or as it may also be read, simply "the yolks of eggs."'*

## TO PREVENT TOOTHACHE

62. If you would always be free from toothache, whenever you wash, rub the inside of your ears with your fingers.

## A FOWL APPLICATION FOR A SMALL TUMOUR

63. Take a cock or hen, (as the patient may be a man or a woman,) and apply the feathered rump to the part, until the bird dies. This will extract the venom.

*This is a similar remedy to Book 1:32, for a viper's bite.*

## TO REMOVE WARTS

64. Whoever wishes to remove warts, let him apply daisy bruised in dog's urine to them, and they will all disappear.

## TO DESTROY FLEAS

65. Whoever wished to destroy fleas, let him steep wormwood* in the sea for an hour, and afterwards dry it in the sun. When sufficiently dry, any fleas coming in contact with it will die.

*Artemisia absinthum, Absinthe Wormwood - bunches of wormwood were traditionally hung in chicken coops to deter flies, lice and fleas. It was one of the 'Seven Sacred Herbs' of the Druids.*

## TO DESTROY FLIES

66. To destroy flies, let mugwort be put in the place where they frequent. Those who come in contact with the herb will die.

*Artemisia vulgaris, featured in the Anglo-Saxon 'Nine Herbs Charm'*

## FOR THE BITE OF A VIPER

67. Let the juice of elder be drunk, and it will disperse all the poison.

## FOR LOSS OF REASON OR SPEECH

68. Whoever shall have lost his reason or his speech, let him drink the juice of primrose*, and within two months afterwards, he will indeed recover.
*Primula vulgaris

## A STRANGE FORECAST OF PREGNANCY

69. Whosoever would know whether a woman is *enceinte* [pregnant] with a boy or girl, let him observe her sitting and standing, and if she moves the right foot first it signifies a son, but if the left, a daughter.

## A STRANGE DIAGNOSIS OF VIRGINITY

70. If you would distinguish between a wife and a virgin, scrape some jet* into water, and give it her to drink. It she is a wife, she will without fail pass water, but if a virgin she will not have a more urgent call than usual.
*A black lignite popular in jewellery in Victorian times.

## TO SILENCE A COCK

71. If you wish that a cockerel does not crow, anoint his crest with oil, and he will be mute.

## FOR OPACITY OF THE EYE

72. Let some ground ivy juice* be put in the eye, and the opacity will be removed, the eye becoming spotless and clear.
*The juice from ground ivy, Glechoma hederacea, not from common ivy, Hedera helix.

## FOR A WEEPING CHILD

73. Let the two lower extremities of a baby, which is much given to weeping, be anointed with hart's marrow*, and it will weep less.
*A hart is usually a male Red Deer over five years old.

## TO REMOVE A SMALL TUMOUR

74. Should a man have a small tumour in a dangerous part of his body, and you should wish to remove it, your object can thus be accomplished. Take the leaves of foxglove, and press them well on any part of the tumour. It will remove it an inch and a half from the herb.

## HYGEIAN* OF THE YEAR

75. Month of **January**. Do not bleed**. Drink three cupfuls of wine, fasting. Take a potion. Let your diet be goat's flesh and wholesome vegetables.
*Relating to Hygeia, the goddess of health; pertaining to health, or its preservation.
**Bleeding, blood-letting was a popular medical remedy.

76. Month of **February**. Bleed from the thumb of the left hand. Obtain a confection and a potion, which will render your eyes healthy.

77. Month of **March**. Use enemata*, the roots of vegetables and the bath. Do not bleed frequently. Do not take an emetic, as it generates cold within. Drink sweet wine, fasting.

*The plural of enema, a procedure in which liquid or gas is injected into the rectum, typically to expel its contents.*

78. Month of **April**. Bleed. Take a gentle emetic, eat fresh meat and take warm drinks. Eat two mouthfuls of hart's tongue (fern) twice a day. Avoid the roots of vegetables, as they will occasion an obstruction. Drink hemp agrimony.

79. Month of **May**. Do not eat sheep's head or trotters, and take warm drinks. Eat hart's tongue twice daily, while fasting. Take a gentle emetic. Use cold whey. Drink of the juice of fennel and wormwood.

80. Month of **June**. Take a cupful or cold water, fasting daily. Do not drink ale or mead. Drink warm milk, and eat lettuce.

81. Month of **July**. Do not bleed. Take an emetic. Make use of flowers and wholesome vegetables. Avoid impurity.

82. Month of **August**. Make use of soups and vegetables. Drink neither ale nor mead. Take white pepper in gruel.

83. Month of **September**. Take three draughts of milk the first thing in the morning, daily. You may after this take what you wish, for vegetables and fruit are then ripe, and bread apt to be mouldy.

84. Month of **October**. Make use of new wine. Eat minnows [small freshwater fish]. Take an emetic. Let your diet consist of fresh meat and vegetables of a wholesome nature.

85. Month of **November**. Do not take butter, as at this time of the year the blood of all men has a tendency to coagulation, which is dangerous. At this time also the heads of beasts and all vegetables are to be avoided, being unwholesome.

86. Month of **December**. Do not drink soup or eat the red cabbage in soup, nor sheep's trotters, and reduce your blood [by blood letting or leeches].

### A GOOD DAY TO BLEED
87. Whoever is bled on the 17th of March, will not be liable to intermittent fevers or coughs in that year.

### ANOTHER GOOD DAY TO BLEED
88. Whoever is bled on the 3rd day of April, will not suffer from disease, from the head to the coccyx, in that same year, unless he is subjected to (undue) abstinence. (Literally, 'unless he doeth abstinence.')

## ANOTHER GOOD DAY TO BLEED

89. The 11th day of the same month is also a good time to be bled, so also are the 4th and 5th day of May.

## ANOTHER GOOD DAY TO BLEED

90. Whoever is bled on the 17th day of September, will not be attacked by colic, ague, nor cough in that year.

*Pughe adds that* 'In a manuscript, apparently written by Llywelyn Sion*, about 1580, the following are enumerated as good days or times for letting blood':-

| The first day after the golden number** in each month, before noon. | The eleventh, in the evening. | The twenty-third. |
|---|---|---|
| The second, at noon. | The twelfth, at all times. | The twenty-fourth, before noon. |
| The third, in the forenoon and after. | The thirteenth, at all times. | The twenty-fifth, at vesper time. |
| The fourth, before anterth***, i.e. before 6 in the morning. | The fourteenth, at all times. | The twenty-sixth, at all times. |
| The fifth, before anterth. | The sixteenth, in the morning. | The twenty-seventh. |
| The seventh, any part of the day. | The seventeenth. | The twenty-eighth, in the evening. |
| The eighth, at noon. | The eighteenth, at the third hour. | The twenty-ninth. |
| The ninth, at all times. | The twentieth, after dusk. | The thirtieth. |
| The tenth. | | |

*\* Llywelyn Siôn (c.1540 - c.1615) of Llangewydd was a poet, farmer, at one time beadle or crier in the courts, a professional copyist by trade, and one of the most important figures in the literary life of Glamorganshire; \*\* A golden number is assigned to each year in sequence to indicate the year's position in a 19-year Metonic Cycle, and used in the yearly calculation of the date of Easter. It can be calculated by dividing the year by 19, taking the remainder, and adding 1. For example, 2011 divided by 19 gives 105, remainder 16. Adding one gives a golden number of 17. 2012 also has a golden number of 17; \*\*\*A liturgical borrowing from the Latin 'ante tertiam', and meaning the same as the Irish Gaelic 'anteirt'. Today it means the zenith or apogee.*

## DANGEROUS DAYS TO BLEED

91. Whoever is bled on the third Monday in January, the first Monday in February, and the second Monday of October, will be in danger of death. There are three days in the year in which no bleeding should take place, nor any medicinal potion taken, which are the last day of April, the first Monday of August, and the last Monday in September.

*The Llywelyn Siôn manuscript above mentions the following are unlucky or dangerous days for blood-letting:*

| January 1,2,4,5,10,12,19 | May 5,6,16,20 | September 16,17 |
|---|---|---|
| February 7,14,18 | June 12 | October 5 |
| March 15,16,18 | July 15,20 | November 7,16,20 |
| April 6,11 | August 2,12,19 | December 6,8,15 |

## THINGS TO BE AVOIDED

92. Whoever is bled on those days [mentioned in 1.91], will die by the 15th or 7th day. And this is the reason. The veins will be full in those days, and if any medicinal potion is taken, it will be dangerous. And if he eats the flesh of a goose, he will die on the third day, or else will be an invalid within a fortnight, or else he will die in the days mentioned of sudden death.

## DANGEROUS DAYS IN THE YEAR

93. Sound teachers have discovered and written as follows, namely, that thirty-two days in the year are dangerous. Know that whoever is born on one of those days will not live long. Whoever is married on one of them, will die before long, or will only exist in pain and poverty. And whoever shall begin business on one of them, will not complete it satisfactorily. These days are:-

In JANUARY there are seven - 1st, 2nd, 4th, 5th, 10th, 16th, 17th.

In FEBRUARY there are three - 16th, 11th, 18th.

In MARCH there are three - 15th, 16th, 18th.

In APRIL there are two - 3rd and 16th.

In MAY there are four - 15th, 16th, 17th, 20th.

In JUNE there is one - 2nd.

In JULY there are two - 15th and 17th.

In AUGUST there are two - 18th and 20th.

In SEPTEMBER there are two - 16th and 18th.

In OCTOBER there is one - 6th.

In NOVEMBER there are two - 15th and 20th.

In DECEMBER there are three - 16th, 17th, 18th.

Whosoever doubts these sayings, let him know that he is wiser than those who first obtained this knowledge.*

*Pughe adds:* *The intelligent reader hardly needs being told, that all this statement relative to good and bad reasons for bleeding has no foundation in fact, and the equivocal structure of this sentence seems to indicate that our ancient mediciners were quite aware of this, and must have indicted it with a certain twinkling eye: we must be guided in the use of the lancet by more certain indications, even the actual condition of the patient carefully and skilfully ascertained. Nevertheless it is curious to observe, that the type of disease seems to change in the course of an uncertain cycle of years, from a sthenic [*strong, vigorous*] to an asthenic [*weak*] form and vice-versa. Thus twenty-five years ago the sthenic constitution prevailed, and the lancet was freely employed, but in late years in consequence of the markedly asthenic tendency of all complaints, this characteristic implement of our art is rarely used, certainly not once where then it would have been used fifty times. From Sydenham* to the present, this fact has from time to time, attracted the attention of medical observers, that father of English medicine having been the first to call attention to it.

*Thomas Sydenham (1624-1689) was known as 'The Father of English Medicine'. See 1.49 above.*

### FOR SWELLING OR HARDNESS OF THE STOMACH

94. Boil duckweed* in goat's milk, and bathe the warm lotion on the stomach frequently.

*Common Duckweed is Lemna minor, but there are many types of duckweed.*

### FOR SWELLING AND PAIN IN THE LOWER EXTREMITIES

95. Take the roots of tutsan and its bark, boiling them in water. When boiled, pour off the supernatant [*floating on the surface*] liquor. Take the residuum and mix with old lard. Then spread on a cloth or a handkerchief, apply to the swollen feet or legs, and the swelling will be dispersed.

### FOR SWELLING AND PAIN IN THE NAPE OF THE NECK [OR THE DORSAL SPINE]

96. Grind the roots of celandine* in a mortar, with fennel, garlic, vinegar or wine, and butter. Bind the poultice around, and it will remove the pain and disperse the swelling.

*One tentatively assumes this is the Lesser Celandine, Ranunculus ficaria, mistaken by some for a buttercup, rather than the Greater Celandine, Chelodonium majus. Lesser Celandine was known as pilewort as it was used to treat piles. The plants are unrelated. The word used in the Middle Welsh text is the Latin 'celidonia'. In Book Two, 'clefyd melyn' refers to Greater Celandine. The modern names are 'dilwydd' for the Greater Celandine and 'cerfagl' for the Lesser Celandine. Both were used extensively in medieval medicine.*

### FOR EPISTAXIS [NOSEBLEED]

97. Boil garlic in milk and water, and drink it. It is proven.

### FOR BURNS OCCURRING IN ANY PART OF THE BODY

98. Take the root of the white lily*, and wash it clean, boiling it briskly in water. Then reduce to a pulp, and mix with oil, and a little white of eggs, spreading it on lint. Let this be applied night and morning. The more plaster you apply the better. Another method is to burn ivy in a clean place, and cover the burn with the ashes of the same, and it will heal it presently.
Another way is to burn fern, and mix the ashes with the white of eggs; or else oil, anointing the burn with it. It will heal it quickly and wonderfully.

*Lilium candidum, the Madonna lily*

### TREATMENT FOR NETTLE RASH, OR ERYSIPELATOUS ERYTHEMA*

99. This is a medicine for nettle rash, (when indicating a bad constitution), so that it may disappear in three days. Take good cheese and pound it briskly in a mortar.

Mix honey with it until it is transparent. Anoint the affected part with the mixture frequently. Lay a cabbage leaf upon it, and it will have disappeared in three days.

*Erysipelas is an acute infectious disease of the skin or mucous membranes, caused by a streptococcus, and characterized by local inflammation and fever. Erythema is a skin condition characterised by redness or rash.*

## TREATMENT FOR THE BITE OF A MAD DOG

100. Pound ground ivy well in a mortar with lard; or pound leeks and vinegar; or pound fennel seed and honey together. Apply to the bite.

## FOR INFLAMMATION OF THE MAMMAE

101. Pound the roots of the tutsan with rancid lard, and apply to the mammae.

## TO CURB INSANITY

102. When a man becomes insane, take daisy, field southernwood* and sage**, infusing them in wine. Let the patient drink it for fifteen days.

*Artemisia campestris, Field Sagewort, Field Wormwood, Field Mugwort; ** Salvia officinalis, Common Sage*

## TO OVERCOME OBSTINATE CONSTIPATION*

103. If the bowels become so constipated that they cannot be moved, obtain duckweed. Boil it briskly in a pot, and then cast it into a pan. Fry with a quantity of blood and butter, eating it hot.

* *Walter Haydn Davies (1903-1984), a Bedlinog miner, wrote in 'The Right Place, The Right Time: Memories of Boyhood Days in a Welsh Mining Community' (1975) of 'Quack-Quack', a local herbalist. Quack-Quack maintained that impurities in the body, rather than germs, viruses or bacteria, caused disease. He said that germs were present in the body but were only harmful if they had some impurity to feed upon. Thus he advised regular use of the bowels to clear the body of impurities and to prevent germs from becoming harmful [- this is similar to claims made by today's colonic irrigation practitioners]. Quack-Quack therefore purged patients, and then advised them upon a suitable diet. The evacuation of impurities from the body and the passing of wind were priorities. He was said to have recited the following to his patients: 'Yr iach a gach yn y bore bach; / Yr afiach a gach yn yr hwyr. / Yr afiach a gach bob yn dipyn bach, / Ond yr iach a gach yn llwyr.' (The healthy defecate in the morning; / The unhealthy defecate in the evening. / The unhealthy defecate little by little, / But the healthy defecate completely.) He also told patients that it was 'Gwell taro rhech na thalu chwech i'r doctwr' (Better to pass wind than pay the doctor sixpence). His preoccupation with digestion and the bowels demonstrated the widespread belief that a 'blockage in the bowels', or retained faeces, was thought to diffuse into the blood and contaminate it with impurities and toxins. These affected the condition of the skin and health in general. The belief is said to be indicative of what has been called the 'plumbing model' of the body, conceiving it as a series of cavities or chambers, connected with one another, and with the body's orifices, by a series of 'pipes' or 'tubes'. If health is to be maintained then blood, air, food, faeces, urine, menstrual blood, etc. must be able to flow freely. The result of any blockage would be illness. Illness resulted from 'morbid humors' produced by rotting food left after digestion. Thus treatment lay in evacuating the morbid humor through the appropriate channel from the affected organ (in this case the intestines). Other means of purging the body of morbid or excess humors similarly evacuated them through an appropriate channel. Therefore emetics such as Ipecacuanha Wine were taken to induce vomiting and expel excess bile or phlegm*

*from the upper part of the stomach. Similarly, diuretics were taken to encourage urination so as to relieve problems in the kidneys.*

## TO CURB PALSY

104. Take field southernwood, pound it in a mortar, and strain the juice to about a small cupful. Give it the patient to drink, on the dawn of God's day of Christmas.

## REMEDY FOR NOSE BLEED

105. Briskly powder betony with salt. Take as much of this as you can hold between your three fingers. Put it in your nostrils. This will stop it quickly.

## TREATMENT FOR ADHESION OF THE LIVER

106. If a man's liver should adhere to his ribs, take in the morning at sunrise some river star tip, (while chanting thy pater noster). Infuse it in new ale. Give it the patient to drink, while in a bath, for nine days.

## COUGH REMEDIES

107. Bruise hemp agrimony in a mortar. Mix the juice with boiling milk, strain and use. Another method is to boil a potful of water until it is wasted to a half. Then mix rye meal with it, and add butter, eating it hot.

## TO DESTROY WORMS IN THE STOMACH OR BOWELS

108. Take the juice of turnips, foment therewith, and they will come out. Another method is to take a handful of the bark of the peach tree, growing in dry ground. Drink it with goat's milk while fasting, and they will all come out.

## TO OVERCOME CONSTIPATION

109. Take salt and second milk\*, equal parts of each. Put on the fire in an evaporating dish, leaving it there until it is reduced into a sort of wax-like mass. Then make cakes (suppositories) of the same, and pass them into the patient's rectum.

*\*The milk which is supplied after the colostrum – this may be human milk rather than cow's milk.*

## ANTIDOTES FOR THE BITE OF A SNAKE

110. For the bite of a snake. Drink the juice of greater plantain, with oil and salt. The juice of mugwort also, when bruised and strained will neutralize poison. Another way is to take the brains of a red cockerel and rue. Mix with sweet milk, curdled milk or wine, and drink. Take also the flesh of the breast while warm, (the cockerel being alive) and apply to the wound. It will extract the venom.

## A CATAPLASM FOR WORMS

111. Take the milk of a cow that has a bull calf sucking her, with barley meal and honey. Boil it in a pan after the manner of porridge, and apply hot to the stomach.

## OTHER REMEDIES FOR WORMS

Another method is to make bread of barley and the kernels of nuts, eating it. Another plan is to bruise fresh rue and mugwort in a mortar, and drink the juice.

## TO HELP A DIFFICULT PARTURITION

112. If a woman is unable to give birth to her child, let mugwort be bound to her left thigh. Let it be instantly removed when she has been delivered, less there should be haemorrhage.

## FOR SWELLING AND PAIN IN THE THIGHS

113. Bruise rue, honey and salt. Apply to the legs, and it will disperse the swelling.

## FOR PAIN IN THE KIDNEYS

114. Take centaury, infused in cold water, and give it to the patient to drink.

## TO HELP EXTREME THIRST

115. Drink centaury infused in hot water. This will quench thirst, and clear the breast and stomach.

## AN APPLICATION FOR SMALLPOX

116. Take the ashes of heath, [lemon] balm or smallage*, and the ashes of hartshorn**, with honey, and anoint with the mixture.

*Apium graveolens, Wild Celery; **Hartshorn salt was a leavening agent, Ammonium Bicarbonate, also called Baker's Ammonia, and a precursor to baking soda and baking powder. It is derived from the use of shavings of the antlers of male red deer (harts), which contain Ammonium Carbonate. In medieval times, the powdered shavings of deer horns would have been used.*

## TO RELIEVE A SURFEIT* [OVEREATING]

117. Take turnip and boil in goat's milk. Let the patient drink it, and he will be relieved.

*The effects of over-indulgence in food and/or drink.*

## A FOMENTATION FOR A BURN OR SCALD

118. Put the leaves of lily in boiling milk, and apply to the affected part until it is well.

## A STRANGE REMEDY FOR RETENTION OF URINE

119. Take the brains of a hare, and mix them with wine. Let the patient smell it for an hour and then drink it.

## A REMEDY FOR THE BITE OF A VIPER

120. Mix the juice of fennel, radish, and rue or wormwood, with oil. Let the patient drink or eat it.

## REMEDIES FOR VOMITING OF BLOOD

121. Boil milfoil with wine or milk, and drink, as this will stop it. Otherwise, boil betonica* in goat's milk, or wine, and this will restrain it.

*Probably Wood Betony, mentioned above*

## A REMEDY FOR CONSTIPATION

122. Boil roots of small thistles*, growing in woods, and give the water to the patient to drink

*This may be the Milk Thistle, Silybum marianum*

## TO REDUCE FATNESS*

123. Whoever is overly fat, let him drink the juice of fennel, and it will reduce him.

*Fennel has been used throughout history as a digestive aid. It can help with trapped wind, poor digestion and more painful conditions such as gastritis and enteritis. Fennel is also a diuretic and therefore is very effective when dealing with kidney or bladder troubles and fluid retention. It is also a general pick-me-up and helps to combat general tiredness and fatigue. If any reader makes a fortune from prescribing this as a miracle diet aid, please remember where you read it first...*

## TO CALM IRRITABILITY OF MIND

124. If a man is irritable of mind, let him drink of the juice of apium, [celery*] frequently. It will relieve him of his irritability, and produce joy.

*Celery juice has been used for centuries for neuralgia, as a nerve tonic.*

## TO EXPEL REPTILES IN THE STOMACH

125. If a snake should enter a person's mouth, or there should be any other living reptiles inside him, let him mix wild chamomile powder in wine, until it is thickened. If he drinks this, it will relieve him of the reptiles.*

*One wonders if tapeworms were considered to be reptiles?*

## TO KILL WORMS IN MAN OR BEAST

126. If worms are generated in man or beast, apply to the stomach the roots of tarragon, and the worm will die immediately. Another way is to mix the leaves of dittany* with strong wine, and let the patient drink it while fasting.

* *Probably Dittany of Crete, Origanum dictamnus*

## FOR INTESTINAL WORMS

127. Let the patient drink a cupful of the juice of plantain, and apply the same herb to the navel. Another way is to take milfoil in wine once, while fasting. The worms will be expelled on that day.

## FOR AGUE

128. Drink the juice of rue in wine, swallow three grains of coriander, drink celery (apium) in sweetened water, and collect plantain while saying your pater noster. Drink it infused in wine and pepper. Another method is to take the juice of bruised mugwort, the juice of wormwood, and tepid oil. Then anoint your whole body on one side three days successively, and it will cheaply cure the ague for you.

## TREATMENT FOR AN OBSTINATE AGUE

129. However, if a man has indeed an obstinate ague, cause him to go into a bath, and let him avoid touching the water with his arms. Let him also take ground ivy, boiling it briskly, and apply hot to his head. He must also be bled in his arm, and he will be cured by the help of God.

## A REMEDY FOR VOMITING AND SIGHING*

130. Mix a handful and a half of betony [betonica] in warm water, and drink it. To cure vomiting, take betonica, and boil in honey, pounding in a mortar, and form into four balls. Administer to him, one daily as a drink, in a warm potion.

* *This is Pughe's translation of 'ucheneideu'. A better translation may be laboured breathing or groaning.*

## AN ANTIDOTE FOR POISON

131. If a man has taken poison let him take juice of dittany, and wine.

## TO STOP BLEEDING FROM THE NOSE

132. Take the tops of three nettles, pounding them together. Put this cataplasm⁺ on the nape of your neck, and if possible into your nostrils. Another method is to pound the milfoil with vinegar in a mortar. Plug the nostrils with this, and it will stay the bleeding.

*A soft poultice, spread on cloth over the skin to soothe.*

## STRANGE TREATMENTS FOR VOMITING

133. Drink milfoil digested in warm wine, until a cure is obtained. Another plan is to immerse the scrotum in vinegar.

## FOR DEAFNESS OCCURRING AFTER A FEVER

134. Take a cow's gall, a woman's milk, and honey, putting it warm into your ears. This is a cure that will not fail.

## THE MANIFOLD VIRTUES OF THE LEEK

135. The following are the virtues of the leek:

It is good to drink the juice to stop vomiting of blood.

It is good for women who desire children to eat leeks.

It is good to take leeks and wine for the bite of an adder, or any other (venomous) beast.

It is good to apply a plaster of leeks and wine to ulcers.

The juice of leeks and woman's milk is a good remedy for a chronic whooping cough, or pneumonia. The juice of leeks, goat's gall and honey, mixed in three equal parts, are useful for deafness. It should be put warm into the ears and nostrils.

The leek is good for headache.

Leeks are good to promote the union of bones, and maturing of boils.

If leeks and salt are applied to ulcers, this will heal them rapidly.

If leeks are eaten raw, they will cause intoxication.

They will strengthen men who have suffered from haemorrhage.

They will relieve flatulency of the stomach.

They are oppressive to the stomach, whether boiled or raw, as they will destroy the nervous energy of it.

Their fumes, rising to the head, will injure the sight.

They produce terrific dreams, unless lettuce or poppy, or something similar is eaten first to temper them, such is their tendency.

They kill the worms that are generated in the stomach or bowels.

## TO STOP VOMITING

136. For those that cannot retain food or drink, but vomit it, milfoil infused in warm wine should be given to them to drink.

## AN ANTIDOTE TO POISON

137. As an antidote for poison, mix two nuts, three dry figs, a handful of rue and thirty grains of salt. Give it to the fasting patient.

## APPLICATIONS FOR PROUD FLESH [GANGRENE]

138. The following is useful when proud flesh forms in a wound, namely, white alum*, reduced to powder, the same powder being applied upon it.

Another for the same purpose. Take a black toad which is only able to crawl, and beat it with a stick, until it becomes furious, when it swells until it dies. Then put it in an earthenware cooking pot, closing it so that no smoke can come out, or air get into it. Then bum it in the pot until it is reduced to ashes, and apply the ashes to the gangrene.

*A white crystalline double sulphate of aluminium, it was often used as an emetic and to stop bleeding in early medicine.

## ANOTHER FOR PROUD FLESH

Another plan is to take a mole, (alternatively a raven), and bum it in the same way, applying the ashes upon the affected part.

## ANOTHER FOR PROUD FLESH

Similarly, make ashes of human flesh, taken if possible from a corresponding part of the body to that in which the disease is situated.

## PROUD FLESH - ANOTHER APPLICATION

In like manner you may take the ashes of the ermine [a stoat in its white winter cost], burnt in the way above mentioned, and apply to the proud flesh.

## ANOTHER FOR PROUD FLESH

Another plan is to take as many as you please of cloves of garlic, burning them upon a clean floor. When they are incinerated, quench the fire with drops of honey, make a powder of the mixture, and apply. Bind it over with a plaster, and in three days afterwards let it be washed. Boil rye meal and a sow's blood together, applying it on the proud flesh when it is ready. Over that a plaster of boiling honey, and a third part of salt should be applied. Do this daily.

## ANOTHER FOR PROUD FLESH

Another plan is to take the jaw of a horse, with all the teeth remaining. Bum a cupful of this to a powder, and mix with pepper and lard. Anoint the affected part with this, tempering with sage. Continue to apply this plaster daily, for a fortnight.

## ANOTHER FOR PROUD FLESH

Another plan is to take honey, the yolk of an egg, good milk and fine confectioner's meal. Mix together and apply to the part twice daily. This is proved.

## THE VIRTUES OF MUSTARD

139. It is useful to expel cold humors.

It is good with vinegar for the bite of an adder or toad.

It is good for toothache.

It will purify the brain.

It will restrain profuse menstruation.

It will provoke the appetite, and strengthen digestion.

It is good for colic, loss of hair, noise in the ears, dimness of sight, cutaneous eruptions, palsy, and many other things.

## URINAL PATHOLOGY* - FOUR URINARY ELEMENTS

140. From the condition of a man's urine, we can distinguish his defects, dangers, fevers (plagues), and diseases, whether he is present or absent. However, we should first show what is the composition of urine. It contains four radical elements:

FIRST. The humor of the blood which circulates in the reproductive organs.

SECONDLY. That (the humor) of the abdominal viscera for the performance of its functions.

THIRDLY. That of the vessels which receive the various fluids of the cholera and fleuma [bile and phlegm].

FOURTHLY. That of the kidneys, supplying those fluids which pass to the bladder. From hence can be discerned all the signs of disease, the fluidity and colour of the urine indicating the evil and good signs.

*Robert Recorde of Tenby (1512-1558), wrote books such as A Treatise of Urine, but wrote from England and in English. Recorde was a polymath who also invented the = and + signs. Apart from mathematical best-sellers and translations, Dr. Recorde also wrote 'The Urinal of Physick' in 1548, which was still in print in the seventeenth century. Urinal diagnosis, urology, is an important diagnostic tool even today.*

## URINAL DIAGNOSIS

141. Should urine abound in water, or resemble red, black, or green wine, or oil, or blood, or the urine of beasts, a skilful person should consider the essential causes of these differences. Attentively studying the same, he will understand which of these humors chiefly predominate: whether they are fleuma; cholera; sanguis; or melancholia*. It is necessary that the urine is collected in a glass vessel, and left to settle until the second hour. Then, by the light of the sun, the physician should judge the indications that it gives.

*These are the four humors of ancient and medieval medicine. Fleuma (Phlegm) is Water (blue, cold and wet). Cholera is Fire, (yellow bile, hot and dry). Sanguis is Air (red blood, hot and wet). Melancholia is Earth (black bile, dry and cold). In turn, these humors gave practitioners the 'four temperaments' of Phlegmatic, Bilious, Sanguine and Melancholic for their patients. Treatment often depended upon the indicated temperament.*

## SIGNS IN ORDER:
### BLACK URINE
141 i. If the urine is black, it will be necessary to renovate that patient's constitution by the most skilful means possible, frequently employing the bath and oil. Then the urine should be again examined, and if it should seem saffron-like and turbid, know that there is a painful disease in the person, produced by heat and dryness.

### SINOPLE URINE
141 ii. If the patient is attenuated and evidently declining in strength, his veins prominent, or red (transparent), and the urine similar in colour to sinople*, it proceeds from the humor of sanguis. By bleeding the patient in the left arm, he will be restored with little trouble.

*A kind of red earth used as a pigment.*

### THICK, OILY, OPAQUE AND SANGUINOLENT URINE
141 iii. If the urine is thick, oily, deep red, not transparent in the rays of the sun and sanguinolent, it indicates languishment and weakness of body, from excess of fever.

### CURDLED URINE
141 iv. If the urine is curdled, it indicates a long continued fever.

### RED AND CHANGEABLE URINE
141 v. If the urine is red, or brimstone-like, and seeming to change its appearance frequently, it indicates a dangerous fever.

### CLOUDY AND GREENISH URINE - A CLOUD ON THE SURFACE
141 vi. If the urine is cloudy and greenish at the commencement of a fever, or in two days afterwards, and when secreted it seems thicker and thicker, the patient is sure to die. If these signs increase in number, though the urine does not thicken, it indicates a tedious fever. If there is a sky appearance on the surface of the urine, it indicates a future fever.

### FOUL URINE
141 vii. If the urine seems foul in fever, it indicates heat and blindness, pain of head and shoulders, with deafness. If the patient is not relieved in seven days, he will die.

### OILY URINE
141 viii. If the urine seems like oil during the heat of a fever, it indicates death, delirium or erysipelas. If it is not quickly removed, it indicates a softening of the brain.

### FIERY URINE, PASSED WITH PAIN
141 ix. If it assumes a fiery hue, and is passed with pain, this indicates that the patient's food and drink are not properly digested. It is accordingly expedient, in such a case, for the patient to restrict himself to a spoon diet.

## BLACK OR RED URINE, WITH SEDIMENT
141 x. If it is black or red, and there is sediment in the bottom, with urine retention, pain in the kidneys, and pain in urination, the patient is in danger. If the urine is passed frequently, and in small quantities, then it indicates a stone in the bladder.

## BLUISH-WHITE URINE, & Co.
141 xi. If the urine is bluish-white, during the heat of a fever, or reddish-brown or red, accompanied with bleeding at the nose, it is attended with great danger.

## WHITE URINE
141 xii. In persons with a diseased liver, when thin urine becomes white, it indicates future agony, but if it disappears suddenly, it indicates a boil.

## BILIOUS URINE
141 xiii. If in the heat of a fever it has the colour of bile, being thick, with a whitish cloud and whitish granules floating thereon, it indicates a long continued languishing.

## COPIOUS URINE
141 xiv. It more is passed than is proper, during the heat of a fever, and the colour is not good, although passed freely, it indicates danger at hand. If the urine is not natural, when passed, and it subsequently assumes a healthy colour, it indicates that the patient will pine away from future torment.

## WHITE GRAVEL IN URINE
141 xv. If a man in the heat of a fever passes his urine sufficiently naturally, but with white gravel in it, the fever not decreasing, it indicates danger.

## WATERY URINE
141 xvi. If it abounds in water, the fever will increase, but he will be in no danger.

## DARK, TURBID URINE
141 xvii. If the urine is dark, during the heat of a fever, the turbidity not subsiding, his illness will resolve itself into an ague in four, or perhaps three days.

## RED, SEDIMENTARY URINE
141 xviii. If it is red, with much sediment, it will indicate a fever.

## TRANSPARENT URINE
141 xix. If it has the colour of water, the fever will increase, but there will be no danger.

## FILTHY, GRAVELLY, CLOUDY URINE
141 xx. Urine during the heat of a fever, if it is viscid and filthy, abounding with a gravelly sediment, with a cloudiness on the surface, indicates a tedious illness.

## SANGUINOLENT URINE [MIXED WITH BLOOD]
141 xxi. The urine of fever having sandy sediment, being sanguinolent in colour, indicates disease of the kidneys.

## FROTHY URINE

141 xxii. If the urine should be frothy, like bubbles on water, let him not be surprised at the occurrence of any disease, as it indicates a fever at hand.

## WHITE, THEN RED, URINE

141 xxiii. If the urine is white in the morning, and afterwards red, it is well. It only signifies the proper flux of the body.

## RED, THEN BLACK, [OR BROWN] URINE

141 xxiv. If it is red first, and afterwards black, or if the urine has a mixture of those two colours, it indicates death.

## GREASY, BUBBLY URINE

141 xxv. If it is greasy on the surface, bubbles ascending therein, it is a bad sign.

## GREASY URINE WITH WHITE SEDIMENT

141 xxvi. If it is greasy on the surface, and there is white sediment in the bottom of the vessel, it indicates pain in the viscera or joints.

## BLUE URINE

141 xxvii. If the urine is blue, it indicates a disease of the viscera.*

*The internal organs of the main cavities of the body, especially those within the abdomen, e.g. the intestines.

## RED AND CLOUDY URINE WITH SEDIMENT

141 xxviii. An ill-looking red urine, containing a gravelly sediment, and having a cloudiness on the surface, is a bad sign.

## WHITE URINE

141 xxix. If it is very white, it is unfavourable. If it is dark in the morning, so much the worse.

## GREASY, PAINFUL URINE

141 xxx. If it is greasy, and preceded by great pain, it is indicative or death.

## MORE URINE INDICATORS

If it is transparent, with a cloudiness, the death of that patient will be nigh at hand.

If it is light-coloured in the morning, and lighter after dinner, it will be all the better.

If it is red with sediment, it indicates no danger. (This contradicts 141 xviii)

A dark hepatic urine indicates danger.

A pale splenetic urine is dangerous.

A red urine from dyspepsia is dangerous.

A clear urine indicates a healthy condition.

And thus it ends.

Pughe adds in a long footnote: The following is the translation of an extract upon the same subject, purporting to have been made from the Book of "Hywel ddu Feddyg" [Hywel, the black Doctor], a descendant of Einion ap Rhiwallon, by

"Ieinē ap Wm. ap ff", A.D. A thousand, [*followed by six symbols*] "The following are the elementary rules of urinoscopy. If the urine exhibits a yellow colour of a faint golden hue, or if it has the hue of refined gold; it indicates that food and drink are perfectly digested in the stomach.

If of a fiery red, like the sunset in the west – if red like oriental saffron – if a fiery red like a vanishing flame – if red like a portion of consuming fire; these four colours indicate that the food and drink have left the stomach in order that their digestion may be completed.

If urine is deep coloured like human liver, or the hue of (blushing) cheeks, like racked red wine, or greenish like the mane of an oxen; these three colours concur that food and drink are properly digested in the stomach.

If water has a leaden hue, or an intensely black colour like black ink, or a dead black, like black horn; these three colours indicate the death of a man.

If it has the colour of clear spring water, if an opaline colour like transparent horn, or the colour of plain milk, or the hue of camel hair; these four colours indicate the non-digestion of the food in the stomach.

If it has a greenish-blue colour, this indicates that less food and drink should be allowed the patient.

If the colour of ill-bled meat, it indicates that the digestion of food has commenced in the stomach.

If a greenish hue like an unripe apple, - if the hue of a ripe apple; these two colours indicate that the food and drink are half digested in the stomach. And thus it terminates."

These extracts as well as the teaching of our "Meddygon" on the same subject, are of but slight value indeed, farther than they show how rude [basic] and empiric was the urinary diagnosis and pathology of our fathers. The first writer on urinoscopy* was Theophilus, called Philaretus**, a monk, who was Physician to Heraclius, who reigned in the first half of the 7th century. His treatise on the urine has little originality, farther than as being the first of a class of writings, distinguished above all others for chicanery and humbug. After him we find a succession of authors (particularly the urinoscopists of the Middle Ages,) pursuing dreamy speculations to a greater pitch of absurdity than can be readily conceived by those whose curiosity has not led them to pay visits of discovery to the bye paths of medicine. In nothing has modern research made greater advances than urinary diagnosis and pathology, thanks to the microscopist and chemist. Vide "Lilium medicina" of Bernard Gordon – Watson (of New York) on ancient medicine.

*A 1910 report found that the Welsh placed a great deal of faith in 'Water Casters' or 'Water Doctors' and, once having obtained a reputation as such, practitioners could build an 'immense practice, people coming from miles around sending him specimens of urine, from which he professes to diagnose their ailments.' 'One such practitioner was J. F. Bridgman of Neath who was said to be extremely busy in his practice. Urine-casting, or uroscopy, had been a diagnostic procedure dating from antiquity but which had been attacked during the sixteenth and seventeenth centuries as irrational and magical, and had undergone decline as a respectable medical practice. And yet the practice continued to be popular among the laity, especially in the more remote parts of the country. Its continued popularity in Wales can perhaps be attributed to the faith placed in humoral conceptions of health and illness – scrutiny of the urine made sense to

102

*determine the state of bodily fluids. Urine-casters either treated their patients themselves or else referred them to another practitioner after identifying their ailment and were the only purely diagnostic practitioners outside orthodox medicine.' 'The Western Mail' 15 June 1926, ran an advertisement: 'Lost. Sunday, June 13th, about 3.30 p.m. from touring car on Carmarthen-Tenby-Road, near Bankyfelin, a 2a Folding Kodak Camera, containing film of owner and family. Substantial reward.- J.F. BRIDGMAN, Herbalist, Alfred-street, Neath.' Thus herbalism must have been a good living. Very, very few people had cars or cameras in the 1920s.*

*\*\*It appears that Philaretus and Theophilus Protospatharius were different persons, however. Theophilus' 'De Corporis Humani Fabrica' and 'De Urinis' were major influences upon physicians for centuries.*

## BLEEDING [BLOODLETTING]

142. When letting blood, the blood should be permitted to flow until the colour changes. If the stream of blood is black, it should flow until it becomes red. If the blood is thick, let it flow until it becomes more fluid [thinner]. If it is watery, let it flow until it becomes thicker.

## HEALTH

143. To secure constant health, drink daily, the first thing in the morning, a spoonful of juice of mallows.

## FOR BIRDS AND FLIES

144. To drive away birds or flies, put mugwort in the places where they frequent, and they will disperse.

## FOR A SPECK IN THE EYE

145. For a speck in the eye, put in it the juice of ground ivy.

## FOR INTOXICATION*

146. In order to be delivered from intoxication, drink saffron digested in spring water.
   *\*This is the same remedy as 1.57 above.*

## FOR A TUMOUR*

147. Apply a cock or a hen to it, until the animal dies.
   *\*This remedy is also repeated elsewhere.*

## FOR FALLING SICKNESS

148. Let a dog be killed, and, unknown to the patient, put some of the gall into his mouth. Falling sickness will never attack him again.

## A PROGNOSIS OF DEATH

149. In order to form a prognosis of the fate of a sick person, bruise violet, apply to the eyebrows, and if he sleeps, he will live. If not, he will die.

## FOR CHASTITY

150. If you would preserve yourself from unchaste desires, eat rue in the morning.

## TO DISSOLVE URINARY CALCULI

151. Take saxifrage*, which grows in stony places (- it has obtained its name from its virtues in this respect). Temper with wine and pepper, drinking it warm. This

will break the bladder stone, and promote the passing of water. It will also promote menstruation, and cure diseases of the kidneys and uterus.

*This is probably Pimpinella saxifrage - Lesser Burnet, Burnet Saxifrage, traditionally used to break up bladder stones. In Latin, saxum means rock or stone, and frangere means to break.*

### ANOTHER WAY TO DISSOLVE URINARY CALCULI
Another way of dissolving the stone is to take saxifrage and the seed of gromwell*, infusing them in boiling water. Let the patient drink this for six days, and he will be cured without fail.

*Lithospermum officinale, European Stoneseed*

### ANOTHER REMEDY TO DESTROY THE STONE – AN EXPERIMENT
Another mode is to take the blood and skin of a hare, burning them to ashes. Then mix a quantity of this powder in warm water, and let the patient drink a spoonful or the mixture, while fasting. This will disintegrate the stone, causing it to be expelled. If you would wish to prove this, put a spoonful of the same powder in water, and deposit any calculus you please in it, and it will instantly slacken [lessen] it.

### THREE THICK INCURABLE ORGANS
152. There are three thick incurable organs: the liver; kidney; and heart. The reason why they are so-called is that when disease has affected any of them, no relief can be given, but a painful death.


### THREE THIN INCURABLE ORGANS
153. There are three thin incurable organs: the pia mater; small intestines; and bladder. They are incurable for the same cause as the others.

### THREE COMPLAINTS WHICH OCCASION CONFINEMENT*
154. There are three complaints which occasion long confinement: disease of the knee joint; of the substance of a rib; and of a lung. For when matter has formed in any, a surgeon does not know when he may be cured, until he sees the patient well.

*Another triad quotes 'the three most difficult treatments for a doctor: an injury to the lungs; an injury to the milk glands; and to a knee.' Triads, groups of three, have been used as mnemonics in Welsh since recorded history.*

### FOR HAEMORRHOIDS
155. Apply the calcareous droppings of the peacock, pounded with fern roots, and it will cure it.

### FOR HYDROPHOBIA
156. For the bite of a mad dog, it is a good thing to eat the root of radish.

### TO CURE BARRENNESS
157. To render a woman fruitful, let her frequently eat lettuce, hot tallow* and pepper.

*Mutton fat, rendered from suet, would be more likely in Wales than beef fat.*

## THE GREATEST REMEDY

158. What is the most difficult treatment (or effort of surgical skill)? To remove a bone from the brain [to trephine or trepan] with safety.

*A trephine is a surgical instrument with a cylindrical blade, specially designed for obtaining a cylindrically shaped core of bone, i.e. cutting holes in bones. Trepanning, also known as trephination, trephining or making a burr hole, is a surgical intervention in which a hole is drilled or scraped into the skull to expose the dura mater. It is often used to relieve pressure beneath a surface. The operation has been carried out from Neolithic times, probably to treat seizures and mental disorders. Trepanning is also used for emergency surgery after head wounds, to remove shattered bits of bone from a fractured skull and clean out the blood that often pools under the skull after a blow to the head.*

## THE LEAST REMEDY

159. What is the simplest treatment? To scratch one's hand until it is sore, then spitting upon it and rubbing it.

## AN ANTIDOTE FOR PAIN

160. Seek dittany, which may be obtained from informed men*. It is the best in all complaints.

* *The Welsh is 'hyspissvyr', which Pughe translated as 'cunning men'. Hysbysrwydd is knowledge. In this context, it may mean 'those who place advertisements', i.e. offer dittany for sale. A 'dyn hysbys' was a wizard, soothsayer or fortune-teller. People went to a dyn hysbys for medical advice, the term coming to mean 'magic healer'.*

## REMEDY FOR A TUMOUR

161. Take daisy and greater plantain in powder, mixing these with drink, until it is thickened. Take also dust scraped from blue stone (sulphate of copper), and administer to the patient in drink. It will cure him, if it is given him before he sleeps.

## REMEDY FOR SWELLING AFTER AN INJURY

162. Take the juice of yellow bedstraw, the juice of plantain, rye meal, honey and the white of eggs. Make into a plaster, and apply to the swelling.

## FOR BOILS

163. Take the juice of the morel*, plantain, barley meal and the white of an egg.

* *The Welsh is 'y morella', and morels are a genus of edible mushrooms, of which there are several types in the UK. The Welsh morel cyffredin is the common morel. However, morel or Morella was recorded in 1400 as also meaning nightshade, usually black nightshade. Whereas Pughe gives us morel as a translation, the use of juice makes it more likely that this is nightshade.*

## FOR STRANGURY

164. Take dead rednettle, and parsley. Make a plaster of them, and apply to the stomach below the navel.

## TO REMOVE WARTS

165. Take the inner bark of the willow, make into a plaster with vinegar, and apply it.

## REMEDIES FOR HEARTACHE*

166. Take the bark of keginderw**, the bark of stinking goose foot, plantain, and shepherd's purse, boiling them in ditch [stagnant] water, until it is boiled down to a third part. Take this water and make it into gruel, with wheaten flour. Another method is to take caraway water and goat's milk in equal parts, mixing plantain juice with them, and boiling river granite in it. Let this be given the patient for nine days, unmixed with any other drink.

*The Welsh is 'rac heint callon'. Modern Welsh is rhag (for) and calon (heart). 'Heintus' is a medieval word for infected, diseased or sickly. Pughe translated 'sickly heart' as heartache: **This word is Middle Welsh, made up of cegin = kitchen, and derw = oak trees. There is no 'k' in modern Welsh, and Pughe did not translate it. It appears that ceginderw is the herb Germander. This should be Germander Speedwell, Veronica chamaedrys, also known as Bird's Eye Speedwell. Its modern Welsh name is Llysiau Llywelyn or Rhyddhwyn. One wonders whether it could be Common Speedwell (a rarer plant), Veronica officinalis, which was also used in medieval medicine, as indicated by its 'officinalis notation'. Another translation is 'oaks of Jerusalem' which is Jerusalem Oak Goosefoot, Chenopodium botrys. Neither this goosefoot nor germander, however, has much of a bark.*

## FOR PAIN IN THE CHEST (DYSPEPSIA)

167. Take a large quantity of blackthorn berries, bruise briskly in a mortar, mixing very new ale with them. Put this mixture in a new earthenware pot, over its edges in the earth, for nine days and nights. Give it the patient to drink the first thing in the morning, and the last thing at night.

## TO MAKE VINEGAR

168. Take clean barley, and put in wine over night until the eve of next day.

## TO PROMOTE THE UNION OF BONE

169. Take comfrey, and bruise with wine, pepper and honey, drinking it daily for nine days. The bones will unite compactly.

## TO MAKE AN EYE SALVE

170. Take the juice ......... * and the juice of fennel root, celandine, lesser celandine, sow's lard, honey, a little vinegar, an eel's blood and a cock's gall. Let them stand in a brass vessel until efflorescence** takes place. This has restored sight to those who had quite lost it.

* This short phrase is omitted, replaced with a line of dots, both in the original manuscript and in Pughe's translation; **Literally to 'flower out', when crystals or sales appear when water evaporates upon exposure to air.*

## THE DIGNITY OF MEDICINE

171. Let all men know that it will be vain to seek anything except by effort. There can be no effort without health. There can be no health without temperance in a man's nature, and temperance cannot exist in a man's nature without moderate heat in his extremities. God has decreed a supervision of the manner in which we should conserve our health, and has revealed it to his own servants, the philosophers and chosen prophets, who are full of the Holy Spirit, and whom God ordained to this profession.

106

172. The Latins, the men of Persia and the Greeks say what we choose we love; and what we seek we think of. Therefore let all men know that God has given the men of Greece a special gift, to discern every art, and the nature of all things, to a greater extent than other nations, with a view to the preservation of human health.

173. The philosophers and wise men knew that man was formed of four elements, each being antagonistic to the others, and each consequently requiring continual aliment, which if it does not obtain, it will succumb. If a man takes too much or too little food or drink, the body will become weak, fall into disease, and be open to injurious consequences. If he partakes temperately of food and drink, the body will acquire strength, and the health will also be preserved.

## MODERATION

174. The philosophers have said whoever shall eat or drink more or less than he should, or shall sleep more or less, or shall labour more or less from idleness or from hardship, (being obliged to overexert himself): or who, used to being bled, refrains from doing so, without doubt he will not escape sickness. Of these things we shall treat presently, and of what is most suitable for our use.

## SAYINGS OF THE WISE AS TO FOOD

175. Wise men have declared, that whoever refrains from eating or drinking immoderately, and will only partake temperately of food and drink, as his constitution requires, will enjoy health and long days, that is, a long life. Philosophers never said anything to the contrary. Desire, love, and the reception of worldly honour, these things fortify and assist life, so that they are gratified temperately. On which account, whoever desires life and permanence, let him seek that which is permanent and tends to prolong life.

## MODERATION - A MEANS TO PROLONG LIFE - HIPPOCRATES AND HIS DISCIPLES

176. Whoever would prolong his life should restrain his appetite, and not eat over abundantly. I have heard that Ipocras* [*the oldest spelling of Hippocrates*] having attained old age, and suffering much from infirmity and the weight of years, was addressed by his disciples, thus: 'Great teacher of wisdom, did you eat and drink abundantly, would you have to endure all the weakness which you do?' Ipocras answered: 'My sons, I eat a proper portion seeing I live. I should not live if, with a view of prolonging mere human life, I took food too frequently. Eating is not the one thing needful, when the prolonging of life is the object aimed at, for I have seen many die from too much eating.'

*Pughe notes that: 'Hippocrates was a native of the island of Cos, and was regarded as the father of medical science. He delivered Athens from a dreadful pestilence at the beginning of the Peloponnesian War, and was publicly awarded with a golden crown, the privileges of a citizen of Athens, and the initiation at the grand festivals. He died in the 99th year of his age, 361 BCE, free from all disorders of mind and body; and after death he received the name of Great, the same honours which were paid to Hercules.'

## EAT SLOWLY AND SPARINGLY - MEN OF ARABIA - TWO RULES TO PRESERVE HEALTH

177. Whoever, restraining their appetite, refrains from gluttony, and eats slowly, these people shall live long; which may be thus proved. The men of Arabia, who dwell in mountains and pathless woods, are the most long-lived of mortals, as these circumstances prevent excessive eating and drinking. The health may be preserved in two ways:

First - by partaking of such food as is most suitable to the time of life and the constitution, restricting himself to that sort of diet which he was reared upon.

Secondly - by evacuating duly, that which is poured into the stomach from above.*

*Here Pughe footnotes: The following "Prescriptions about health and life" are attributed to Cattwg the Wise *(the 6th century Saint Cadog ap Glywys):*

177.1 He that would attain a long life, let him play until he is twenty, labour until he is forty, and rest to the end of his days.

177.2 Let him arise with the lark, sing with the lark, and retire to rest with the lark.

177.3 Let him eat when he has an appetite, drink when he is thirsty, and rest when he is fatigued.

177.4 Let him avoid food which is too dainty, drink that is too strong, and work that is too heavy and troublesome.

177.5 Let him avoid too much food, too much drink, and too much labour.

177.6 Let him avoid contention, love peace, and divest himself of too many cares.

177.7 Let him be merry, generous, and just.

177.8 Let him have but one wife, be strong in the faith, and have a clean conscience.

177.9 Let him be meditative in the morning, industrious at noon, and social in the evening.

177.10 Let his meditation be pleasant, his games innocent, and his air salubrious.

177.11 Let his clothes be not old, his furniture be clean and sweet, and let him be content with his lot in life.

177.12 Let his dress be light, his food be light, and his heart be light.

177.13 Let his disposition be affectionate, his genius lively, and his friends numerous.

177.14 Let him keep the law of his country, the rule of his vocation, and the commandments of his God.

177.15 Thereby, his body will be healthy, his mind easy, and his conscience pure.

177.16 His life will be long, his end will be bliss, and his God will love him – Myvyrian Archaiology iii p.56

## A THEORY OF DIGESTION

178. Let all men know, that the human organism is antagonistic to food and drink, decomposing both in the process of digestion, and that every animal or human being is naturally verging upon disease. Also, animal organisms are corrupt from superabundant heat, which dries the spirit (anima) by which the body is nourished. Animal bodies also are corrupt from excessive heat of the sun, which dries the animal spirits; and this is particularly the case with the bodies of the animals upon which we feed. When the body is hot, strong aliments are required, as then they can be digested.

## FAT AND DRY CONSTITUTIONS

179. When a man's body is fat and dry, luxurious juicy food is proper for him, for they will easily assimilate. In this way a man may preserve his health. Let him confine himself to such food as is suitable to his constitution. This has been proved.

## A HOT HABIT

180. If a man's body is constitutionally hot, hot aliment [food] is proper for him.

## A COLD HABIT

181. If a man's body is constitutionally cold, cold aliments are proper for him.

## A HUMID OR DRY HABIT

182. If the body is constitutionally humid or dry, cold aliments are forbidden him.

## WHAT FOOD IS MOST SUITABLE FOR A WEAK OR STRONG STOMACH

183. Strong food is most suitable for a hot stomach; as such a stomach is comparable to fire consuming loose flax. Weak food is most proper for a cold stomach; as such a stomach is compatible to fire consuming straw.

## A HEALTHY DIGESTION

184. The signs of a healthy digestion are that the body is active, the understanding clear, and the desire for food frequent.

## SYMPTOMS OF INDIGESTION

185. The symptoms of indigestion are heaviness of body, with irritability of feeling added, a languid performance of duty, swelling of the face, frequent yawning, dimness of sight, frequent eructations*, attended with a bitterness of taste in the mouth, this bitterness occasioning cardialgia, which extending to the body and limbs, occasions a dislike for food.
*Belching

## HOW TO ACT WHEN RISING FROM BED, AND SUBSEQUENTLY DURING THE DAY, WITH OTHER HYGIENIC MATTERS

186. When rising from bed, walk a while and stretch your limbs, contracting your head and neck. This will strengthen your limbs, and the contracting of the head will cause the (animal) spirits to rush from the stomach to the head, and from the head. When you sleep, they will fall to the stomach again. In the summer, bathe in

cold water, for this will keep warmth in the head, which will occasion a desire for food. Then array yourself in fair garments, for a man's mind delights in fair things, and his heart is rendered lighter. Then clean the teeth with the dry bark of the hazel*, as they will become all the fairer in consequence. Your speech will be also most distinct, and your breath sweeter.

The standing posture should be at times practised, as it will do you much good, relieving the dura matter (membrane of the brain,) clothing your neck with power, investing your countenance with greater beauty, giving strength to the arms, improving your sight, preserving you from paleness, and adding power to your memory. Conversation, walking in company, and eating and drinking according to your usual habit, should be done in moderation. Use moderate exercise in walking or riding, as this will invigorate the body, and remove cardialgic pains, so that a man will be more hearty, stronger, and the stomach will be warmer as well as your nerves more elastic.

* *Pughe notes:* Giraldus Cambrensis assures us that the Welsh, in the 12th century, paid great attention to their teeth, rubbing them with either the leaves or the bark of the hazel, and refraining from hot meats and drinks, so that they were of dazzling whiteness.

## WHAT TO EAT
187. When you eat, take that for which you have the greatest relish if you can, particularly leavened bread. If you eat simple food it will be easier for the stomach to digest it. If, when unused to it, you should nonetheless eat two kinds of food, plain and strong food, eat the strong first, for the inferior portion of the stomach is hotter than the superior, as the lime is nearer, from whence more heat will be derived.

## RULES FOR EATING AND DRINKING
188. When you eat, do not eat away all your appetite, but let some desire for food remain. Drink no water with your food, as it will cool your stomach, preventing its digesting the food, and quenching the warmth of it. But when you drink water, drink it sparingly, choosing the coldest water you can obtain. When you have eaten, take a walk in some well-sheltered level piece of ground. When you feel inclined to sleep, do not sleep too much. Rest on your right side, then turn on the left, and double yourself. It you should feel pain in your stomach (cardialgia) and heaviness, put on extra clothing. In order to withdraw the heat from the stomach, drink warm water, as by producing vomiting this will remove unhealthy matter from your stomach. Much walking, before food, will heat the stomach. Much walking after food will injure the stomach, because undigested food will fall to the inferior part of the stomach, and there generate many diseases.

Sleeping before food will make a man thin, but sleeping after food will make a man fat. The night is colder than the day, and consequently the stomach will digest sooner by night than by day, because the colder the weather, the better the stomach digests, as the heat falls from the extremities, and concentrates itself about the stomach. If a man who is in the habit of eating twice daily, should do so once only, it will injure the stomach. If a man in the habit of eating once only daily, eats twice, it will be hurtful to the stomach. If from eating at one period of the day, we change to another, it will do harm to the stomach.

At all times, if necessity should arise, obliging one to make a change in one's habits, let it be done gradually. Also do not eat until the stomach has become empty, and this you may know from the sense of hunger and the thinness of your saliva. If you eat without hunger, the animal heat will freeze. If you eat when hungry, you animal spirits will be as hot as fire, and whoever does not then take food, his stomach will fill up with insalubrities [unwholesomeness], which will produce headache.

## PART 5

## THE PHYSICIANS OF MYDDFAI

## BOOK TWO

This has been compiled by Iolo Morganwg (Edward Williams) 1747-1826, and many of its remedies are in the three untranslated mss. in the British Museum and Jesus College Oxford. The book contains later remedies, using ingredients not available in the twelfth-thirteenth centuries, which are similar to those noted by Culpeper, Gerard and others in the seventeenth century and before. It is thought by this author that the work is genuine, gathered from many sources. Normally a medical book would begin with remedies for the head, and end with the feet, but groupings of remedies recur in different places. If Iolo had wished to forge a realistic medical primer he would have ordered the entries differently.

A 1916 inventory of manuscripts mentions MS. B 20, the Book of Thomas Bona, so called *'because it was purchased by Iolo from a collector of that name in Carmarthenshire. The book however contains poetry written in different hands of the 16th and 17th centuries, some of the poems being in the writing of their authors.'* Surely Iolo would not fabricate a manuscript from Bona's brother William and risk his reputation? Historians seem to forget the terrible fires at Hafod Uchtryd in 1807 and Wynnstay in 1853, which destroyed a good proportion of the manuscripts collected by Edward Lhuyd, and which Iolo had studied and presumably copied.

This author has details of Iolo buying mss. which had come from Margam Abbey, and Gwyneth Lewis' doctoral thesis has shown that many of the triads allegedly 'made up' by Iolo were genuine, existing for centuries before his birth. There is not the time or space to devote to a defence of Iolo Morganwg here, unfortunately, but he was unfortunately traduced by those who believed that south-east Wales had no literary heritage (it was the home of the Silures, and by far the richest part of Wales). Iolo has also been slandered by generations of historians who did not realise that taking laudanum for chronic asthma was the only remedy in his days.

Please note that the translations for forty remedies (5, 47, 72, 73, 83, 91, 92, 93, 116, 138, 139, 140, 142, 143, 144, 146, 185, 211, 212, 217, 219, 256, 264, 268, 269, 270, 276, 317, 333, 334, 339, 343, 350, 352, 365, 366, 439, 445, 647 and 775) are new, and were missing from Pughe's 1861 translation. Others, such as 349, were not translated fully. It appears that these were expurgated by the Reverend John Williams ab Ithel, as they deal with the private parts of people, and some refer to venereal diseases. The original Welsh version of these missing remedies in Pughe's edition has never been translated for publication, and is included, in the event of a mistranslation by this editor.

The National Library of Wales refers to the manuscript as NLW MS 13111B: *'Meddygon Myddfai; Llyfr Harri Siôn, [1767x1826] / 'Iolo Morganwg' and*

*[Harri Jones]. A composite volume containing two Welsh medicinal texts. Pp. 1-236 are in the hand of Edward Williams ('Iolo Morganwg') and contain a corpus of medicinal prescriptions, a Latin-Welsh list of herbs, etc., reputedly compiled by Hywel Feddyg ab Rhys ab Llywelyn ab Philip Feddyg of Cil Gwryd in Gower [co. Glamorgan] from the books of his ancestors Rhiwallon and his three sons Cadwgan, Gruffudd, and Einion, the original 'Meddygon Myddvai' (physicians of Myddfai, co. Carmarthen) and those of their descendants. The text was allegedly transcribed by Edward Williams in 1801 from a volume in the possession of Thomas Bona of the parish of Llanfihangel Iorwerth, co. Carmarthen, physician, which, in turn, had been transcribed by Wiliam Bona, brother of Thomas, in 1743 from a volume which had belonged to John Jones of Myddfai, physician, 'y diweddaf o dadidad o'r Meddygon ym Myddfai' (the last, by male descent, of the physicians of Myddfai). The Welsh text was published in John Williams ab Ithel (ed.): The Physicians of Myddvai; Meddygon Myddfai. . . (The Welsh MSS Society, Llandovery, 1861), pp.89- 298, with an English translation by John Pughe of Aberdovey, co. Merloneth, ibid., pp. 301-462. Two pieces of paper pasted on to p. 256 are inscribed in the hand of Edward Williams 'Llyfr Meddyginiaeth. Cynnulliad Harri Jones o Bont y Pwl. Cefais hwn am driswllt gan Joseph Jones, Mab yr Harri Jones uchod. Iolo Morganwg', and 'Llyfr Meddyginiaeth. Llyfr Meddyginiaeth Harri Siôn' respectively. These are followed on pp. 257-370 (previously paginated 1-114) by a corpus of medicinal prescriptions, etc., in a hand other than that of Edward Williams, presumably compiled by the Harri Jones referred to in the aforementioned inscriptions.'*

# THE THREE REMEDIES OF THE PHYSICIANS OF MYDDFAI
## *WATER, HONEY AND LABOUR*

## BOOK II

## THE BOOK OF REMEDIES OF HOWELL THE PHYSICIAN

The book purports to have been compiled by Howell the Physician, son of Rhys, son of Llywelyn, son of Philip the Physician, a lineal descendant of Einion, the son of Rhiwallon, from the Books of the first Physicians of Myddfai. William Bona made a transcript from the Book of John Jones, Physician, the last lineal descendant of the family, AD 1743. The late Iolo Morganwg took a copy of this MS. in 1801, and it is his copy, then in the Llanover Library, that formed the text of this volume. *According to Enwogion Cymru, 'Hywel Veddyg of Cilgwryd in Gower, was the son of Rhys ap Llywelyn ap Phylip Veddyg, a physician of the family of Rhiwallon of Myddvai. He left a book of his practice after him, which, in 1743, was in the possession of John Jones, the last who practised at Myddvai; and of which Dr. William Bona had a copy, which was transcribed by Iolo Morganwg in 1801. (- Owen's Cambrian Biography.)'*

## INTRODUCTION

## THE BOOK OF REMEDIES

The following Work is a book of remedies, which have been proved to be the best and most suitable for the human body, through the research and diligent study of Rhiwallon the Physician, and his three sons, Cadwgan, Gruffydd and Einion, who were Physicians to Rhys Gryg ap* Gruffydd ap Rhys ap Tewdwr, their Lord, who gave them rank, lands, and privileges at Myddfai, for their maintenance in the practice of their art and science, and the healing and benefit of those who should seek their help.

Herein, therefore, by the help of God, is exhibited the art of healing the injuries and diseases to which the human body is most subject, and the method of their management. In the name of the FATHER, of the SON, and of the HOLY GHOST. AMEN, and so may it ever be.

* *Ap means 'son of' in Welsh, the same meaning as 'mac' in Gaelic.*

## FLATULENT DYSPEPSIA*

1. Take parsley seed, bruise well and boil in parsley juice obtained from the leaves and stems. Let it be drunk warm, the pain being present.

* *A disorder of digestive function, characterized by discomfort or heartburn or nausea.*

## ACUTE GASTRODYNIA*

2. Take buckbean** and powder well. Also, burn a quantity of gorse*** or broom**** seed in an iron pot, and reduce to fine powder. Pour a gallon of strong old mead upon the ingredients, then cover it up well and boil, and let it stand covered until cold. You should then drink as much of it as you may require, while fasting night and morning. At other times you should drink nothing but water, until you have recovered your health.

*Gastrodynia is an old name for pain in the stomach. In many texts it was interchangeable with cardialgia, giving one an impaired appetite, with gnawing or burning pain in the stomach. Other writers call it 'neuralgia of the stomach', but the term was often applied to various forms of gastric pain and to pyrosis (acid reflux or heartburn). Again, cardialgia could be a pain in or near the heart.*

**Also known as bogbean and marsh trefoil, Menyanthes trifoliate.*

***Common gorse, Ulex europaeus*

****Common or Scotch broom, Cytisus scoparius*

## ANOTHER REMEDY FOR ACUTE GASTRODYNIA

3. Drink a decoction of blessed thistle* for nine mornings, and refrain from drinking it for nine mornings following, then drink and refrain as before for nine mornings each; and again in the same way for nine mornings more. Let your diet be wheaten bread**, and the milk of kine***.

*This is Cnicus Benedictus, also called Holy Thistle, of extensive use in medieval medicine. A decoction is made by boiling it down to its essence, using all parts of the plant.*

**This may similar to Irish Soda Bread – see Book One.*

***Kine is an archaic word for cattle.*

## A COLLYRIUM*

4. Take a penny pot** full of the best white wine, and as much in quantity as a hen's egg of copper ore. Heat the ore in the fire until it is red, and quench it in the wine, repeating this process nine times. This fluid should be put in a well-covered glass vessel. Keep so covered for nine days, and it will then be fit for use when wanted. A drop or two should be put in the eye night and morning. When wine cannot be obtained, strong old mead [honey wine], or old cider (the wine of apples) may be used.

*Collyrium was a lotion used as an eye wash, from the Greek κολλύριον, eye-salve.*

**A penny pot was half a pint.*

*This entry is missing in Pughe's translation.*

## ARALL

5. Golch dy lygaid a'th ddŵr dy hunan, yna eu cadw yng 'nghaed tra rifer cant.

## ANOTHER EYE WASH

5. Wash your eyes with your own urine, and then keep them closed while you count to one hundred.

## TO BREAK AN IMPOSTUME* OR ABSCESS

6. Take a small portion of the herb called the herb of grace**, a portion of leavened bread, and half a spoonful of glue. Boil these ingredients in the sediment of old ale, mixing them well together until the mass thickens. When required for use, let it be applied hot to the impostume.

*Imposthume or Impostume comes from the Old French empostume, via Late Latin apostēma, and originally from Greek. It means separation (of pus), from 'aphistanai' - to remove. It was used from early medieval times onwards to mean a collection of pus or purulent matter in any part of the body; an abscess.

   **Herb of Grace is Common Rue, Ruta graveolens.

## FOR TOOTHACHE

7. Take distilled water of red roses*, a small portion of beeswax, and a little fresh butter, say an equal quantity of each. Let the ingredients be mixed together in a dish upon embers, then let a linen cloth be dipped in it, and applied to the affected jaw as hot as it can be borne.

   *Probably Rosa Gallica officinalis, the 'Apothecary's Rose', brought to Britain by the Crusaders in the 13th century.

## OINTMENT FOR AN ULCER

8. Take four portions of rosin, two of wax, one of lard, and four of verdigris*. Let these ingredients be boiled together on a slow fire, and strained through a coarse cloth. It should be kept in a well covered leaden vessel.

   *Verdigris is the common name for the green coating, the patina formed when copper (or brass or bronze) is weathered and exposed to air or seawater over a period of time. It is usually copper carbonate, but near the sea will be copper chloride. If vinegar (acetic acid) is present, it will be copper acetate. The word comes from 'verte grez', the Old French for 'green of Greece', as it was a pigment used by Greek artists. The pigment could be made by hanging copper plates over hot vinegar in sealed pots, until the green crust formed and could be scraped off. However, at the time of the physicians of Myddfai, a simpler method may have been used. A wooden block could be soaked in vinegar and copper strips attached. The block was then placed in a dung-heap for a few weeks, and dug up after the verdigris had developed.

## FOR ALL KINDS OF ACHES

9. Take linseed*, boil in milk, and apply to the painful part.

   *Linseed is the seeds of the Flax plant, Linum usitatissimum.

## TO HEAL A WOUND

10. Take yellow wax*, melt on a slow fire, and take bruised cumin seed. Mix with the molten wax, and then stir these ingredients with a stirrer until cold. Apply this as a plaster to the wound.

   *This is a yellow to brown solid wax made by melting a honeycomb with boiling water, straining and cooling, now called beeswax and used in polishes.

## ANOTHER REMEDY TO HEAL A WOUND

11. Take bruised linseed, the white of an egg, a small portion of cream of sheep milk, and a little honey. Make these into a plaster and apply to the wound.

## FOR A BURN OR A SCALD

12. Roast a dozen eggs stone hard, then take out the yolk and put in a frying pan. Fry them until they become an ointment, and strain. Anoint the injured part with the ointment, then take a bladder, spread mucilage of twigs from the lime tree upon it, and apply to the injured part.

## FOR HAEMORRHOIDS

13. Take smoke-dried goat's flesh, desiccate completely, and reduce to as fine a powder as you can. Lay some on live coals in a fireproof utensil, and put the same in a commode and sit upon it.

## AN OINTMENT TO PROMOTE THE REMOVAL OF A SLOUGH FROM AN ULCER

14 Take a spoonful of good vinegar, a spoonful of honey, a little verdigris, and the same quantity of aloes*, and boil together. Keep ready at hand for use.
*This is Aloe vera, indicating trade at that time with the Mediterranean. Pughe notes: 'It cleanseth wounds and suddenly healeth them' – London Dispensary 1679.

## A LOTION TO WASH AN INFLAMED PART

15. Take greater plantain*, honeysuckle, and white roses, distil together, and in the product put some camphor**. Let it remain in this water constantly.
*Also known as Common Plantain, Healing Blade, and Soldier's Herb, Plantago major was used as a wound dressing on battlefields for millennia.
**A waxy solid found in the wood of the Camphor Laurel tree, Cinnamomum camphorum

## FOR AN INFANTILE AGUE OR INTERMITTENT FEVER*

16. Boil the leaves of common cinquefoil** in milk, using as much of the herb as will be expedient. Let this be the child's*** only drink until he is well. This is also generally the most successful remedy for those of mature years.
* This was characterized by paroxysms consisting of chill, fever, and sweating, at regularly recurring times, and followed by an interval or intermission the length of which determines the epithet. Quotidian ague had an interval of 24 hours between paroxysms; Tertian ague had a period of 48 hours; Quartan ague was 72 hours and Quintan ague was 96 hours. The term ague was also applied to Marsh or Malarial fever, with symptoms recurring every 48 hours. 'Aigue' entered English usage in the 14th century, from the Middle French 'ague'. The word shares the same origin as acute, from the Latin 'acutus' meaning sharp or pointed. A 'fièvre aigue' in French was a sharp or pointed (or acute) fever.
**Potentilla erecta was used for stomach pains in medieval times.
*** 1545 - Thomas Phaer, who died in Cilgerran published 'The Boke of Chyldren' (The first book of children's diseases in English). MP for Carmarthen and Cardigan, he was possibly Welsh, of Flemish descent. An addendum to his 'The Regimen of Life', 'The Boke of Chyldren' anticipated many later trends in medicine. He recognised children as a special class of patients, and listed the 'manye grevous and perilous diseases' to which children were susceptible, including meningitis ('apostume of the brayne'), colic, nightmares ('terrible dreames and feare in

*the slepe' and bedwetting ('pissing in the bedde'). Phaere counselled against unnecessary treatments for childhood diseases such as smallpox and measles, and condemned physicians for using Latin, to and the consequent confusion for the patient: 'How long would they have the people ignorant? ... Would they have no man to know but only they?'*

## ANOTHER REMEDY FOR AN INFANTILE AGUE OR INTERMITTENT FEVER

17. Let some crab apples be roasted, and take some of the pulp, and half as much honey. Let this be the child's only sustenance for a day and a night.

## FOR A MALIGNANT INTERMITTENT, PROCEEDING FROM THE HEART*

18. Take some white wine whey and reject the curds. Then take some horse dung, warm as it comes from the beast, and mix well with the posset**. Then strain and boil a small portion of the blessed thistle in this, or if more convenient add a spoonful of distilled water of the same. Let the patient drink as much as he can of this for nine mornings, while fasting.

*\*This seems to be a recurring fever of increasing intensity. In Thomas' 'The Eclectic Practice of Medicine' of 1907, it is also referred to as 'pernicious intermittent', 'congestive intermittent' and 'congestive chills'. There is a black pigment in the blood cells, and it is described as 'an intense intermittent, where the paludal poison is so intense as to rapidly break down the blood, resulting in a local or general congestion which early threatens life.'*

*\*\*A posset was usually a warm drink of milk, curdled with wine or ale, and often spiced.*

## FOR OPACITY OF THE CORNEA*

19. Take the juice of parsley, and half as much of honey, and drop into the eye with a feather. Keep the eye closed afterwards, for as long as a hundred is counted. Let this treatment be perseveringly followed.

*\*There can be several causes of an opaque or cloudy cornea, causing poor vision.*

## ANOTHER REMEDY FOR OPACITY OF THE CORNEA

20. Take the juice of celandine*, and drop into the eye. Close the eye for as long as a hundred is counted. Let this treatment be perseveringly continued.

*\*This is probably the Greater Celandine, Chelidonium majus, named 'clefyd melyn' in the text.*

## TO CURE A PAIN IN THE CHEST

21. Take wall pepper* in small fragments, the dregs of small beer**, wheat bran and mutton suet. Pound well in a mortar, boil together on a slow fire and then apply to the chest.

*\*Biting stonecrop, Sedum acre.*
*\*\*Weak, low alcohol beer.*

## TO OVERCOME HABITUAL CONSTIPATION

22. Take a new laid egg and remove the white, fill up the egg with fresh unsalted butter, then warm and eat it. Do this frequently if you are naturally disposed to constipation.

## TO PRODUCE A DIURETIC EFFECT

23. Take some haws* [Hawthorn berries], put them in a vessel of red earthenware, mix with it a good quantity of honey, then put in an oven with bread. Take four spoonfuls, three times a day.

*The Common Hawthorn, Crataegus monogyna is also known as Whitethorn and Mayblossom.*

## ANOTHER REMEDY TO PRODUCE A DIURETIC EFFECT

24. Separate the stones of haws from the pulp, and dry well. Reduce to a fine powder and keep in a dry place. Then, when you need it, take a spoonful of this powder and a spoonful of honey, and make a confection of it. This should be taken at night when going to bed, and again in the morning while fasting, subsequently refraining from food for three hours. If needed, let this be repeated, and you will have a thousand chances of being cured.

## FOR WORMS IN CHILDREN

25. Take as much wheat flour as will stand upon three golden crowns*. Bolt this through a fine silken sieve, and put it in a glass vial. Pour on this as much spring water as will suffice to bring it to the consistency of milk, and no more. Then let it be given the child to drink, and dead worms will be seen in his evacuations. This is a very excellent recipe.

*Gold coins in medieval times were generally nobles, with the first gold crowns not being minted until Henry VIII's monetary reforms of 1526. A large coin, the crown was worth 5 shillings.*

## ANOTHER REMEDY FOR WORMS IN CHILDREN

26. Take the child's hair, cut it as small as you can, and mix as much as will stand on a golden crown, with the pulp of a roasted apple, or with honey. This will kill the worms.

## FOR A MALIGNANT SCALD* OR RINGWORM

27. Take some snails and prick them all over with a needle until a kind of water exudes from them. With this water, wash the scald or ringworm. Then bind some honeysuckle leaves on the affected part. Let this be done night and morning, and in a short time you will be cured.

*Scald head was a common term given to Porrigo, or ringworm of the scalp. There are several diseases of the scalp characterized by pustules (the dried discharge of which forms scales), and by falling out of the hair. Ringworm is an infection of the skin caused by a fungus. Ringworm can affect your skin anywhere on your body (tinea corporis), your scalp (tinea capitis), your groin area (tinea cruris, also called jock itch, from jockstrap), or feet (tinea pedis, also called athlete's foot). Incidentally 'jock' is a slangword of unknown origin for penis, so calling a Scotsman a 'jock' could be derogatory in origin.*

## FOR A HAEMOPTYSIS*, THE CONSEQUENCE OF THE RUPTURE OF A BLOOD VESSEL IN THE LUNGS

28. Take the dung of mice and dry in the sun, or at a distance before the fire, and then powder it. Let as much as will stand upon a groat** be put into half a wineglass of the juice of plantain***. Mix with some burnt honey. Let the patient drink this night and morning, continuing this treatment until he is cured.

*Coughing of blood from the respiratory tract below the level of the larynx.

** A groat was a large silver coin about an inch in diameter, also known as Fuppence, as its value was four pence. Some readers may remember when we called two-penny and three-penny coins 'tuppence' and 'thruppence'.

*** Also known as Common Plantain, Healing Blade, and Soldier's Herb, Plantago major was used as a wound dressing on battlefields for millennia.

## TO CURE FOETID BREATH.
29. Take rosemary* leaves and the flowers if available, and boil in white wine with a little myrrh** and pellitory of the wall.*** You shall witness a wonderful result if you frequently gargle your mouth with this.

*Rosmarinus officinalis. Officinalis denotes that it was a medicinal herb sold by apothecaries and pharmacists in their shops. Rosemary is renowned for antiseptic and other properties.

**The dried gum resin of Commiphora myrrha, native to Somalia, Yemen and Ethiopia.

***Also known as Lichwort, Parietaria officinalis.

## FOR A VESICAL CALCULUS*
30. Take the powder of golden rod**, called in Latin Virga aurea, and mix a spoonful of this with a newly laid egg which has been gently roasted. Give it the patient for breakfast. Do not permit him to take any food for four hours afterwards, and he will pass urine in less than half an hour afterwards. Let him continue to do this for ten or twelve days and he will get rid of the stone without pain. This is also very useful in flatulent dyspepsia.

*A stone, or stones in the bladder, being an abnormal concretion usually consisting of hardened mineral salts.

**Aaron's Rod, Solidago virgaurea, was known in history as Woundwort.

## FOR AN EPIPHORA*
31. Take red cabbage leaf, and spread some white of egg upon it. Cover your eyes with this when going to bed.

*An overflow of tears caused by eye irritation.

## FOR THE BITE OF A MAD DOG
32. Take as much as can be contained in half a walnut shell, of powder of spear thistle, which has beeen dried in the shade. Mix with a wine glassful of the best white wine, and drink it three times daily for three days. By the help of God you will be cured.

*Spear Thistle is also known as the Plumed Thistle and Scotch Thistle, and is Cirsium vulgare.

## FOR INFLAMED EYES
33. Take juice of ground ivy*, and woman's milk, equal parts of each. Strain through fine linen, and put a drop in the painful eye, and in both eyes, if needful.

*Also known as Gill-over-the-ground, this is Glechoma hederacea.

## ANOTHER REMEDY FOR INFLAMED EYES
34. Take distilled fennel* water, and a portion of new honey, then mix together. Put a drop or two in the eye. It is proven.

*Foeniculum vulgare

## ANOTHER REMEDY FOR INFLAMED EYES

35. Take the leaves of red fruited bramble,* and the leaves of common plantain**. Boil in spring water until it is reduced to half, and apply to the diseased eye.

*Bramble fruit can be either blackberries or raspberries, and raspberry (Rubis idaeus) leaves are probably used in this instance.*

**This is probably Plantago major, Greater Plantain, but may be another of the plantain family.*

## A COLLYRIUM* FOR AN ACUTE OPHTHALMIA

36. Take a handful of red sage**, and boil in as much smith's water*** as will cover it, until it evaporates to a half. Then filter well. Put a pennyworth of aloes, and as much white copperas****, in the liquor when it is removed from the fire, and wash your eyes with this.

*A lotion or liquid wash used in eye care.*

** *This is Salvia officinalis purpurea, the purple form of sage.*

*** *The water in which blacksmiths quench iron.*

****Copperas was also known as Green Vitriol, and is a form of Ferrous (Iron) Sulphate, but White Copperas was Zinc Sulphate. There is also a 1464 account of 'a cure for sore eyes using white coperose.' Later in the text, blue copperas is mentioned, copper sulphate.*

## FOR A PTERYGIUM* OR WET IN THE EYE

37. Take the white of an egg warm from the nest, rejecting the yolk. Add to this the size of a small nut of aloes in powder, and a little burnt honey. Incorporate together well, and add as much water as will enable you to filter the mixture through a fine cloth. Put a drop or two in each eye (or rather in the one requiring it), three times a day.

*This is a benign (non-cancerous) growth of the clear thin tissue that lies over the white of the eye, the conjunctiva. Often a triangular piece of tissue, it is sometimes called 'Surfer's Eye' today.*

## FOR AN ACUTE PAIN IN THE LEG

38. Take a quantity of leavened dough in a very advanced state of acidity, the same weight of mutton suet, and of black soap*. Incorporate them together and spread on linen cloth. Then apply to the inflamed leg, changing twice a day, and by the help of God it will be cured after three or four dressings.

*Today's soap is commonly made from any animal or vegetable fat, which is treated with an alkali-like sodium hydroxide. Early medieval soaps were often made with ash as a makeshift alkali and pig-fat (lard), resulting in what was called 'black', or 'speckled' soap.*

## TO STRENGTHEN THE SIGHT

39. Take eyebright* and red fennel**, a handful of each, and half a handful of rue. Distil, and wash your eye daily with this.

*Red Figwort, Euphrasia officinalis; **See 2.59 below*

## FOR A HEADACHE

40. Take a piece of raw beef, and lay it on the nape of the neck, taking it away each night in going to bed. Do this as often as needed. It is proven.

## FOR GOUT

41. This disease is mostly confined to the feet and hands. Take wood sage*, pellitory of the wall, wheat bran, cow's dung and salt. Boil together in wine or cider vinegar, and apply as a plaster to the painful part.

*Teucrium scorodonia.*

## TO MAKE A PLASTER FOR ALL KINDS OF ACHES

42. Take a pound of crude wax, half-a-pound of rosin*, one-sixth of a pound of dus**, and a pound-and-a-half of ram's suet. Boil together and strain into a clean basin, then place the basin on a cinder fire in a stove. Saturate a piece of linen in this mixture, and apply to the painful part.

*Also called Colophon or Greek Pitch (Pix Graeca), this is a solid form of resin obtained from pine trees.*

**Pughe translates the mutated 'tus' as 'thus', but the plant is as yet not known.*

## FOR A COUGH

43. Take coarsely powdered mustard seed, boil with some figs in strong ale, and drink.

*[Figs and grapes were grown in the warmer climate of early medieval times].*

## FOR A RINGWORM

44. Take the roots of red dock* and salt them, then put them in vinegar, and give them a boil. Then wash the ringworm with this liquor.

*Bloody Dock, Bloodwort and Redvein Dock are all names for Rumex sanguineus var. sanguineus.*

## FOR HYSTERIA

45. Take rosin and pound it well, then put it in white wine, and the gum of the bay tree.* Swallow it, and you will obtain benefit.

*The Bay Laurel or Sweet Bay, Laurus nobilis.*

## TO CURE ONE WHO TALKS IN HIS SLEEP

46. Take southernwood*, and pound it well. Add some wine or old mead**. Strain well and let the patient drink a portion of this, night and morning.

*Artemisia abrotanum.

**Mead is strong alcohol, made from honey and water and sometimes spices. 'Old mead' used rainwater that had been kept for several years.*

*47 is missing from Pughe's translation:*

## I WRAIG A FYTHO'N CAEL GORMOD O'I BLODAU

47. Cymmered droed ysgyfarnog, a llosged yn bylor, a chymmered ganel y bylor, y ddau hanner yn hanner, a doded mewn gwin coch, ag yfed o hono lwnc syched yn gyntaf a diweddaf nawniwarnod, a hi a gaiff les o hynny.

## FOR A WOMAN WHO HAS HEAVY PERIODS

47. Take the foot of a hare, and burn it until it is powder. Take the middle part (we have translated ganel as ganol) and cut into two halves and place in red wine. Take a mouthful to start, and finish off in nine days time and she will benefit from that.

## FOR TOOTHACHE

48. Take shepherd's purse* and pound into a mass, then apply to the tooth.
*Capsella bursa-pastoris.

## ANOTHER REMEDY FOR TOOTHACHE

49. Take the root of the water flower de lys,* and masticate. If there is a cavity in the tooth, put a fragment of the root in it, but avoid swallowing the saliva, as the juice of this root is poisonous. If you swallow it you will become delirious for days, if it does not prove fatal.

*Iris Pseudacorus, the Yellow Flag Iris.

## FOR A DANGEROUS COUGH

50. Take leaves of sage, rue, cumin*, and pound them like pepper. Then boil together in honey, and make into a confection. Take a spoonful of this night and morning, and by the help of God you will obtain benefit.

*Cuminum cyminum

## FOR SORENESS AND GANGRENE OF THE MOUTH

51. Take half a handful each of rosemary tops, sage, honeysuckle, and mallows*. Boil together well in as much spring water as will cover them, until it is reduced to a third. Then take some pure honey boiled in spring water, with as much as a pigeon's egg of alum**. Boil this in the filtered decoction of herbs until reduced to a third. Then keep in a well-corked glass bottle, and wash your mouth with it.

* Malva sylvestris, the Common, or Blue Mallow; **Hydrated potassium aluminium sulphate

## A DRAWING OINTMENT

52. Take mercurial ointment and May butter*, rosin, sheep's suet, and new wax. Then take round birthwort**, great ox eye***, betony****, milfoil*****, hoary plantain******, sage, smallage*******, marigold********, and pound well. Boil the butter and herbs together on a slow fire for two or three hours, and if the butter dries up, add more as there may be need to. When this boiling is finished, strain off the butter well under a press, and add the wax and the mercurial ointment to it, as well as the rosin and the suet. Boil together on a fire for an hour, then let it cool in a clean vessel and keep.

*Butter clarified in sunlight to make it more rancid and purgative; **Aristolochia rotunda, English Mercury; ***Probably the Dog Daisy, Leucanthemum vulgare; **** Stachys officinalis, Bishop's Wort, Wood Betony; *****Probably Achillea millefolium, Yarrow; ******Plantago media; *******The Welsh is 'perllys y morfa', This means 'Marsh Parsley', which is Apium graveolens, Wild Celery. See 2.65 below; ********Calendula officinalis

## AN ANTIDOTE FOR POISONED FOOD OR DRINK

53. Take rue, bruise well and pour white wine upon it, (as much as will cover it). If there is no wine, use ale or mead. Let the liquor and the herb be stirred well and strained. Let a draught of this be given to the patient in the morning while fasting, and another in an hour, and he will be cured.

## FOR INFLAMMATION OF THE MAMMAE

54. Take agrimony*, betony, and vervain**, and pound well, then mix them with strong old ale***, strain well, and set some milk on the fire. When this boils, add

124

the liquor to it and make a posset, giving it to the woman to drink warm. Let her do this frequently and she will be cured.

*Agrimonia eupatoria; **Verbena officinalis; *** This now refers to a rich, dark, sweet, high strength beer. However, until the 15$^{th}$ century and the arrival of hops to make beer, ale was the main alcohol, typically bittered with 'gruit', a mixture of herbs and/or spices which was boiled in the wort in place of hops. 'Old' ale was typically over a year old.

## FOR HOARSENESS

55. Take the spotted persicaria* and boil, then pound in a mortar well. Rub the throat with it, and the patient will be cured.

*Pulmonaria officinalis, Lungwort

## FOR STRANGURY*

56. Seek some mouse chickweed** and wild sage***, as much of the one as of the other. Then make into a powder, and mix with drink. Cider is best, or else old mead, if no cider can be obtained.

* A condition marked by slow, painful urination, caused by muscular spasms of the urethra and bladder; **Cerastium vulgatum, Mouse-ear Chickweed; ***Salvia verbenica, Wild Clary

## TO EXTRACT A TOOTH WITHOUT PAIN

57. Take some newts, by some called lizards, and those nasty beetles which are found in ferns during summer time. Calcine* them in an iron pot and make a powder of this. Wet the forefinger of the right hand, and insert it in the powder. Apply it to the tooth frequently, refraining from spitting it off, when the tooth will fall away without pain. It is proven.

*Heat to a high temperature.

## FOR HAEMATURIA*

58. Take agrimony, bruise well, and mix the mass with wine, ale or mead to drink. You will obtain a cure.

*The presence of red blood cells in the urine.

## FOR DIARRHOEA

59. Take the roots of the red fennel*, pound well in a mortar, and mix with goats' milk, drinking for nine mornings. It will be of benefit, and halt the purging. It is proven.

*Pyrethrum inodorum, the name which Pughe gives in his text, is Corn Feverfew or (scentless) Mayweed, now named Chamamaelum inodorum or Tripleurospermum inodorum. Red Fennel, however, is what we know as Bronze Fennel, Foeniculum vulgare purpurescens or ssp. Purpureum. The Welsh is 'y ffenigl cochon' so it seems that Pughe has mistranslated the herb, giving the wrong Latin name.

## FOR AN OBSTINATE PAIN IN THE STOMACH

60. Drink the juice of tansy* in old ale, and you will be effectually cured.

*Tanacetum vulgare

## FOR DYSPNOEA* IN THE CHEST

61. Seek the roots of elecampane**, wash clean and scrape. Then boil in white wine vinegar when scraped. Dry them, reduce into powder, and boil the powder

in honey. Add powdered pepper to this. Keep in a box and take a spoonful night and morning. This will cure the patient. If there is dyspnoea and cough with expectoration in a person, seek three cinders and set before the sick person. Then let him spit upon the cinders. If the expectorated matter smells offensively, he will die. If not, he will recover.

* *Breathlessness or shortness of breath; difficult or laboured breathing;*
** *Inula helenium, Horse-Heal*

## FOR THE BITE OF A MAD DOG

62. Seek some plantain and a handful of sheep's sorrel* Then pound them well in a mortar with the white of eggs, honey, and old lard. Make into an ointment and apply to the bitten part, so that it may be cured.

* *Rumex acetosella*

## TO PROMOTE THE FLOW OF MILK IN A WOMAN'S BREAST

63. Seek some red fennel, and administer to a woman in ale, and it will produce enough milk to nurse her child.

## FOR DEAFNESS

64. Seek red onion, and boil in oxymel*. Then add to this a handful of oat malt, rue and red fennel. Boil in the liquor. Put this, in the warmth of milk, into the ear night and morning. Plug the ear with black wool, so that it may not come out. It will improve the hearing wonderfully. It is proven.

* *A common medicinal preparation dating back to antiquity, oxymel is basically a mixture of honey and vinegar. The simplest method of preparing it is to mix together 4 parts honey with 1 part apple cider vinegar, but there are many different recipes.*

## TO PREPARE A BLESSED COLLYRIUM TO CLEAR THE EYE

65. Take red roses, lovage*, vervain, red fennel, maiden hair**, house leek***, greater celandine, and wild thyme****. Wash them clean, and macerate in white wine for a day and a night, then distil from a brass pot. The first water you obtain will be like silver. This will be useful for any affection of the eye, and for a stye.

*In Remedy 52 Pughe gives Smallage as an ingredient, which is itself Wild Celery. The original is 'perllys y morfa' (Marsh Parsley, which is Smallage). Here, he again translates as smallage, but the original Welsh is 'perllys y mor' (trans. Sea Parsley, which is Lovage).*

**This is the well-known Common Maidenhair Fern, Adiantum Aethiopicum*

***Common Houseleek, Sempervivum tectorum*

****Popular throughout the ages in medicines, this is also known as Creeping Thyme, Thymus serpyllum*

## FOR AN EPIPHORA

66. Take the flowers of betony and eat them, and this will clear the eye.

## ANOTHER REMEDY FOR AN EPIPHORA

67. Anoint the eye with the juice of greater celandine and fresh honey, and you will obtain great benefit.

## ANOTHER REMEDY FOR AN EPIPHORA
68. Take white wine, the juice of greater celandine, and the juice of red fennel. Boil in white wine until it is reduced to a third. Anoint your eye with this, and it will keep it clear and strong.

## FOR A STYE OR PAIN IN THE EYE
69. Obtain the yolk of an egg, and wheaten meal, and add a little sulphate of copper. Incorporate them together and lay upon a cloth. Apply to the eye in going to sleep. It will cure it by the following day. Let this be done for three days.

## FOR PAIN IN THE EYE
70. Seek the gall* from each of a hare, a hen, an eel and a stag, with fresh urine and honeysuckle leaves. Then inflict a wound upon an ivy tree, and mix the gum that exudes from the wound with the mixture, boiling it swiftly. Strain it through a fine linen cloth. When cold, insert a little of it into the corners of the eyes. It will be a wonder if he who makes use of it does not see the stars in mid-day**, in consequence of the virtues of this remedy.

*Gall is bile, the bitter-tasting yellowish-brown to dark green fluid produced by the liver to aid digestion in most vertebrates.
**Stars are dimmed so much by the brightness of daylight that we cannot usually discern them in our more polluted atmosphere.

## TO STRENGTHEN THE EYE
71. Seek house leek, red rose leaves, and greater celandine. Pound together and boil in white wine, or strong and clear old ale. Boil briskly, and strain through a fine clean linen cloth. Wash your eyes with this night and morning, and you will be cured.

*72 is missing from Pughe's translation*

### I WYBOD AM FORWYN AI BOD WEDI CADW EI MORWYNDOD AI NA BO
72. Cymmer bylor y milwydd a dod ar ei diod, agos ni bydd morwyn, hi a gyfyd i wneuthur dwr; os morwyn nid ysgyg.

### TO FIND OUT IF A GIRL IS A VIRGIN OR NOT
72. Take the powder of yarrow* and put into her drink. If she is not a virgin, she will get up to pass water. If she does not budge, she is a virgin.

*Milwydd can also mean camomile or milfoil.*

*73 is missing from Pughe's translation*

### I WYBOD PUN AI MAB AI MERCH A FO YNGROTH GWRAIG
73. Cais laeth bronn y wraig, a dod ef ar ei dŵr hi ei hun, os nofio wna'r llaeth yn ucha, mab yw; o sir gwaelod yr â, merch yw.

### TO FIND OUT THE SEX OF A CHILD IN A WOMAN'S WOMB
73. Take some milk from the breast of the woman and put in into her urine. If it floats, it is a boy. If it sinks, it is a girl.

## FOR A COLD OR CATARRH, AND ALL KINDS OF PAIN IN THE SHOULDERS, ARMS, AND LEGS

74. Take wild thyme, and bruise until small. Boil in the lees* of strong ale until it is thickened, and apply to the pain as hot as the patient can bear it. Let this be persevered with for nine days - and he will be effectually cured.

*The deposits of dead or residual yeast left over in the bottom of the container when the ale has fermented.*

## FOR A THORN IN THE FLESH

75. If a thorn enters into a man's body, either in his feet or hands, take the root or leaves of the black chameleon thistle*. Add the white of eggs and refined rye meal (or barley if there is no rye). Apply to the thorn in the form of a poultice, and this will extract it.

*This is Pughe's translation of 'yr ysgall duon', which he translated as Black Thistle, Cirsium vulgare, also known as Spear Thistles or Scotch Thistle. However Spear Thistles are mentioned previously in the text as Cirsium vulgare, Scotch Thistle, in 2.32, when Pughe translates 'ysgall gwylltion.' Ysgall y blaidd and ysgall march are this same plant. However, 'Ysgall ddu' is noted in Hugh Davies' 'Welsh Botanology' of 1813 as Carthamus corymbosus, and now known as Cardopatium corymbosum or Echinops corymbosus, the Black Chameleon plant. It is found in Greece and many Mediterranean countries.*

## FOR TERTIAN AGUE*

76. Take a large handful of betony, a handful of year-old broom** and a handful of sage. Wash clean and bruise the plants a mortar. Mix with strong ale, strain and let it be drunk nine times successively. This will restrain the ague.

* An intermittent fever, attended by alternate cold and hot fits. The interval of the paroxysms gave rise to the following varieties of ague. An interval of 24 hours constitutes a quotidian ague; of 48 hours, a tertian; of 72 hours, a quartan; and of 96 hours, a quintan ague.*

**Common Broom, Cytisus scoparius*

## FOR SUPPRESSION OF URINE

77. Seek broom seed, and ground into fine powder. Mix with drink and let it be drunk. Do this until you are quite well.

## ANOTHER REMEDY FOR SUPPRESSION OF URINE

78. Take broom seed, counting nine, and devoting the tenth to God. Grind the seed into fine meal and take in drink, or as a confection in boiled honey. If a woman or maid should do this, neither pain or abscess will ever take place in her mammae [breasts].

## FOR A SPRAIN

79. Obtain the lees of strong old ale, the suet of a black wether* or a goat, and wheat groats**. Boil well and spread on a cloth as warm as can be borne, and apply to the injured part three times. This will cure it.

*A castrated male sheep. Welsh Blacks are a common breed in Wales; **The hulled grains of wheat*

## FOR GOUT

80. Seek an equal portion each of avens*, pimpernel**, betony, vervain and four portions of ground ivy. Boil them in as much white wine as will cover them, and let a good draught of this be drunk night and morning. Thus you will obtain a cure. Let this be drunk the first thing every morning, and the last thing every night, for nine mornings, in order to relieve the stomach. Then apply a piece of fresh beef half-an-inch thick to the foot or hand, and this will completely cure you.

*Geum urbanum, Wood Avens or Herb Bennet; **Anagallis arvensis, Scarlet Pimpernel*

## FOR DYSPNOEA AND HOARSENESS

81. Take a large quantity of vervain, boil in until till reduced to a third, and strain. Add the root of mallow, cut small, and boil again. Let this be taken warm at night and cold in the morning, keeping it in an earthenware grenn.*

* *Pughe notes:* Grenn, a measure equivalent to 1/9 of a ton [c.250 pounds]. 'The load of two men upon a bar in every grenn.' - Welsh Laws. *Later in the book we find that a grenn is 16 gallons.*

## FOR THE EVIL*

82. Take the juice of rue, cumin and powdered pepper Boil in honey and make a confection of them. Let this be taken the first thing in the morning, and the last at night.

*This may be scrofula, also known as King's Evil. 'The Evil' is Pughe's translation. The Welsh is 'periglys', however, and means danger, jeopardy or risk, possibly from the Latin periculum. It may be a catch-all term for disease. In 2.258 scrofula is 'y manwynon' and the King's Evil is 'y frech yn y gwaed'.*

*Missing from Pughe's translation.*

## RHAG Y GAFFO WR GAN WRAIG

83. Cais ebod march ceilliog a llinhad, au tymheru ynghyd, au berwi yn iwd, ai roi ar gadach lliain wrth y clwyf, ag arfer o'r plaster hynny hyd oni ddarffo iddo dynnu y llosg tân i gyd o'r clwyf, yno rhoi'r eli a berthyno wrtho, ag iach a fydd.

## PROTECTION FROM WHAT A MAN CAN RECEIVE FROM A WOMAN

83. Take the dung of an uncastrated stallion, and add linseed. Blend them together and boil to make pottage. Place on a bandage upon the sore. Apply that poultice until it removes all the burning from the wound. There apply the appropriate ointment, and it will be healthy.

## FOR BLACK JAUNDICE*

84. Seek the tail of salmon, dry slowly and reduce to a powder. Let it be taken on ale, and the patient will be cured.

*This was a common name for Weil's Disease, Leptospirosis. It was also known as 7-Day Fever and Ratcatcher's Yellows, and can be fatal.*

## FOR DEAFNESS

85. Take some pieces of elm wood*, and lay them upon the embers, then receive the water that exudes from the rods in a clean vessel. Get the oil of a black eel, as much honey, and as much of the juice of betony, and mix them together. Drop

into the ear, and plug with the wool of a black lamb. This will effectually cure the patient.

*The Welsh is llwyfi, which can mean the elm or lime (linden) tree.*

## FOR PLETHORA*

86. Seek bean meal**, honey, and the yolk of eggs. Form a cake of them and bake on the hearth under a pan, with embers covering the pan. Let the patient frequently have some of this cake to eat.

*From Greek times it was believed that many diseases were caused by 'plethoras', overabundances in the blood, and that they could be treated by exercise, reduced food intake, sweating and vomiting. If persistent, blood-letting was advised.*

***Flour ground from chick peas, broad beans, lentils etc. In times of famine, it was used to make bread.*

## TO AVOID ENEMIES

87. If one goes to battle let him seek vervain, and keep it on his person. He will escape from his enemies.

## TO MAKE HEALING PLASTER

88. Seek half a pound of pitch, quarter of a pound of wax, half a pound of suet, and powder of gall stone. Boil these ingredients together, stirring them well so that they may be thoroughly incorporated. Then the mixture should be poured into a pot or into water, so that it may be formed into a roll. This plaster, being spread upon linen or white kid*, is useful for all ulcers from which there is a profuse watery secretion.

*Leather made from the skin of a young white goat.*

## FOR SUPPRESSED MENSES*

89. Seek rue, pound it well, and express the juice into wine or strong ale. Strain and let it clear. Then let the woman drink it, and she will recover.

*A failure of menstruation when expected, amenorrhea.*

## TO IMPROVE THE HEARING

90. Seek young ash shoots, the size of rods. Cut, and lay upon a tripod over the fire. Then collect the drops which will exude from the ends. Take a spoonful of honey, the ends of houseleeks, the heads and stalks of leeks, some mustard in flour, and a shell full of the oil of eels. Let the whole be boiled together, carefully stirring the mixture while boiling. Let it be injected warm with a syringe into the ear, the ear then being filled with the wool of a black lamb, and the patient will be cured.

*This entry is missing from Pughe's translation*

## RHAG HWYDD YNGWIALEN GWR

91 Cais ddail y gwinwydd, a berw, a gulch yn dda, yna cais ddail y llinhad, a'r malw, a berw mewn llaeth, a dod o beutu'r ar liain manwe.

## A REMEDY FOR A MAN'S SWOLLEN PENIS
91. Take the leaves of the vine and boil, and wash well. Then take the leaves of linseed and mallow. Break them up and boil in milk, before wrapping around the penis in a linen cloth.

*This entry is missing from Pughe's translation*

## ARALL
92. Rhostia wïau yn galed, a thyn y melyn a gwna'n bylor mân, a gwna'n eliw, a gwasg ef drwy gadach lliain, a dod ar y wialen, ag y mae'n dda rhag y gwst mawr a fo mewn asgwrn, a rhag amrafael glefydau eraill.

## ANOTHER REMEDY FOR A MAN'S SWOLLEN PENIS
92. Roast eggs until hard, and take out the yolk and make into a powder. Then make into a lotion and press through a linen cloth and place upon the penis. It is also good for arthritis and a number of other ailments.

*This entry is missing from Pughe's translation*

## ARALL
93. Cais floneg yr Affrig* a chennin, a dod yn blasder wrth y wialen, ag iach y bydd. Ti a elli ymarfer a'r plasder hwn gyda's meddyginiaeth nesaf o'r blaen at hwn, a da fydd hynny.

## ANOTHER REMEDY FOR A MAN'S SWOLLEN PENIS
93. Take African lard (or grease) and leeks, and smear upon the penis, and it will be fine. You can use this ointment with the medicine above this, [remedy 2.92] and that will be fine.

* *Bloneg is fat, lard or grease, or could be sap. It is not yet known what this substance is.*

## A PLASTER FOR ERYSIPELAS, AND THE REMOVAL OF PROUD FLESH*
94. Take the juice of wood sage and honey, mixed with salt and vinegar. Mix the ingredients together well, then add a portion of rye meal and boil so that a cataplasm* may be formed. Make use of this cataplasm in conjunction with the drink recommended for gout, and the patient will soon recover.

* *An excess of granulation tissue (caro luxurians) is informally known as 'proud flesh'. Granulation tissue is the fibrous connective tissue that replaces a fibrin clot in healing wounds. Such tissue typically grows from the base of a wound and can fill wounds of almost any size it heals; **A poultice or plaster*

## FOR AN AGUE OR ARDENT INTERMITTENT
95. Take two pennyworths of treacle, a pennyworth of saffron*, and a little hartshorn** grated fine. Put into a cupful of ale and mix well together, drinking it for three mornings. Then seek some sprigs of red raspberries, the leaves of sweet-briers***, wood sorrel***, and malt. Make a drink, and take a hearty draught of it three or four times a day. Whoever does this will recover.

**Crocus sativus; **It was thought that this was Pasqueflower, Pulsatilla vulgaris, but the Welsh 'corn carw' means deer horn. It is the horn of the Red Deer stag over 5 years old; ***Sweet Briar, Rosa rubiginosa, Rosa eglanteria; ****Common Wood Sorrel, Oxalis Acetosella*

## AN APERIENT* DRINK

96. Take a pennyworth of stibium** and grate as fine as flour, then mix with half a pint of sound ale. Warm, and let the patient drink it in the morning while fasting. Afterwards get a quart of posset***, and in half an hour let him drink it three times. When it has acted, make a warm drink with spring water. Put some good butter and honey in it, then let the patient drink it two or three times and he will recover.

*Laxative;* ** *Regulus of Antimony. Stibium is Latin, an obsolete name for Antimony, the grey chemical element mainly found in nature as the sulphide mineral, Stibnite. This soft metal, with fire retardant properties, has been known and used for 5,000 years. By the 19ᵗʰ century, the metallic 'antimony pill' had become a popular remedy, used to purge and 'revitalise' the bowels. It was swallowed and allowed to pass through the body, after which it is customarily recovered for reuse, giving rise to the name 'the everlasting pill'. According to the 'Medico-Pharmaceutical Critic and Guide' (1907), edited by William J. Robinson: 'It is possible that a minute amount was dissolved by the gastro-intestinal juices and this amount, plus the suggestion, was sufficient to produce cathartic action. Then again the everlasting pill probably aided peristalsis by its mechanical weight and motion. The bullet was passed out, recovered from the faeces and used over and over again. This, as Dr. J. A. Paris says, was economy in right earnest, for a single pill would serve a whole family during their lives and might be transmitted as an heirloom to posterity.'; ***A hot drink of milk curdled with wine or ale, often spiced, popular from medieval times.*

## ANOTHER APERIENT DRINK

97. Take the fruit of buckthorn*, express the juice and mix two spoonfuls with a full draught of good ale wort**. Let the patient drink it, and if it does not act, let him drink another draught without the buckthorn. When it has acted, let him take for food some warm oatmeal gruel made with spring water, mixing with it some honey, butter, and unsifted wheaten bread. Let this be done three times in nine days, and it will purge from the body all corrupt humors. After this course let him live for nine days further on milk food, and wheaten bread with the bran retained, alternately with the warm water and flour as previously mentioned.

*Rhamnus cathartica, Common or Purging Buckthorn; **Liquid extracted from the mashing process when brewing. Wort contains the sugars that will be fermented by yeast to make alcohol.*

## ANOTHER APERIENT DRINK

98. Take a handful of the leaves of damask roses*, boil in the wort of good ale, and drink, attending to the diet as in 2.97 for nine days.

*Rosa Damascena*

## ANOTHER APERIENT DRINK

99. Take honey, and the juice of the fruit of buckthorn, in equal quantity. Boil together on a slow fire, and keep in a well-covered glass bottle. Take two or three spoonfuls when required, and half an hour afterwards drink a hearty draught of the wort of strong ale.

## A CONFECTION FOR A SORE MOUTH

100. Take a spoonful of the juice of sage, a spoonful of the juice of elder, two spoonfuls of the juice of cloudberry*, the pulp of a hot apple, and three spoonfuls of honey. Boil on a slow fire. Stir continually until it becomes a thick

confection. Keep in an earthenware pot, covering it well, so that it may be kept for use. When a case of sore mouth occurs, take as much as a pigeon's egg and let it be retained in the mouth until it is dissolved, and it will be of service.

*Rubus chamaemorus according to Pughe, but the Welsh is 'mwyar gleision', blue berries, which seems to indicate the Bilberry plant, Vaccinium myrtillus.*

## ANOTHER CONFECTION FOR A SORE MOUTH

101. Take elder leaves, honeysuckle leaves, sage, rosemary, and briars*. Boil well in as much water as will cover them, then sweeten with honey and wash your mouth with it, retaining the liquor in your mouth for as long as you can. Then eject it three times, and afterwards drink a hearty draught of it to cool your stomach.

*The Welsh is 'dail drysu', tangled leaves, and may refer to either Dog Roses or Brambles.*

## ANOTHER CONFECTION FOR A SORE MOUTH

102. Take four spoonfuls of honey, the juice of four oranges*, three spoonfuls of the juice of sage, three of the juice of blackberries, and three of the juice of cloudberries*. Boil on a slow fire until it becomes a thick confection. Keep in a covered pot, and put as much as a pigeon's egg in your mouth, retaining it until it dissolves.

*Oranges were not well-known in Europe until around 1650; **Probably bilberries, see 100 above.*

## FOR A COLD HUMORAL CATARRH

103. Take half a pint of the juice of cleavers*, and a spoonful of honey in it night and morning.

*This is Goosegrass, Galium aparaine.*

## ANOTHER FOR A COLD HUMORAL CATARRH

104. Take half-a-pint of blackberry juice, containing a spoonful of new honey, night and morning.

## FOR INFLAMMATORY CATARRH

105. Take equal parts of the juice of cleavers, the juice of water cress*, the juice of sorrel**, and the juice of elder. Drink half-a-pint of this, night and morning for nine days. Live the next nine days upon a milk diet and wheaten bread, ground through and through. Let no other food or drink be taken, and it will be well to take a cathartic two or three times before this medicine, in order to clear the system of corrupt humors.

*Nasturtium officinale; **Common, or Garden Sorrel, Rumex Acetosa*

## FOR HUMORAL FLATULENCE, WEAKENING THE BODY AND MIND

106. Take the juice of apples, raspberries, plums or blackberries, strained. Set upon a slow fire, adding to it a spoonful of honey for every draught, giving it a slight boiling. Then drink a hearty draught of this for nine days, and take for food bread made of highly roasted acorns. No other food should be taken during this time, and you will recover. The best juice of fruit, should they be in season, is the juice of sloes, and of blackberries. When no acorns can be procured, dry the roots

of nettles at a distance from the fire, and grind to powder. Make it into bread, and subsist on this.

## ANOTHER REMEDY FOR HUMORAL FLATULENCE
107. Take a spoonful of mustard seed three times a day. Wash down the throat with good old mead, and subsist upon a milk diet with well-baked wheaten bread. Let your meals be slight and frequent.

## AN OINTMENT FOR THE ANKLES AND JOINTS
108. Take rhodri, or as others term them radishes, and the suet of sheep or goats. Pound them well together until they become an ointment. Then put the ointment in a pan, adding a little honey and salt. Boil them well on a slow fire, and strain well. With this anoint the painful joint, and it will be cured by the help of God.

## TO EXTRACT IRON OR FRAGMENTS OF WOOD FROM A WOUND, AND TO OPEN IT
109. Take the roots of nettles, goose grease and honey. Pound them into a plaster and apply to the wound. It will mysteriously open the wound and extract what may be in it.

## FOR INFLAMMATORY WOUNDS, WHEREBY THE PATIENT IS PREVENTED FROM SLEEPING
110. Take equal quantities of holly bark, mallow, the middle bark of the elder. Add lard and wine in the same proportions. Boil well until it becomes thick, then take a cloth and spread the ointment on the wound, also spreading some warm on a tent*. Insert this in the wound, and cover it over with the anointed cloth. Apply some powdery unguent on the wound with the tent, and by the help of God it will be healed.
   * *This is Pughe's translation of goreth. Goreth is a tent for a wound, or seton. Pabell is the Welsh for tent.*

## A GOOD HEALING SALVE FOR WOUNDS
111. Take oil of olives*, or, if none can be obtained, some lard and wine, in equal quantities. Boil together well, stirring it continually while boiling. When it has thickened, keep in an earthenware vessel or bladder, covering it well. When required anoint the wound therewith.
*This author remembers as a child in the 1950s that olive oil was quite rare, being only sold in the very few delicatessens that existed, or in chemist shops. It was used mainly mixed with vinegar as a suntan lotion by when going to the local beach.*

## AN OINTMENT FOR AN EXTERNAL INFLAMMATION
112. Take the cream of cows' milk, and white wine or strong apple cider, or else strong old mead. Boil well together, equal quantities of each, until it becomes thick, stirring it continually. When cold, keep in a bladder* or box, and when needful anoint the part therewith.
*Animal bladders, from time immemorial were useful liquid storage containers.*

## FOR BRONCHITIS WITH DYSPNOEA
113. Take the roots of parsley, red fennel, river star tip*, and pound well. Take three quarts of strong black wort** and boil what is proper of the herbs in it, until

the three quarts are reduced to one. Then take six pennyworth of powdered anise, and as much clarified honey as will sweeten it well. Boil in the above liquor, and set aside to keep in a warm place. This is termed an expectorant medicine, and will certainly destroy the cough.

*The Welsh is 'a chynglynedd yr afon', with a spirant mutation meaning 'and cynglynedd of the river.' However, in Book 1 River Startip is 'gwessyn'.

** The Welsh is 'o frecci du cadarn'. Breci is a wort or concoction used in the brewing process, du is black and cadarn means strong.

## TO PREPARE CLARIFIED HONEY

114. Take one proportion of honey, and four of proportions of spring water, and put in a clean brass pot to boil. When the wax and other impurities rise to the surface, remove them with a bassel* until the pot ceases to produce scum.

Then boil upon a moderate fire until the water is completely evaporated, and the honey left clarified in the pot. Put it afterwards in an earthen pot, and cover it up well. It is the best sort of honey for medicine or dietetic purposes.

* Pughe notes: From baselard, an ornamental dagger much worn in the time of Henry V (1386-1422). A spatula is the term now in use.

## AN ANODYNE OINTMENT

115. Take the pulp of crabs and boil in wine, until the wine is evaporated completely. Mix rosin, clear honey, and old lard with this, then boil well and strain. Anoint the painful part with this ointment frequently, and by the help of God the pain will be removed.

*This translation is missing in Pughe. The Welsh is:*

## I BERI I WRAIG ESGOR ESMWYTH AG EBRWYDD

116. Cymmer sudd y marchfynt*, neu fynt y dŵr, wedi eu pwyo'n dda gyda gwin gwynn, ai hidlo'n lân, a rho iddi i'w yfed. O bydd gwraig a dyn marw yn trigo gyda hi. Yfed y sudd hynn a sudd marchalan** hanner yn hanner, ag ef ai rhyddha hi drwy Dduw.

## TO CAUSE A WOMAN TO GIVE BIRTH EASILY AND QUICKLY

116. Take the juice or infusion of horsemint* or water mint**, and pound well with white wine before filtering and giving to her to drink. If a woman and a dead man dwells with her***. Drink half and half of this juice and the juice of elecampane**** and it will liberate her through God.

*Now spelt Marchfint, meaning Horse Mint, Mentha silvestris, recommended by Culpeper for colic and other ailments; **Also called Marsh Mint, Mentha sativa; ***The Welsh is 'O bydd gwraig a dyn marw yn trigo gyda hi'. The baby Jesus was called 'dyn bach', so dyn (man) could mean baby here. Marw, instead of dead, might mean dying. The idiom is difficult to translate – it may mean 'If a woman and a dying baby…' but still makes little sense; ****Elecampane is Horse-heal, Inula helenium.

## FOR A BURN OR SCALD

117. Take the roots of lily, wash them clean and boil briskly in water. Then mix them well with the white of eggs, ointment of petreolum*, or the ointment of

lime twigs. If the lime ointment cannot be obtained, use good cow's cream, or fresh unsalted butter. Apply this to the bum, and the more the better of it.

*The old spelling, still used across much of the world, is petreolum, not petroleum. This appears to be petroleum jelly, what we now know as Vaseline, but the raw material for petroleum jelly was not discovered until 1859, and commercialised as Vaseline in 1870. Iolo Morganwg died in 1826 and this translation was first published in 1861. The Welsh is pederhamon.*

## FOR A SWELLING, HEAT, OR SPRAIN, A RIGOR, SUCCEEDING A JOURNEY, OR FOR ERYSIPELAS ON THE LOWER EXTREMITIES; HOWEVER GREAT MAY BE THE PAIN, REDNESS OR CORRUPT CONDITION OF THE DISEASED PART, EVEN THOUGH MANY OTHER MEDICAMENTS MAY HAVE FAILED, THIS WILL HEAL IT

118. Take white alum and reduce to powder. Then mix it with spring water giving it three boilings, and should any scum appear, remove it carefully until none remains. Then keep it most carefully. A pennyworth of this solution in a quart of water will be enough to make a lotion, which should be applied frequently to the diseased part with a linen cloth, and it will reduce the swelling, the heat, the redness, and the pain. Indeed if you continue to wash it in this way, any disease - even phagadenic* ulcers, or gangrenous erysipelas - will be cured by this water, thus perseveringly applied by a fireside. When the whole is used, make another supply, and observe that a pennyworth of the alum will be enough in a quart of water. Do this and you will be cured. It is proven.

*Gangrenous*

## FOR A SUNBURN OR A SIMILAR EFFECT FROM ANY OTHER HEAT

119. Take Marsh Pennywort* and cream, half and half. Boil upon a slow fire until it becomes a thick ointment. Keep it in a covered box.

*Pennywort, Hydrocotyle vulgaris*

## FOR ITCH OR PSORIASIS

120. Take the root of elecampane washed clean, and boil in pure water. When the roots are softened, pound, and then add thick cows' cream. Mix it for an ointment and anoint your whole body with it as you go to bed, every three days, (that is three times in nine days.) Drink a hearty draught of the water in which the roots were boiled, three times a day for nine days, and you will be cured of the eruption, and will be strong in body, for the water is useful to heal and strengthen the stomach and lungs.

## AN OINTMENT FOR PNEUMONIA

121. Take suet and honey, boil together, and when they have boiled enough, take nine pieces of fine flannel and dip in the ointment. Let each cool, and when cold apply the nine to your chest, from one armpit to another, and from the shoulder to the navel. Let it remain there for nine days, then remove one away daily until the whole are removed. When this is going on, take wheaten bread, ground thoroughly, with some pure honey spread thereon every morning. Then take some of the same bread with cow's milk at noon, and then baked apples and

136

goat's milk at night. Take between the meals a spoonful of pure honey. This by the help of God will cure you.

## ANOTHER MEDICINE FOR PNEUMONIA
122 Take white horehound*, and pound well. Then add some pure water, letting it stand for three hours. Strain well through a fine cloth. Add a good deal of honey to the strained liquor, and put on a slow fire to warm. Take half a draught of this every three hours, and let your diet be the best wheaten bread and milk. When thirsty, take an apple, and cover it with good old cider, eat the apple. In an hour drink the cider, and let this be your only diet.

*Common Horehound, Marrubium vulgare*

## ANOTHER MEDICINE FOR PNEUMONIA
123. Take half a man's meal of cows' milk, and add two spoonfuls of pure honey. Take for food some good wheaten bread with this drink, three times a day. Between the meals take a spoonful of the juice of white horehound, and a spoonful of honey mixed in it. When neither these herbs nor any other can be obtained fresh, in order to get their juice, then get the herbs dry. Boil them in enough water to cover them, in an iron pot, until it evaporates to half. Then express well through a fine cloth. After this add half the quantity of honey, boiling the second time until it is evaporated to a third, keeping it in a well-corked glass bottle.

## ANOTHER MEDICINE FOR PNEUMONIA
124. Take for your only food a slice of the best wheaten bread with honey, and for your only drink the breast milk of a healthy young woman, for nine days without intermission. Then instead of the breast milk, take goat's milk for another nine days, and subsist upon that for a longer period if necessary.

## FOR STRANGURY AND THE STONE
125. Take milfoil and saxifrage, and pound with warm water. Let the patient have this liquor for nine days as drink. Do not let him take any other drink, and by God's aid he will recover.

## ANOTHER REMEDY FOR STRANGURY* AND THE STONE**
126. Take the blood and skin of a hare and make a powder. Mix with the cider of red-skinned apples, mead, or beer, and drink the powder with any, but preferably cider or mead. Let the patient drink this only. It will disintegrate the stone, causing it to be expelled. If you should wish to prove this, take a spoonful of this powder in water, and put in a hole made in an acid stone, and by next day it will certainly have dissolved it.

*Painful, frequent urination of small volumes, caused by spasm of the urethra or bladder; **Bladder stones are painful and can occur in the urinary tract. Kidney stones are hardened masses caused by concretion of phosphates or urates.*

## FOR STRANGURY AND RETENTION OF URINE
127. Take smallage, a herb very much like garden parsley, having a roast meat sort of taste. Add rue and betony, and a quart of white wine. Pound the herbs well, and boil in the wine until it is reduced to half. Then strain well through a fine cloth, and give it to the patient in three draughts, and he will certainly be cured.

## FOR A PAIN IN THE CARDIAC REGION

128. Take centaury, pound well, boil in old ale and express well. Afterwards boil to half, take this with twice as much honey, and boil moderately. Take a cupful of this while fasting for nine days, and it will remove the pain and oppression from the region of the heart without fail.

## ANOTHER WAY OF PREPARING THE SAME MEDICINE

129. Take centaury, boil well in old ale, then remove the herbs from the ale, and pound well in a mortar. Boil again well, and express through a fine cloth. Take this juice mixed with twice the quantity of honey, boil moderately and habituate yourself to take it while fasting for nine days. Through the help of God it will heal the oppression and pain about the heart.

## A VALUABLE OINTMENT FOR ALL KINDS OF ACHES

130. Take old lard, a he-goat's and a sheep's suet, yellow wax, wormwood and primrose. Bruise in a mortar, boil in butter,and then put in the suet, lard, and wax. Boil well and express strongly through cloth. Keep carefully and it will ease all sorts of aches.

## AN OINTMENT FOR ALL NERVOUS DISORDERS

131. Take earthworms and the bulb of an onion, make a hole, and put the earthworms in. Then light a fire underneath to roast them, after that apply to the affected part, leaving it there for three nights without removing.

## AN OINTMENT FOR GENERAL USE

132. Take a gander's fat, the fat of a male cat, a red boars' fat, three drams of blue wax,* watercress, wormwood, red strawberry plant and primrose. Boil them in pure spring water. When boiled, stuff a gander with them, and roast it at a distance from the fire. The grease issuing from the gander should be carefully kept in a pot. It is a valuable ointment for all kinds of aches in a man's body, and is like one that was formerly made by Hippocrates. It is proved.

*Pughe notes: Cupriated wax.

## FOR OPACITY IN A MAN'S EYE

133. Take a rook's gall and mix well with the white of an egg, and put in your eye. Take a little fine linen and lay it upon the eye. Do this night and morning, and you will surely be cured.

## FOR AN INJURY IN THE ELBOW, KNEE, OR LEGS

134. Take lard, or pig's fat once it has melted. Spread on a cloth or flannel, and apply to the swellings. If it is the elbow or knee, mix some juice of rue with it, and it will cure an injury of the joint. It is proven.

## FOR A SWELLING AND HEAT, OR INFLAMMATION OF AN ERYSIPELATOUS NATURE, OR ANY OTHER KIND

135. Take elm bark and bruise well, rejecting the epidermis. Boil down to the thickness of honey, remove the bark, and add barley meal and unsalted butter. Boil into a cataplasm, place it on a flannel and apply to the disease. If it is supposed that there is a fragment of bone therein, use a large quantity of bark in

the poultice, and it will bring it into union with the adjoining bone, if it is used with perseverance.

## FOR PAIN AND NOISE IN THE EAR
136. Take a loaf of wheaten bread, ground through and hot from the oven. Divide in two, and apply to both ears as hot as it can be borne. Bind, and thus produce perspiration, and by the help of God you will be cured.

## FOR CARDIALGIA IN A MOIST STOMACH
137. Take grains of paradise* and powdered cloves, eat for a week, and by God's aid you will be cured.

*In medieval times grains of paradise, or simply 'grains', cost even more than the black pepper of India. They are the peppery seeds of either of two African zingiberaceous plants, Aframomum melegueta and Aframomum granum-paradisi, also called Guinea grains, Melegueta pepper and Alligator pepper. The spice was termed grains of paradise because of its high value. It was gradually replaced by black pepper.*

*This is missing from Pughe's 1861 translation*

## I BERI I'R BLODAU GERED AR WRAIG
138. Cymmer dafod yr hŷdd, a berw mewn dwr yn ffest, a rhoi yn glaiardwym i yfed, ag iach y bydd.

## TO START A WOMAN'S PERIOD
138. Take the tongue of a stag* and boil. Give it to her to eat lukewarm and she will get well.

*Tafod yr hydd is hart's tongue fern, so we are unsure at present whether this is an animal or plant cure, but an animal seems more likely. The circumflex does not appear in modern Welsh.*

*This is missing from Pughe's 1861 translation*

## RHAG PISO GWAED
139. Pwya arlleg a berw mewn llaeth yn yr amser, ai yfed nos a bore, i iach y bydd.

## TO STOP URINATING BLOOD
139. Mash garlic and boil in milk for a time. Drink morning and night time and she will get well.

*This is missing from Pughe's 1861 translation*

## RHAG TRAUL NATTUR AR WRAIG, A RHAG GORMODD O FLODAU
140. Cymmer risg derwen ifanc o'r hanner at yr haul, a thynn o'r bôn tua'r brig, a thynn yr uchaf ymaith, a briw yn dra mân mewn llaeth buwch unlliw, a chymmer werth ceiniog o saffar yn bylor mân, a brew y cyfan yn dda ar dan araf, a chwedyn ei hidlo ai yfed y bore a'r nos yn dair diod neu chwaneg, ag yn wir iach y bydd trwy Dduw, Amen.

## FOR A WOMAN WITH HEAVY PERIODS
140. Take the bark* of a young oak from the side facing the sun, and pull from the base towards the top. Take off the upper layer and mash into small pieces in

the milk of a cow of one colour. Take a penny's worth of powdered saffron and stew everything well on a slow fire and then sieve. Drink evening and morning in three drinks or more, and truly she will be well by God. Amen.

*Rhisg is a variant of rhisgl, which means bark.*

## A PLASTER TO REDUCE A SWELLING

141. Take tutsan, cinquefoil, vervain, mallows, lard, and butter. Boil the herbs well in water, then remove and pound the herbs well. Set them on the fire in the water a second time, with butter and lard. Mix and boil until it forms a cataplasm, and apply to the swelling, and it will reduce it without fail.

*This is missing from Pughe's 1861 translation*

## RHAG GWAYW Y FAM A LLEWYGON

142. Cymmer gan gwenith, a dŵr yn oer, ai yfed yn dair diod, ag iach a fydd yn gwir, gyda nerth Duw.

## FOR THE MOTHER'S PAIN AND FAINTING

Take wheat flour and cold water in three drinks, and she will be truly well with the strength of God.

*This is missing from Pughe's 1861 translation*

## I WRAIG A FO AI FFRWYTH YN CERDDED GORMODD

143. Cymmer flwr gwenith a llefrith yn oer, ag yfed ef felly, ag iach y budd yn wir.

## FOR A WOMAN (WHO IS MISCARRYING?) WHOSE BABY IS MOVING TOO MUCH

143. Take wheat flour and milk, and drink cold and she will be truly well.

*This is missing from Pughe's 1861 translation*

## RHAG Y FAM YN CODI AR WRAIG

144. Cais gymaint o ffafen o'r tus*, a dod ar dri marweryn a chymmer y tarth i'th enau, ag ef a ostwng yr hywydd, ag hefyd cymmer gorn y carw** wag arfer ef un yr un modd, a iach y fyddi.

## TO AVOID SWELLING OF THE WOMB

144. Take many beans of frankincense, place upon three embers and inhale the vapour via the mouth. It will reduce the swelling. Also take a stag's horn and use it in the same manner, and you will be well.

*We believe this is frankincense, spelt in Welsh as 'thus' today; **Corn y carw is probably buckthorn, hartshorn or plantain.*

## FOR JAUNDICE

145. Take the leaves which grow on the branches of the hawthorn and the mistletoe, boiling them in white wine or good old ale, until reduced to half. Then take off the fire and strain. Drink this three times a day and you will be cured.

*This is missing from Pughe's 1861 translation*

## RHAG Y FAM O'R BYDD YN CWNNU AR WRAIG YN HWYDDEDIG O'R CYLLA

146. Cymmer isob, a'r llysiau llwydon, a gwna ddiod ag hwynt trwy hen gwrw iachus, a hidla'n lan trwy liain wedi'r berw, a dyro i'r wraig dair diod ar dri phryd, ag ef a estwng y clwyf yn wir, a dda yw'r ddiod honn rhag y tostedd* a'r cyllwst, o herwydd y llysiau llwydon sy dda i'r clefydau hynny yn wir, ag felly rhag pob gwynnogwst yng nghorph dyn, ai un y cylla, ai yn y llynnor**.

## TO AVOID SWELLING OF THE WOMB, IF IT ARISES FROM SWELLING OF THE STOMACH

146 Take hyssop and St John's wort and make a drink from them, in wholesome old beer. Strain completely through a cloth after boiling, and give it to the woman in three drinks on three occasions. It will truly reduce the swelling. This drink is good for strangury and colic, because St John's wort is really good for these ailments, and also for every ache in a person's body, either in the stomach, or from an ulcer.

*Tostedd is strangury, lithiasis, colic; **Llynor is a variant of linor, meaning pimple, boil, ulcer, sore, blister.*

## A DRINK FOR RIGOR* OF STOMACH AND BODY

147. Take a handful of rosemary, a handful of hyssop, a handful of sage, a handful of feverfew, and a handful of red fennel. Pound well and boil in a gallon of good strong wort made from barley malt. Keep it in an earthenware vessel, cover carefully, and set aside for three days. Then take three draughts of it, fasting every morning, and another at night warmed to blood heat. Take also a pennyworth of grains of paradise, a pennyworth of saffron, and a pennyworth of canella bark powdered fine in a mortar. Cast a portion of this upon the surface of the drink, doing this in the drink as long as it lasts. It has been proved valuable for all pains in a man's body.

*The Welsh is cryd, meaning shivering, ague, fever. Rigor is the sudden feeling of cold accompanied by shivering and a rise in temperature, especially at the onset or height of a fever.*

## FOR PNEUMONIA

148. Take a proportion of sea beet* (called in Latin beta), rejecting the branches and tops, and take three gallons of pure water, boiling the sea beet in it. Then take the beet out, letting the decoction boil. After a while remove from the fire, and let it cool to the temperature of wort, then pour it upon some fresh lees of ale, permitting it to ferment as long as it will do so. Then give it the patient for nine meals as his only drink. Then take the beet and mix with butter and powdered melilot, giving it the patient to eat for nine meals, and by the help of God he will recover. It is also an excellent medicine for tertian ague.

* Beta vulgaris subsp. maritime. Also known as Wild Spinach or Sea Spinach, it is the ancestor of all cultivated beets and chards.*

## FOR AGUE

149. Take a handful of the water flower de lys* and three quarts of good strong ale. Pound the herbs, and boil in the ale till it is reduced to three quarts, then strain. Then take a pennyworth of the powder of the grains of paradise, and boil a

second time slightly. Take it four times a day before the ague fit, and you will recover.

*The Yellow Flag Iris, Iris pseudacorus*

## FOR THE INTERNAL PAIN CALLED STONE

150. Take the herb called butterwort*, which grows in meadows and on mountains, its leaves embracing the earth, and having a blue barren flower. Gather your cowl** full of these herbs, and pound them well in a large wooden milk pail. Then take twice as much watercress, and pound that briskly. Afterwards take a red cock, kill, defeather, eviscerate, and clean well. Then put the cock into a brass pot, in at least two gallons of pure water, and boil in the water with the herbs, until the bones become loose. Take the cock out and remove its bones. Return the flesh again to the pot, as well as the herbs, boil briskly a second time until you find the mixture thickening, and the ebullition ceasing in consequence of its thickness. Now take it off the fire, and strain the whole through a strong cloth. Take the strained matter and set upon the fire, then take a half-pennyworth of powdered pepper, and cast into this liquor. Afterwards remove it from the fire to cool, stirring continuously. Administer some of this to the patient with his food and drink each meal, till the morbid product is found passing away from him in a dissolved condition. I have proved this to be effectual in the case of those of all ages. It is called 'The blue confection*** for the Stone'.

*Common butterwort is Pinguicula vulgaris; ** A hood or hooded robe normally worn by monks. Physicians were an integral part of the monastic order. When to monasteries were dissolved, much herbal lore was lost forever; ***See Book 1:17 for blue confection again.*

## WHEN A MAN IS SWOLLEN FROM THE POISON OF A SPIDER

151. Take nine cloves of garlic, and peel carefully. Add a spoonful of treacle and a quart of strong new ale. Mix these together and give them to the patient to drink freely. At the same time cover him with an abundance of clothes so that he may perspire well. If he can retain this position for an hour he will escape [illness], even though the integument had become mottled. This medicament is also useful for a person bitten by an adder.

* There are over 700 native species of spider in Britain, and about a dozen can give a nasty bite. They are the tube web spider, the false widow, woodlouse spider, walnut orb weaver, cellar spider, black lace weaver, mouse spider, rustic wolf spider, bark sac spider, stone spider, cross (or garden) spider, Bruennichi's Argiope, and the money spider.

## FOR SWELLING AND PAIN IN THE SHOULDERS, OF THE JAWS, AND UNDER THE EARS

152. Take celandine, the roots of red fennel, heads of leeks, red wine and butter. Pound them together and apply them cold as a plaster to the affected part, and you will truly recover by the help of God.

## FOR SCABS AND ERUPTIONS UPON A MAN'S FLESH

153. Take celandine, the root of elecampane, and wood sorrel. Boil them in as much water as you please, until it is evaporated to half. Wash the diseased part with this fluid, and it will be healed.

## FOR PAIN IN THE BACK

154. Bleed from the back of the foot near the big toe, and fillet the limb*, having bathed it in warm water, and the patient will surely get well.

*'A chorda'r esgair' is the Welsh original, which Pughe translates as fillet the limb. Cordio is to tie or bind, so 'bind the limb' makes more sense.*

## FOR PAINFUL ERYSIPELAS IN THE LEGS AND MEMBERS.

155. Take the herb called the buckthorn plantain, and boil in three gallons of water, until it is reduced to a quart. Bottle, then add a gallon of ale, and boil until it is reduced into a bottle again, finally straining it. Keep it in a clean vessel and let the painful part be anointed with it frequently.

## FOR STRANGURY AND THE ATTENDANT PAIN

156. Take saxifrage and parsley, pound them well together, and boil with honey in old ale, finally straining. Drink this night and morning, and you will be cured in the name of God.

## FOR ULCERATION OF THE EARS

157. Take the seed of the ash, otherwise called ashen keys*, and boil briskly in the urine of the sick man. Bathe the ear with this and put some in the ear, soaked into black wool. By God's help it will cure it.

*Joined together at the top, the seeds have the appearance of a buch of keys.*

## FOR JAUNDICE

158. Take the largest apple you can have, and scoop the eye out, removing the core of the apple with a bone or wooden scoop. Fill it up with the juice of the white oxeye, (by some called the great daisy) and saffron, then re-insert the eye in its place. Bake the apple under the fire embers, and when sufficiently baked remove from under the embers, and pound thoroughly. Let the patient eat it, and he will certainly recover.

## FOR A CHRONIC GASTROCELE*

159. Take the bark of blackthorn, scrape off the epidermis, and boil the under-bark in water for as long as beef is boiled. Afterwards boil a hard egg, and take its yolk and fine wheat flour, mixing together well. Then take a third part of the liquor in which the bark was boiled, and the mixture of meal and yolk. Make bread with them and bake on the hearth stone. This should be eaten night and morning. The patient should carefully abstain from any drink other than the liquor of blackthorn or red wine, and he will recover. - Philip the Physician.

*A hernia of part of the stomach.*

## FOR FAINTINGS OF THE HEART

160. Take the juice of fennel, and honey, measure for measure. Boil well, eating as much in quantity as a hen's egg night and morning, and you will recover.

## FOR HARDNESS OF THE ABDOMEN

161. Take two spoonfuls of the juice of holly, drinking it three times a day for nine days, and by God's help you will recover.

## FOR A MOIST STOMACH

162. Take the roots of leeks, and make into powder by desiccating them at a distance from the fire, and powdering in a mortar. Take a spoonful of this powder in a good draught of red wine. Drink it the last thing at night, two hours after your supper, for three days, when by God's help you will recover.

## FOR A PNEUMONIA

163. Take a handful of each of the three following herbs: mugwort*; gystlys – that is to say tansy; and red fennel. Pound well and make them into a potion, with good sound old ale. Boil this on a slow fire, straining carefully, and drinking it cold for three meals, and by God's aid it will remove the pain under the pectoral muscle and shoulder, curing the patient. Another way of preparing it is to pound the herbs well, pouring upon them three cupfuls of ale or old mead. Having left them to stand to cool for half-an-hour, strain well through a clean cloth. Give it in three portions to the patient once every three hours, and by God's help he will recover.

   *Llysiau llwydon is the same as llysiau Ifan, Artemisia vulgaris.*

## AN OINTMENT FOF ALL SORTS OF DOLOURS*

164. Take broom flowers, or when not to be had the branches and leaves. Find primroses, roots of water hemlock, leaves of eryngo, mugwort, and red dock. Pound all well in a mortar, and make an ointment by means of butter. Anoint the diseased part frequently and it will be cured.

*Pughe translates gwayw as dolours, meaning painful grief, heartbreak, sorrow, depression. However, it should be translated as sharp and sudden pain, shooting pain, stitch, gripes, painful spasm, agony or stabbing pain.*

## FOR SOLUTION OF THE LIVER*

165. Take a little wild tansy. Pound well with wine, express, and then drink it three times a day for three days. By God's help you will recover. When no wine can be obtained, take strong sound ale or mead instead. Borage will remove the red hue of the evacuations, if it is pounded with wine and drunk. It will strengthen a man's memory and intellect, being truly a warm astringent tonic.

* *Pughe notes:* One of the imaginary diseases of the old humoral pathology, probably bilious diarrhoea or dysentery, as evidenced by the reference to blood in the stool.

## TO RESTRAIN THIRST, IN A HEALTHY OR SICK MAN

166. Take centaury, and pound with warm water, then strain. When cold let it be drunk, and it will remove cardialgic pains, and cure the patient.

## FOR PAIN IN THE FEET, AND SWELLING IN THE LEGS

167. Take the roots of dwarf elder*, and remove the bark, boiling it well. Then pound them in a mortar with old lard, and apply as a plaster to the diseased part.

   *Sambucus ebulus, Danewort*

## FOR OPACITY OF THE CORNEA

168. Take the leaves of the red garden strawberry, and pound with a hen's fat and unsalted butter. Anoint your eye when you go to sleep with this ointment, so that it may enter into your eye, and you will recover.

144

## ANOTHER FOR OPACITY OF THE CORNEA

169. Take a hen's fat, unsalted butter and powdered aloes, boil them together and let them cool. Then anoint your eyes when you go to sleep.

## FOR STRANGURY

170. Take the juice of the leek, honey, powdered pepper, and vinegar. Pound well until they are incorporated, and administer to the patient in three doses, and it will cure him.

## FOR DYSPEPSIA, STRANGURY, AND PAIN IN THE PERINEUM

171. Take two handfuls of tansy, pounding them in a mortar. Then boil them in spring water for the time required for beef, when they will become a thick mass. Cast some barley meal upon the surface, mix well and lay upon a cloth or flannel. Apply this cataplasm to the painful part frequently, repeating it nine times. Afterwards take two quarts of perry [pear cider] and a quart of blessed water* of rulandus, or the emetic water. Add some to the wine as warm as the patient can take it, and let him drink it night and morning. Do not permit him to take the warm drink first and then the emetic water afterwards. Let him follow this plan as long as the liquor lasts.

While the patient is taking these things, procure some ram's flesh, boil well in spring water, then remove from the fire. Take out the meat and let the water cool. Remove the surface fat, make it into a ball and melt. Boil this tallow with some of the blessed water upon a slow fire until it becomes an ointment, the vessel containing it being well-covered meanwhile.** Let the affected part be rubbed backward and forward with this ointment. Take some oven-baked or griddle-baked bread, and ram's flesh for food, and do not take any other kind of food for a long while, for in persevering in this plan you will recover, as has indeed been fully proved.

* *Pughe notes:* Aqua Benedicta Rulandi was a wine of antimony, and identical in property and strength with that now in use; ** *Pughe notes:* This again has its modern representative in the antimonial ointment of the London Pharmacopia.

## TO HEAL A BURN, EVEN WHEN INVOLVING THE JOINTS OR VEINS

172. Take the shield fern*, (by some called the great fern), and extract the juice of the roots, the outside being first scraped. Mix this with some white of eggs. Spread on the injury with a feather, night and morning, and the patient will recover.

*Marchredyn generally means the Common Polypody, which is a small fern. Marchredyn gwrychog is the Hard Shield Fern. It could be the Soft Shield Fern, Polystichum setiferum or the Hard Shield Fern, Polystichum aculeatum. However, the Common Male Fern, Dryopteris filix-mas, is also known as the Male Shield Fern, and was of common use in medieval medicine. It is the commonest and hardiest British fern after Bracken.*

## TO REMOVE A DEAD BONE IN MAN OR BEAST

173. Take cucumber, called in Latin cwcwbri, bugle and pepper in wine. Drink this nine times while fasting, and you will certainly recover.

## FOR INFLAMMATION OF THE MAMMAE

174. Take groundsel, tutsan, and old lard. Pound them well in a mortar and apply to the inflamed organ, as an emollient first. Then next day take plantain, and a gloveful of betony, boil them with water to half, and lay them on a flannel or cloth. Apply this to the affected part, when the patient is going to rest, giving her a cup of wine, and she will obtain natural sleep that night. i. h. u. y.*

   * *It is not known what these letters represent.*

## TO DESTROY PARASITES ON THE HUMAN BODY

175. Take rue, pound well, wrap up in a cloth, and rub the flesh smartly with it. This will destroy them. It is also excellent for those hectic perspirations which so weaken a man.

## FOR ANY KIND OF WOUNDED INTEGUMENT*

176. Take feverfew, bruisewort, ribwort plantain, common plantain, and sage, an equal portion of each. Bruise them briskly in a mortar, and boil in unsalted butter till the butter disappears. Then strain well and keep in a box. Anoint any bruised skin with this.

   *The inegumentary system is the organ system which protects thebody from damage, including the skin, hair and nails.*

## THE FOLLOWING IS A POTENT OINTMENT FOR EXTRACTING EVIL HUMORS FROM WOUNDS

177. Take feverfew, mugwort, devil's bit*, plantain and mallows. Pound them well and add some unsalted butter, fresh yellow wax, rosin, and suet. Boil well, and the virtue of the herbs will be communicated to the butter, suet, wax, and rosin. Strain through a cloth, and keep in a box. It will extract the venom from all sorts of wounds, and heal them.

There are three wounds of membrane which the surgeon should not meddle with: the membranes of the brain; a wound of the intestines; and the urinary bladder, for they should be left to God. Nevertheless, they will be frequently healed, as is often the case in men wounded in battle. Neither food nor drink should be allowed such patients, except sweet milk, and woman's milk.

   *Devil's Bit Scabious, Scabiosa succisa*

## FOR WORMS IN THE STOMACH

178. Make a powder of turnips, by slicing and roasting them before the fire. They should be ground and given to the patient to eat cold, for nine mornings fasting, or at nine separate times, and he will be cured.

## FOR THE BITE OF AN ADDER

179. Take the juice of plantain, ground ivy and olive oil, an equal quantity of each. Give the patient a good draught of it, and anoint the wound with the same. It will destroy the poison and cure the patient.

## ANOTHER FOR AN ADDER'S BITE

180. Take the brain of a red cock, and the juice of the fern called hart's tongue.* Pound them well, and then mix well with white wine or milk. Let the patient drink a full draught of this, also washing the wound with it, and he will be healed.

*Hart's-tongue Fern, Asplenium scolopendrium, also formerly known as God's Hair.*

## FOR A FRECKLED FACE

181. Anoint the face with a bull's, or a hare's blood.

## FOR SWELLING IN A MAN'S JOINTS OR LIMBS

182. Take centaury and pound it well. Strain it well in combination with water through a clean linen cloth. Let the patient drink it.

## FOR EXCESSIVE THIRST

183. Take centaury, and a little bastard pellitory*, and pound them well. Express them into strong wort of barley malt, or let the herbs stand in the wort, in an earthenware vessel until the next morning. This, given to the patient to drink in the morning, will remove his thirst.

* Sneezewort, European Pellitory, Achillea ptarmica*

## FOR AN INTERNAL SWELLING

184. Take plums, boil in goat's milk, and when cold let the patient drink it in the morning, and as late as he can in the evening.

*Pughe's translation is missing. The entry should be:*

## RHAG RHWYSTR PISO A LLOSGFA MEWN GWIALEN GWR NEU WRAIG

185. Cymmer ymhenydd ysgyfarnog, a dyro mewn gwin gwynn sur, a rhoi i'r claf i yfed.

## TO REMEDY THE INABILITY TO URINATE AND INFLAMMATION IN THE ROD* OF A MAN OR WOMAN

185. Take the brain of a hare and place in sour white wine. Give this to the patient to drink.

*Gwialen means rod or penis, and here must refer to the urinary passage.*

## FOR RINGWORM

186. Take some brimstone, and grind fine. Boil dock root and ox tallow together. When cold, add the powdered brimstone and mix as much with the tallow as will make a hard ointment. This will destroy ringworm.

## FOR HEADACHE

187. Whoever is frequently afflicted with a headache let him make a lotion of vervain, betony, chamomile, and red fennel. Let him wash his head three times a week with this, and he will be cured.

147

## FOR DEAFNESS

188. Take ram's urine, the oil of eels, the house leek, the juice of traveller's joy*, and a boiled egg. Let him mix these, and drop the lotion into the ear little by little, and it will cure him.

   * *Old Man's Beard, Wild Clematis, Clematis vitalba*

## AN OINTMENT FOR AN OLD SPRAIN

189. Take a handful of ivy leaves, and pound well with goat dung and fresh butter. Mix them together well. Apply as a plaster to the sprain, and it will be healed.

## FOR HEADACHE

190. Take ground ivy, pound well with red wine, and apply as a plaster to the forehead of the patient.

   He that does not take food when hungry, his stomach will be filled with wind and disease, which will produce headache. Taking dry bread with salt mutton as food will cure it.

## FOR ALL KINDS OF PAIN

191. Take a quantity of broom flowers, water flower de lys, primrose, a handful of the roots of red nettle, water hemlock, the leaves of eryngo and the leaves of plantain when in seed. Add a quart of seeds.* Mix and pound well with unsalted butter, and boil briskly. Strain through linen, and keep in a covered box. This is a precious ointment for any kind of pain.

   * *Pughe notes here:* Probably the four greater hot seeds - Anise, Carui, Cumin, and Fennel. *Carum carui is caraway.*

## TO DESTROY WORMS IN A MAN'S STOMACH, WHEN NAUSEA IS PRODUCED

192. Take the herb called honeywort*. Pound it well with some white wine. Warm some of it and administer to the patient while fasting for three mornings, and it will cure him.

   *Llysiau'r mêl, literally herbs of honey – Common Honeysuckle, Lonicera periclymenum, the Woodbine.*

## FOR PAIN IN THE BACK OR HIP

193. Take mouse-ear chickweed*, and pound well. Boil it with butter, and strain, then anoint the back with it before the fire, and the patient will get well.

   * *Cerastium fontanum*

## FOR CHRONIC HEPATITIS

194. Take the root of melilot*, anise-seed, betony and elecampane. Pound them well with strong wort or white wine. Strain carefully and drink night and morning, until the pain is removed, when by God's help you will obtain a cure.

   * *The Welsh word used, Melottai, can mean liquorice, beet or mallow, whereas Pughe's translation is Melilot, the same as the English word Melilot. To add to the confusion, Melilotus officinalis (Melilotus indicus) or Yellow Sweet Clover was known as Wild Laburnum and Wild Lucerne, and prescribed for illness from the time of Galen onwards.*

## TO CURE DIMNESS OF SIGHT

195. Take the juice of red fennel, celandine, a little vinegar or verjuice, an eel's blood and a cock's gall. Mix these ingredients together, and set aside in a clean vessel until fermentation takes place. Take some of the clear liquor and put in a blind man's eyes. Science tells us that by these means, sight lost may certainly be recovered.

## FOR THE PAIN AND SWELLING OF ERYSIPELAS

196. Take fern root, pound well, and then mix with a little warm water, rubbing it with your hands. Then express through linen, and make a plaster from it with barley meal and the white of eggs. Spread with your thumb on a cloth, and apply to the disease.

## FOR ALL COMPLAINTS OF THE EYES, PARTICULARLY OPACITIES

197. Take wild or garden tansy*, and boil well in white wine until the virtue of the herbs is extracted. Then remove from the fire, strain clean, and permit it to cool and clear. Afterwards take of the clearest portion, and put some camphor in it, and leave it until it is dissolved. Introduce some of this collyrium to the eye, and it will cure whatever disease afflicts the eye. Aristobolis** states that this is proven.

*Grieve distinguishes between wild and garden tansy – one assumes that either is useful, but in this context it appears to be the same plant. Tanacetum vulgare, known as Common Tansy has been used for centuries in herbal practice. Earlier, in Book 2:163 Pughe uses Gysthys for Tansy. Tansy is also sometimes known as Mugwort; **Probably Aristobulus of Cassandreia, the Greek military engineer and historian who accompanied Alexander the Great.*

## FOR GASTRIC PAINS

198. Take a little tansy, and reduce to fine powder. Take with white wine and it will remove the pain.

## ANOTHER FOR GASTRIC PAINS

199. Take some tansy, and southernwood, then boil together well with salt. Eat them frequently when fasting, and you will recover.

## FOR AN OEDEMATOUS* WOUND OF THE SCALP, IN CONSEQUENCE OF A FALL

200. Take an ounce of bay salt**, three ounces of crude honey, one of cumin, and two of turpentine. Mix these ingredients well on the fire, and then spread on a linen cloth for a plaster. Apply to the head when it has been warmed. It will remove the oedema and contusion. Let neither oil, tallow, nor any other grease whatever be added to any plaster required for the head.

*Meaning with excessive fluids; **Sea salt*

## FOR A MALIGNANT DISEASE OF THE MAMMAE

201. Take hemlock leaves, bruising them well and boiling with fresh butter in a pan on the fire. Apply to the breast as warm as possible on a white cloth, and it will cure it. Or the leaves may be pounded well with some fresh butter or olive oil, being spread as before upon white linen. Apply to the breast as hot as it can be borne.

## FOR CANKER OF THE MOUTH*

202. Take a cupful of wine or claret, and a sprig of rosemary, boiling them together. Put in a piece as big as a nut of frankincense, a spoonful of honey, and two of water, mixing them well together. Wash the mouth frequently, and it will be cured.

*This is an apthous ulcer, a canker sore – a mouth ulcer which is a contagious open sore.*

## TO PRODUCE GOLDEN HAIR

203. Take the bark* of rhubarb, and infuse in white wine. Wash your head with it, dry with a fine clean cloth, and then dry by the fire, or in the sun if it is warm. Do this once and then again. The more often you do it the more beautiful your hair will become, and without injury to the hair.

*While rhisgl is translated as bark, perhaps the meaning should be stem?*

## TO REMOVE WARTS FROM THE HANDS

204. Take the juice of sheep's sorrel* and sea salt. Wash your hands with this and let them dry spontaneously. Do this again and you will see the warts and freckles disappear. It is also a useful remedy for eruptions and ringworm.

*Rumex acetosella, also known as sour weed, red sorrel and field sorrel.*

## TO KNOW WHETHER A PATIENT WILL LIVE OR DIE

205. Take breast milk where a boy is nursed, and some of the urine of the sick person, and drop the milk from the end of your finger to the urine. If it remains on the surface of the urine, the sick person will live. If not, he will certainly die.

## ANOTHER TO KNOW WHETHER A PATIENT WILL LIVE OR DIE

206. Take daisy flowers, and pound well with wine, giving it the patient to drink. If he vomits it, he will die of that disease. If not, he will live, and this has been proven true.

## FOR A BURN

207. Take fern roots, and pound well with butter. Apply this as a plaster to the injury and it will remove the ardent pain.

## FOR A VIOLENT HEADACHE

208. Take the leaves of foxglove, and pound with milk and mutton suet, until it becomes a plaster. Apply to the head as warm as the patient can bear it.

## HOW TO PREPARE ANOTHER REMEDY FOR A VIOLENT HEADACHE

209. Take oaten groats, the leaves of foxglove, suet and sweet milk*. Pound together until the ingredients are incorporated into a plaster. Set in a pan upon the fire until it is warmed, and apply to the head as warm as it can be borne.

*Sweet milk may be whole milk which is 2-3 days old, when the taste sweetens.*

## FOR SMALLPOX

210. Take quicksilver [mercury], oil of turpentine, white lead*, blue stone**, and lard. Melt these ingredients into an ointment, mixing them well in order to kill the quicksilver, one portion being taken in hand (to kill the mercury) when the other is finished. Long pepper*** and treacle in sage wine should be administered in order to drive out the eruption.****

*This is the basic lead carbonate used as the principal white paint in classical European oil painting, formerly used as an ingredient for lead paints and as a cosmetic, and is poisonous.*

** *Coprys or copras glas means Blue Copperas, a hydrated blue crystalline form of copper sulphate. It is essentially a copper salt made by the action of sulphuric acid on copper oxide. It was also known as blue vitriol, Salzburg vitriol, Roman vitriol, and is a naturally occurring odourless crystalline substance that is electric blue in colour, highly toxic, and unsafe to work with. It was used as a fungicide in agriculture, which is why rural people had it easily to hand. The old-fashioned pesticide called Bordeaux Mixture is a combination of hydrated lime and copper sulphate, also used to control fungus on grapes, melons and other berries. Reckiit's Crown Blue has been available worldwide since the 1890s and so for most of the 20th century, and this author remembers his mother using it on his white school shirts. It was invented to avoid the toxic side-effects for liquid laundry whitening using blue copperas. It is still used as a herbicide for control of invasive exotic aquatic plants and the roots of other invasive plants near various pipes that contain water. Most species of algae can be controlled with very low concentrations of copper sulphate. It also inhibits growth of bacteria such as E.coli.*

*** *Piper longum or Indian Long Pepper was used as a spice across Europe, until displaced by the milder Piper nigrum from the New World, from which white, black and green pepper are obtained.*

**** *In the 1750s, the British general, Lord Jeffrey Amherst, was fighting the French, and their allies the Native Americans. Knowing that smallpox was contagious, he intentionally infected a group of Native Americans. To do this, he obtained scabs from smallpox victims, ground them into blankets, and gave the blankets to his enemies. The Native Americans had never encountered the virus before and had no immunity to it, so the disease spread quickly with deadly results.*

### This is missing from Pughe

### RHAG Y FRECH FAWR

211. Cymmer werth dwy geiniog o eliw twrpant, a gwerth dwy geiniog o eliw bae, gwerth chwech cheiniog o arian byw, gwerth dwy geiniog o'r gwm a elwir mastig, gwerth dwy geiniog o rwd gwyrdd a elwir ferdigrw, gwerth dwy geiniog o goprys glas, gwerth ceiniog o gamffyr, gwerth ceiniog o elyf*, gwerth ceiniog o losgfaen pyloraid, ag ob* rosin, pwys o blwm gwynn os bydd y claf yn wlyb, cymysg hwy ynghyd, ag elia'r claf, profedig yw.

### PROTECTION FROM POX (VENEREAL DISEASE, SYPHILIS)

212. Take twopence worth of oil of turpentine, and twopence worth of bay (laurel) oil, sixpence worth of quicksilver, twopence worth of the gum called mastic, twopence worth of green rust that is called verdigris, twopence worth of blue copperas, a penny worth of camphor, a pennyworth of oil, a pennyworth of flowers of sulphur**, an obolus*** of resin and a pound of white lead if the patient is wet****. Mix together and salve the patient, it is tried and tested.

* *In other parts of his translation, Pughe translates elyf not as oil, but as alum or aloes; **In the next entry, Pughe translates losgfaen pyloraid not as 'flowers of sulphur' but as 'powdered brimstone.';* ***Pughe notes: Obulus, efallai; gwerth dimai – *An obolus is a Greek unit of measurement, a tenth of a gramme, and efallai means perhaps; to the value of a halfpenny;* ****Perhaps wet with sweat?*

### This is missing from Pughe

## ELI ARALL RHAG Y FRECH FAWR

212. Cymmer bunt o floneg twrch neu fadd i wr, os gwraig bloneg hwch, a hanner pwys o'r ystor a elwir tus gwedi ei bwyo'n dda, ag wncyn o arian byw, hanner wncyn o goprys gwynn, wncyn o rwd gwyrdd, ag ychydig o elyf heb ei losci, ag ob o losgfaen pyloraid, pwya nhwy nghyd yn dda fal nad adwaenir un oddiwrth y llall, ag elia'r claf; profedig yw.

## ANOTHER OINTMENT (REMEDY) FOR POX (VENEREAL DISEASE, SYPHILIS)

212. Take a pound weight of the lard of a wild boar for a man, or if a woman a sow's lard, and half a pound of the gum called frankincense. Pound thoroughly with an ounce of quicksilver, half-an-ounce of white copperas, an ounce of verdigris, a little unburnt alum and an obolus of powdered brimstone. Then mix them thoroughly together so that they are wholly unrecognisable, and salve the patient. It is tried and tested.

## A HEALING OINTMENT FOR BRUISES

213. Take feverfew, ribwort plantain, garden sage and bugle, equal parts of each. Pound them well, and boil in unsalted May butter. Then express through fine linen, and keep in a box. Anoint the disease with it, and the ointment will cure it. If there is dead flesh therein, take some aloes, or sulphate of copper, or red precipitate of mercury in powder. Mix with some of the ointment, and then it will destroy the dead flesh, and promote the healing of the sore.

## FOR WARTS ON A MAN'S HANDS OR FEET

214 Take puffballs*, and pound with salted butter or fresh butter. Make a plaster, and apply to the part where the warts are situated, and it will unroot them.

*Much rarer than in the earlier life of this author, this is probably the Giant Puffball, Calvatia gigantean, a fungus which can reach a foot in diameter.*

## FOR A WART

215. Take an eel and cut its head off. Anoint the parts where the warts are situated with the blood, and bury the head deep in the earth. As the head rots, so will the warts disappear.

## FOR A THORN OR ARROW-HEAD, WHICH HAS ENTERED A MAN'S BODY AND CANNOT BE EXTRACTED

216. Seek the roots or leaves of the spear thistle, and the white of an egg. Mix together and apply to the wound. It will extract the foreign substance.

*This is missing from Pughe*

## RHAG Y WAEDLING NEU FRATH

217. Cylyma fys bach y dyn ag efe a ettail y gwaedu.

## FOR BLEEDING OR A BITE

217. Bind the small finger of the person and it will stop the bleeding

## FOR THE BITE OF A MAD DOG

218. Seek some cowslips, pound them, and mix with milk. Administer to the patient as his only drink for nine days, first straining it through a fine cloth.

152

Others boil the cowslips with sweet milk*, strain them under a press, and administer as a drink to the patient, for nine days. The patient should drink as much as he can of the potion, abstaining from all other aliment for this time.

*Pughe translates 'pen llefrith' as 'sweet milk', and a folk recipe uses a cup of fresh milk and five dried figs to make it. Wash the figs, put them into a small pot, and pour in the milk. On medium heat, bring milk to a boil and cook down for 15 minutes, cover the pot with a lid, let it draw for about 30 minutes or until cool down. Strain the figs from the milk. Pen llefrith, or the top of fresh milk, indicates using cream in this medicine, but in 2:224 Pughe uses hufen llaeth to mean cream. As noted in 2:209, sweet milk may mean milk a few days old – in 2:209 he translates llefrith, not pen llefrith as sweet milk.*

*This is missing from Pughe:*

## I BERI I WRAIG BLANTA
219. Cais lynger ysgyfarnog, ai harennau, a pheth o'r gwaed, a thrwy wynebion yr isgell y brewer y cig, eu maeddu, a dod ynddo hanner wncyn o rawn paris yn byloraid, ag ychydig o win gwynn main, a rhodder hynn iddi pan ei I wely, a hi a fydd gyflawn o anian naturiol.

## TO CAUSE A WOMAN TO BEAR CHILDREN
219. Take tapeworms from a hare, and also its kidneys and some of its blood. Through the surface of the infusion boil the meat, and mix. Add half an ounce of ground cardamine* and a little weak white wine. Give it to her when she goes to bed, and she will be full of natural** disposition.

*'Grawn paris' was known as grawn de Paris or grawn Paradwys, meaning cardamine, lady-smock, cuckoo-flower; **Anian can also mean semen.*

## TO PREVENT DREAMS
220. Take vervain, and hang about a man's neck, or give him the juice in going to bed, and it will prevent his dreaming.

## TO DESTROY A WORM IN THE TOOTH
221. Take the roots of the cat's ear*, bruise, and apply to the patient's tooth for three nights, and it will kill the worm.

*Thankfully not a real cat. Melenydd is Hawkweed, probably Mouse Ear Hawkweed, Pilosella officinarum. However, see 2.774. Culpeper tells us: 'The green herb bruised and bound to any cut or wound doth quickly close the lips thereof, and the decoction or powder of the dried herb wonderfully stays spreading and fretting cankers in the mouth and other parts.' It was thought that worms in the teeth caused toothache.*

## TO CURE ALL KINDS OF ERUPTIONS
222. Take some onions and pound in water or vinegar. Wash the affected part with this, and it will remove all sorts of eruptions.

## FOR NOISE IN THE HEAD, PREVENTING HEARING
223. Take a clove of garlic, prick in three or four places in the middle, and dip in honey. Insert in the ear, covering it with some black wool. Let the patient sleep on his other side every night, leaving the clove in the ear, unchanged for seven or eight nights. It will prevent the nose running, and restore hearing.

## A SAFE PLASTER FOR ALL SWELLINGS
224. Take some cream*, or in the absence of cream, fresh milk, and set on the fire. Add some crumbs of white bread, wax, and a little honey. When this has boiled nearly enough, add a portion of mutton suet, and olive oil**. If the heat in the swelling is considerable, add some white of eggs, mix well and apply to the swelling.

*Here Pughe uses 'hufen llaeth' to mean cream. See 2:218; **As a youngster, olive oil was only available from chemist shops, usually used to dissolve ear wax. A very few delicatessens would sell it for cooking. Some of my parents' generation mixed it with vinegar as suntan lotion.*

## A PLASTER TO REMOVE PAINS, ACHES, AND INFLAMMATION
225. Procure if you can the milk of a single-coloured cow, oatmeal, a little mutton suet and a handful of parsley. Pound these together and boil well, then apply warm to the diseased part, and it will speedily ease it.

## TO DISPERSE A SWELLING
226. Take the juice of plantain, the white of eggs, clarified honey and barley meal. Mix them together and apply as a plaster to the swelling. Proven.

## ANOTHER REMEDY TO DISPERSE A SWELLING
227. Seek the juice of water pimpernel, the white of eggs, honey and wheat or barley meal. Make a plaster, then apply to the disease, and it will heal it.

## TO REMOVE PAIN AND SWELLING
228. Take rye meal, white of eggs, and the juice of plantain. Then apply as a plaster to the area, anointing it first with honey, and by God's help it will cure it. If required, this should be done two or three times.

## TO REMOVE A SWELLING
229. Take the leaves of foxglove, mutton suet, oatmeal and milk. Apply as a plaster to the swelling and it will cure it.

## TO PROMOTE THE FORMATION AND POINTING Of AN ABSCESS
230. Take the leaves of foxglove. Pound with wine, suet and barley meal. Apply it as a warm plaster.

## ANOTHER TO PROMOTE THE FORMATION AND POINTING Of AN ABSCESS
231. Take curds in ale, together with sheep's milk.

## TO DESTROY FLEAS
232. Take a hedgehog and roast it, receiving its oil in a vessel. Anoint a stick with some of this oil, and lay it where there are fleas, and as many as are to be found in that room will be attracted to it.

## FOR ALL MANNER OF ACHES IN THE THIGHS, FEET, ARMS, OR ANY OF THE JOINTS

233. Take a small quantity of broom flowers, lily flowers, eryngo leaves and red dock leaves. Pound them well and make an ointment of them with butter. Then anoint the diseased part with this, and it will be cured.

## FOR VERTIGO, CALLED MIGRAN*, OR HEMICRANIAL HEADACHE

234. Take a live hare, behead it, skin it and boil or roast. Then open the head, taking some rosemary flowers, and powder the same. Put them in the head, mixing with the brains and baking or roasting it. Let the brain be then eaten, the patient sleeping afterwards, and it will be found really useful.

 * *This is Migraine, from the Greek hemi (half) and kranion (skull), as it affects half the head. It causes severe headaches and is three times as common in women as in men.*

## FOR THE FALLING SICKNESS CALLED FFLAMGWST, AND IN LATIN EPILEPSIA

235. Take the blood of a newly born lamb, which has never suckled. Mix with two spoonfuls of good ale, and drink it while fasting for three mornings. This is proven and wonderful.

## TO ALLEVIATE WHOOPING COUGHS* WHEN PRODUCING CEREBRAL DISTURBANCE

236. Seek a pennyworth of cumin seed, two pennyworths of the seed of English galingale, called glingal**, and the same of canella***. Powder these ingredients well together, then take on a warm drink, and it will be of benefit.

 * *This is Whooping Cough, caused by the highly contagious Bordetella pertussis bacteria. Known as the 100 Days Cough, it is difficult to treat, and vaccination has prevented epidemics in Britain. There is a bout of coughing, a 'whoop' sound as one gasps for breath and vomiting. Globally there are almost 50 million cases a year and almost a third of a million deaths from the disease.*

 ** *The Welsh is Ysnoden Fair, and the plant is Sweet Galingale, Cyperus longus.*

 *** *Canella is the fragrant cinnamon-like inner bark of a West Indian tree, Canella winterana, used as a spice and in medicine. However, Pughe possibly wrongly translates from 'canel', which is actually cinnamon itself, Cinnamomum verum, traded from earliest times.*

## FOR MALIGNANT CARBUNCLE OR PLAGUE

237. Seek a good handful of red sage, a handful of rue, and the same of garlic. Pound well, in strong ale, wine or good mead. Strain through a fine cloth. By God's help you will recover.

## FOR A PROLAPSUS ANI*

238. Take the herb called cleavers, whose seed adhere to the hose [trousers or lower garments] of those who get among them, and are found in round grains of the size of pepper on the terminal branches of the plant. Pound them well and boil in butter until an ointment is formed, which should be expressed and the anus anointed therewith.

* *Usually caused by constipation, this is a condition in which inner anal canal and rectum comes out through the anal opening with its mucosa. It usually occurs in old age and causes much discomfort.*

## FOR MIGRAINE OR VERTIGO

239. Obtain frankincense, yellow wax, and honey. Compound them well together, then apply in the form of a plaster to the forehead, and it will be truly useful. *(See 2.234)*

## FOR A CHILD WHO HAS BECOME PARALYSED IN HIS LIMBS

240. Perhaps he has lost the power of his limbs from weakness in his spine. If so, take oil of turpentine, and oil of olives, and mix together, anointing the child's back with this night and morning. This will strengthen him.

## FOR PAINS IN THE THIGHS, FEET, ARMS, AND ALL JOINTS

241. Take oil of turpentine, butter, sheep and goat's suet. Boil well in a pan, straining through a cloth. Anoint the painful part with it well.

## FOR A STITCH ORIGINATING UNDER THE ARM OR BREAST, AND EXTENDING THROUGH THE SHOULDER

242. Make an ointment with thick cream, broad leaved dock, and nettles. Apply this as a plaster, so as to bring it to the surface. It is indeed a good application.

## FOR THE BITE OF A MAD DOG

243. Take primrose, pound small, and express the juice under a press. Mix with milk, giving it the patient to drink nine times.

## FOR RHEUMATISM, OR STIFFNESS IN THE SHOULDER AND LIMBS

244. Make an ointment with butter, rue, frankincense, and three pennyworth of the blessed water.* Anoint three times a week for a summer's month, or if it is winter, remain in a warm room, and beware of cold.

* *Aqua Benedicta Rulandi.*

## FOR AN INSANE PERSON

245. Take betony, boil in a quart of strong ale, and use for drink, and you will certainly recover.

## FOR A MAN WHO IS WEAK IN HIS INTELLECT, OR MAD*

246. Take a quart of red wine vinegar, and half as much of the juice of celandine,** mixing them together. Then take a cupful of a potion prepared from spring water and betony, (bruised together and strained) the first thing in the morning, and the last thing at night. Let the same herbs be boiled for him in order to strengthen his head, an emulsion being prepared from linseed, in which the herbs should be boiled. The patient should be confined in a dark room. This is an effective treatment.

*Gwallbwyllo is to have lost one's reason, at one's wit's ends, manic, demented, insane;* ** *Celandine is an active and drastic cathartic.*

## FOR THAT INFIRMITY OF THE HEAD WHICH IS TERMED BRAIN FEVER OR FRANTIC DELIRIUM, OCCASIONING DERANGEMENT OF MIND, AND CALLED IN LATIN PHRENESIS. IN THIS COMPLAINT THE PATIENT IS HARDLY CONSCIOUS WHAT HE UTTERS. IT IS OCCASIONED BY WATER UNDER THE FONTENELLE, PRESSING ON THE BRAIN AND MEMBRANES, AND HINDERING SLEEP AT NIGHT

247. Obtain linseed, and pound in a brass mortar. Make an emulsion with pure water, boiling it as you would make porridge. Powder as much anise-seed and ginger as can be held in the hollow of your hand. Mix this anise-seed and ginger with the emulsion and give to the patient to drink, four times in the day and night for nine days. The diet should be nourishing, any drink of a tonic nature, and the patient should be put to sleep in a dark room.

## FOR INFLAMMATION, ATTENDED WITH SWELLING AND PAIN IN THE MEMBERS, FEET AND HANDS

248. Take asparagus, pound it well and make into an ointment with butter. Then anoint the diseased part with it. It is truly useful.

## FOR ALOPECIA

249. Take watercress*, bruise well and express the juice. Wash your head with this and scrub it well. The same juice may also be taken internally, and you will be cured.

*Watercress is a traditional cure for hair loss, owing to the presence of biotin (Vitamin B7) and zinc, and therefore is present in many modern shampoos. It also contains iron, silica and pyridoxine (Vitamin B6). The deficiency of any or all of these components can cause alopecia.*

## FOR HYSTERIA

250. First take an emetic, then the following dry herbs: cloves, mastic, grains of Paradise, wood of aloes, a pennyworth of each. Pound together well, let a portion be taken dry every morning, and in an emulsion at other times.

## TO REMOVE AN EXFOLIATION OF BONE FROM THE SKULL

251. Take betony, vervain, and rue. Pound well with honey, wheaten flour, and the white of eggs. Make it into a plaster, and apply to the injured part.

## A PLASTER TO REDUCE A SWELLING

252. Take barley flour and the white of an egg, mix, and apply as a plaster to the injury.

## FOR HAEMATURIA*

253. Take a handful of each of the following herbs: parsley, plantain, and shepherd's purse. Pound thoroughly, and strain with goats' whey. Drink a cupful while fasting every morning. Continue this and you will recover.

*Haematuria is blood in the urine. It may signify a kidney stone, or a tumor in the urinary tract (including the kidneys, ureters, urinary bladder, prostate or urethra).*

## FOR AN EPITHELIAL* CANCER

254. Take ground ivy and foxglove. Pound well and then boil in stale urine, with tallow or suet. Strain, and anoint the injury therewith.

*The epithelium is the membraneous tissue covering most of the external surfaces of the body and its organs.*

## TO OBTAIN SLEEP

255. Take eryngo and mugwort called orpin*. Mix with milk, and form into pills, administering unto the patient, and he will sleep presently.

* *The Welsh is 'llysiau Ieuan a elwir yr orpin'. Generally llysiau Ieuan or Ifan are Mugwort, Artemisia vulgaris. However, llysiau Ifan can also be St John's Wort, Hypericum. Orpin, or Orpine, is Sedum telephium, a Stonecrop.*

*This is missing from Pughe*

## RHAG GWRAIG GWEDI EI LLOSGI GAN WR

256. Cymmer arian byw werth dwy geiniog, eliw gliwydden werth dwy geiniog, camffyr werth ceiniog, coprys glas ob, a bloneg, ai gymysgu ai ddodi ar y dolur.

## FOR A WOMAN WHO HAS HAD INFLAMATION FROM A MAN

256. Take twopence worth of quicksilver, twopence worth of ointment of lime twigs, a pennyworth of camphor, an obolus of blue copperas, and lard. Mix and place upon the sore.

* *Eliw glinydden is ointment of lime twigs, according to Pughe.*

## FOR AN INFLAMMATION WHICH IS THE RESULT OF MECHANICAL IRRITATION, BOTH HEALING IT, AND SOOTHING THE ITCHING

257. Obtain parsley, pound it small, and boil well in butter. Cast a pennyworth of black soap into the boiling ointment, mixing it well. Strain, and anoint the diseased part night and morning. It is proved. In order to promote the healing of this skin, so that it may be as white as the whole skin, obtain oatmeal gruel made with water. Apply an oatmeal poultice as a broad cake to the part, first washing it with the gruel. This will presently heal it.

## FOR SCROFULA, CALLED BY SOME THE [KING'S] EVIL

258. Take four pennyworth of oil of olives, two pennyworth of white lead, a pennyworth of frankincense, blue stone [referred to as blue copperas elsewhere], a pennyworth of wax, a pennyworth of oil of turpentine, three pennyworth of mercury, a pennyworth of colophane* and lard. Mix these ingredients together, and apply repeatedly to the affected part, removing the former before each fresh application.

* *Black Rosin*

## FOR A SWELLING IN A MAN'S THROAT THAT PREVENTS HIM FROM SPEAKING*

259. Take hog's lard and stale urine and boil together. Dip a piece of flannel in this, wrap it round the throat, and use for three days. However, if there is an

abscess, put some clarified butter on flannel, and it will mollify it, and also prevent it from suppurating.

*Possibly quinsy?*

## A PLASTER TO REDUCE A SWELLING, RESULTING FROM AN ACCIDENT

260. Take mallows, chamomile, maiden hair fern, chickweed and ground ivy. Boil them well in the stalest urine you can get. Apply to the affected part as a plaster, and it will reduce the swelling.

## TO STRENGTHEN THE TEETH AND MAKE THEM WHITE

261. Take elecampane, and scrub your teeth briskly with it. It will make them firm, white, and healthy.

## FOR LIVID INFLAMMATION OF THE FLESH

262. Obtain eryngo, the leaves of red alder, parsley, broom flowers and stinking iris. Pound them well together and make into an ointment by using butter and black soap. Anoint the painful part with this, and it will heal it.

## TO RESTRAIN A HAEMORRHAGE

263. Obtain beans, or rather bean meal and suet. Boil them together and apply as a plaster to the injury. It is really useful.

*This is missing from Pughe:*

## RHAG HWYDD A GWY* DOLURUS MEWN PWRS NEU ARENAU DYN

264. Cais y llyriad** mawr, sef llydan y ffordd, a llwyn hidydd sef y bychan o'r erllyriad a elwir astyllynes, a dant y llew, a dyrnaid da o fwydynod y ddair, y rhai mwyaf a geffych, a bloneg tew, a dod nghyd mewn mortyr am ben eu gilydd, a phwya'n dda fal nas nabydder un oddi wrth y llall, a dod yn blaster oer wrth y dolur ac iach y bydd; profedig yw.

[Gwŷn, mae'n debyg*]

## FOR SWELLING AND ACHING PAIN IN A MAN'S SCROTUM OR TESTICLES

264. Take Plantago major, namely waybread and Plantago lanceolata, namely the smallest of the plantains called ribwort [plantain]. Add dandelion, and a good handful of earthworms, the biggest you can get hold of, and thick lard. Put them together in a mortar and mix them thoroughly together so that they are wholly unrecognisable, and place as a cold poultice on the ache and he will be healthy. It is tried and tested.

*Gwy means liquid; Pughe's footnote of 'Gwŷn, mae'n debyg' seems to signify that it is pain with liquid; **Erllyriad is the same word as llyriad, meaning itself greater plantain or waybread. Mawn means peat or turf. It is not known whether llyriad mawn is a different plant, or if mawn may be a misprint of mawr, meaning large or great.*

## FOR NAUSEA

265. Obtain a pint of the juice of fennel, and boil it with a pint of clarified honey. Take a spoonful every morning while fasting, as well as the last thing at night, for nine days.

## FOR A MAN WHO TALKS IN HIS SLEEP

266. Take a pint of the juice of betony, and a pint of ale wort and mix together. Drink, and by God's help it will do you good.

## FOR RECEDING GUMS*

267. Take two pennyworth each of blessed water**, distillation of white wine*** and white wine vinegar. Mix them together, and wash your mouth with the same as long as it lasts.

*The Welsh is 'rhag cig yn cwympo o gylch y dannedd'. 'Cylch y dannedd' does not occur in Geiriadur Prifysgol Cymru, and may mean retraction of the gums. 'Teeth ridge' is an alternative for 'gums'. Could it mean 'collapse of the teeth ridge'? 'Cig yn cwympo' can mean collapsing flesh. Pughe's heading is* 'ForAbsorption of the Gums'; ** *Pughe notes:* Aqua Benedicta; *** *Pughe notes:* Brandy

### *This is missing from Pughe:*

## RHAG Y MANWYNION OS BYDD PRYFED YNDDO

268. Cais cig ci wedi ei flingo, a thorr e'n dafelli bychain fel golwython chwilbob, a dod wrth y dolur o'r pryd i gilydd, a thyn ymaith a sych y clwyf yn lân, ag or bydd pryfed fal penn y dannedd fe au tynn ymaith, a dod gig arall o'r unrhyw wrtho o'r pryd i gilydd hyd ymhen pedair nowaith, ag ymhen ei sychu un lân, ag i iachau a sychu'r dolur cais eliw gliwydden werth with ceiniog, a phlwm gwynn werth grôt, ai ferwi ynghyd yn dda, a'i ddodi ar y clwyf noeth ychydig y bore a'r nos, a chraf yr hen a dod y Newydd, ag o'r bydd heb dorri dod wrtho blaster glaiarllys* a menyn.

## FOR SCROFULA IF THERE ARE WORMS (OR LARVAE) IN IT

268. Take the meat of a flayed dog, and cut it into small slices like thoroughly baked chops, and place near the sore from time to time. Remove and wipe the wound clean, and if the larvae are shaped like the top of the teeth it will draw them out. Place more meat of the same sort upon the sore from time to time for four nights, and at that time wipe it clean. And to make the wound healthy and to dry it, take ointment of lime twigs worth eight pence and a groat's worth of white lead, and boil it well. Place a little upon the bare wound morning and night. Remove the old and place the new, and if it has not broken, place upon it a poultice of claerllys* and butter.

*Then spelt claiarllys, this is now claerllys, and is given variously as brookweed, water pimpernel, samolus valerandi, woad, water speedwell, brooklime, houseleek, golden stonecrop and wall pepper.*

### *This is missing from Pughe:*

## ELI RHAG Y MANWYNON, A'R FRECH FAWR A'R CANCAR

269. Cais werth grôd o gamffyr, gwerth ceiniog o ystor, ac o gwyr morwynain ob, o driagl ob, o eliw ecsedr werth ceiniog, a'r cymaint arall o eliw'r baedd, ag eliw yr eliwydden yr un gymaint a'r eliwau eraill, eliw rhos yr un gymain a'r eliwoedd eraill, a thair llwyaid o fêl, a phwya a maedd hwynt oll ynghyd yn dda, yna eu berwi trwy laeth geifr, a thynn i'r llawr, a brew eilwaith hyd ymhen y naw waith, a

160

hidle trwy liain crai, a dod i gadw mewn corn, ag a hwnnw ira'r clwyf, a hwnnw a dynn y pryf o waith riddwn o gig ag esgryn.

## OINTMENT FOR SCROFULA AND POX AND CANCER

269. Take four pence worth of camphor, a pennyworth of storax*, an obolus of pure wax, an obolus of treacle, a pennyworth of ecsedr** ointment and as much again of boar's oil, and as much olive oil as the other oils. Add as much rose oil as the other oils, and three spoonfuls of honey, and mix and knead everything thoroughly. Then boil them in goat's milk and filter through an unbleached linen cloth and keep it in a horn, and with that bathe the wound. That will draw the larva [o waith riddwn]*** from flesh and bones.

*This can variously be resin, gum or frankincense; **The meaning is unknown as yet; ***This phrase is untranslated, perhaps 'repelling its work'.*

### *This is missing from Pughe:*

## RHAG CIG DRWG A FO'N PYLLU AG YN MAGU PRYFED

270. Cais bwys dwy geiniog a frawn morfil, a elwir yn y Lladin spermaceti, a phedair ceiniogbwys o rwd gwyrdd, a phwya'n dda ag yn fân a rho am ben peint o laeth gafr, a hidla'n lân drwy liain crai, a dyro i'r claf i yfed ar hen gwrw da, a da iawn yw.

## FOR BAD (PUTRID) FLESH THAT IS BECOMING PITTED AND WHERE MAGGOTS (LARVAE) FLOURISH

270. Take the weight of twopence of whale brawn, which in Latin is called spermaceti*, and the weight of fourpence of verdigris. Grind well and fine, and place on a pint of goat's milk, and filter through an unbleached linen cloth. Give it to the patient to drink in good old beer, and very good it is.

*This is the valuable wax extracted from the head cavities of the Sperm Whale. A large whale could supply 500 gallons. It was originally mistaken for the whale's sperm, hence the name. Sperma means sperm in Greek, and ceti is whale in Latin.*

## FOR HAEMATURIA

271. Take milfoil, and a third part of the juice of red fennel. Temper it with red wine, and let the patient drink it warm, and he will get well.

## FOR DYSENTERY AND ITS ATTENDANT PAIN

272. Pick sloes when fully ripe. Dry them either in a strong heat of the sun, or before the fire, (but at a distance), so that they may become dry enough to be powdered. Let the powder be kept in a glass bottle, well corked. When there is a person ill with this complaint, mix a spoonful of this powder with a pint of good, strong and sound old ale, strong old cider, or good old mead. Warm it well and give it to the patient to drink for three mornings while fasting. It will remove the pain and cure the disease.

Also for this disease obtain some strong new linen cloth, and put in it as much in quantity as a goose's egg of the finest wheaten meal you can obtain. Tie up the meal in this new cloth, and boil in a gallon of spring water until reduced to a quart [two pints, a quarter of a gallon]. Then let it cool, and boil a little with milk as gruel. Let the man have this for his daily food. It is proven.

## TO REMOVE THE PAIN ATTENDANT UPON DYSENTERY
273. Take wheaten bread* and old cheese. Slice it thin and boil in milk, mixing a good quantity of pepper therewith. Make use of this, for it is good.

*Wheaten bread is still a term used in Ireland for brown soda bread.*

## FOR PARALYSIS OR HEMIPLAGIA*, THE BLOOD BECOMING SLUGGISH AND VISCID IN THE VEINS
274. Take a handful of the leaves of foxglove, and a handful of the leaves of red nettles. Pound them well, and then boil in a quart of good honey. Strain carefully and keep in a vessel. Boil therewith three pennyworth of the blessed water** or distilled wine*** or cider. Then take two gallons of stale urine, boiling it well, and skimming it carefully as it boils. Take a quantity night and morning, and anoint your joints well therewith by the fire. Rub them afterwards with the preserved ointment, rest your shoulder on an elevated place, and exercise yourself in walking frequently. It is good.

*Pughe gives 'hemiplagia'. Today, hemiplegia is total paralysis of the arm, leg and trunk on the same side of the body; ** Pughe notes: Of Rulandas; *** Pughe notes: Brandy.*

## FOR A SWELLING UNDER THE NAVEL, SOMETIMES LONG, SOMETIMES ROUND, LIKE A BALL BETWEEN THE FLESH AND SKIN
275. Take a quart of red vinegar, and pound a handful of leeks, roots and leaves. Boil a pennyworth of stale bread well with the mixture. Apply this as a fresh plaster every night, and it will remove the swelling.

*This is missing from Pughe:*

## RHAG TRAUL NATUR FFORD Y WIALEN
276. Cais had ffunel, a had anis, a mâs, a phylora nhwy yng ynghyd a bwrw ar gawl neu lynn twym, a chymmer hyd ym mhen nawnydd, a da yw yn wir.

## FOR WEAR AND TEAR OF THE PENIS' PASSAGE
Take fennel seed, anise seed and mace and pulverize together. Pour onto broth or a hot drink and take it for nine days. It is very good.

## FOR A THORN
277. Take betony (by some called bitton), old lard and agrimony. Pound them together and apply to the thorn. This will extract it.

## FOR A POISONOUS THORN
278. Take boar's lard, black soap, and the yolk of eggs. Mix them together and apply as a plaster to the part. It will extract it.

## FOR PAIN IN CONSEQUENCE OF A THORN
279. Take tops of broom and a boy's urine. Boil them briskly, and apply as a fomentation to the part and it will ease it. The fat of a wild cat* is also good. Take also oil of olives, and a pennyworth of camphor, pounding them well together and applying as an ointment to the part.

* *The European Wildcat, Felis sylvestris sylvestris was once common in Wales, but there are now only 400 left in Britain, all in Scotland. Untameable, suffering from habitat destruction and hunted for its fur, it survived in Wales until 1862.*

162

## FOR A WHITLOW ON THE FINGER

280. Take rue, cumin, bacon fat and wheat flour. Boil in white wine and oil of turpentine*. Mix together carefully and apply to the part. When ripe, let it be opened and dressed, it will then heal like any other wound or contusion.

*Also called Wood Turpentine, and Turpentine Spirit, is it distilled from the resin of trees, usually pine trees. It has been used in medicine for centuries, although toxic.*

## ANOTHER FOR AN IMPOSTUME*

281. Take mugwort, and bruise briskly. Mix with the yolk of eggs, apply to the part and it will cure it. There will be a spreading inflammation of the skin, a livid hue and a burning pain at the bone. The tendons will slough away in an impostume of the finger. Thus is the disease known.

*Pughe notes*: Or Whitlow

## ANOTHER FOR AN IMPOSTUME

282. Take a snail out of its shell, and bruising it small, pound into a plaster. Apply to the finger. This will ripen and break the impostume, and then it should be dressed like any other wound.

## ANOTHER FOR AN IMPOSTUME

283. Take water pimpernel and pound it well, and mix carefully with oil of roses. Apply as a plaster to the part.

## ANOTHER FOR AN IMPOSTUME

284. Take rue and wild valerian. Pound them well and boil with rosin and yellow wax. Apply as a plaster to the affected part. It is useful for all kinds of swellings in a finger or any other joint.

## ANOTHER FOR AN IMPOSTUME

285. Take rue, water pimpernel, southernwood, wild valerian, a snail and lard. Pound them into a plaster and apply to the part, changing every night. Others boil the bruised herbs in lard, adding the snail (bruised and boiled carefully) to the mixture, compounding the whole into a plaster, and so using it.

## ANOTHER FOR AN IMPOSTUME

286. Take a little sulphate of copper, dried and powdered. Mix it well with the yolk of eggs. Apply to the part and it will heal it quickly, easing the pain and reducing the swelling.

## TO IMPROVE THE SIGHT

287. Boil fennel in water, and wash your eyes with the same water morning and evening, and it will improve the sight for you.

## FOR A WEB IN THE EYE*

288. Take a cow's, a hare's, and an old cock's gall, with a small quantity of the blue matter formed of rue and celandine. You should have equal parts of each, the cow's gall only being in excess. They should be tempered together with wine. Being applied to the eye it removes the web.

*In the Proceedings of the Royal Society of Medicine: Section of Opthalmology, 11 October 11 1951, the President's Address was 'Of the Web in the Eye', which is the 'senile cataract'.*

## AGAINST INTOXICATION

289. Take a handful of betony and pound well, expressing in water and straining carefully. Drink some of this before you have taken any food or drink, and you will not get drunk that day.

## A GOOD EMETIC FOR THE HEAD AND STOMACH

290. Take three spoonfuls of the juice of betony for three mornings successively. Put in your nostrils with the feather tip of a wing, and it will be a good emetic for the head and stomach.

## FOR INTERMITTENTS AND FEVERS

291. Take dandelion and fumitory. Add to some drink, of which take a good quantity morning and noon. You will be certainly cured.

## TO DESTROY A CANCER

292. Take a piece of unbumt limestone, black pepper, orpiment* [called in Latin auripigmentum], strong vinegar, rue, honey, barley meal, equal parts of each. Boil in a pan or pot until they can be reduced to a powder, then they should be powdered and boiled a second time. This powder is good to destroy a cancer or scrofula.

* *Pughe adds:* Yellow sulphurate of Arsenic.

## ANOTHER TO DESTROY A CANCER

293. Take the root of the dragons*. Cut them small, then dry and make into a powder. Take nine pennyweights of this powder, and boil well in wine. Give it to the patient to drink, warm, for three days fasting, and it will cure him. I warrant him he will never have it again.

* *Pughe adds:* Arum dracunculus. *Dracunculus vulgaris is commonly known as Black Dragon, Snake Lily, Brlack Arum, Dragon Arum, Dragonwort and Dragons. Native to the Balkans and Greece, it must have been imported into medieval Britain. However, it is possible that Pughe's translation is wrong, and perhaps it refers to another herb far more commonly used in Britain. The Welsh is llysiau'r ddraig, 'dragon's herb'. Tarragon (Artimisia dracunculus) is known as Dragon's Wort (wort means plant). Also known as Dragon's Herb, the belief in the Doctrine of Signatures gave it its name. The serpentine shape of its root gave the belief that it could cure snake bites, so it was named dracunculus, Latin for little dragon. As such, Tarragon features in all the medieval herbals, whereas the Arum is not as commonly used.*

## FOR DEAFNESS

294. Take a small branch of ash, a foot in length, putting the middle part in the fire, and keeping the water proceeding from the two ends. Then take the juice of rhubarb, wine, and the fat of a newly caught eel. Take an equal part of these substances, mixing all together, and put in the ears as you go to sleep. It is also useful in these cases to drop some stale urine into the ears, covering it over with black wool.

## THUS IS A MAN PRESERVED FROM HYDROPHOBIA [*RABIES*]

295. Let him not eat cheese, nor butter, nor eggs, nor sea fish, nor beef, nor rye bread, nor new bread. Let him drink nothing but sweet milk, water, or buttermilk,

with a draught of wine or mead once in twenty four hours. Let him also refrain from venery*, and by help of God he will be preserved.

*The pursuit of sexual pleasure*

## FOR AN INCISED WOUND OR INJURY OF A TENDON, VEIN, ABDOMINAL WALLS, OR BONE, WHEN INFLAMING AND SUPPURATING

296. Take goat's milk and linseed. Boil them together, then take the milk of a one coloured cow and bean meal, and mix together. Boil it for a long period of time, then remove it and apply as a plaster to the affected part. Leave it there till the next day or longer, and it will reduce the swelling and pain, extract the venom from the flesh, promote the union of the tendons, remove dead flesh, disperse contusions, and procure sleep for the patient. If needful some healing salve should also be used.

## TO RE-OPEN A WOUND OR ABSCESS WHICH HAS CLOSED OVER, AND TO HEAL IT

297. Again, to the same ointment [as above]* add a portion of wax, rosin, black soap, a small quantity of honeysuckle leaves and plantain. Pound together, boil on the fire, strain through a cloth and keep in a pot. Apply this in the manner of a salve, and the wound will be healed.

*Pughe explains: i. e. the healing salve.*

## TO PROMOTE THE SECRETION OF URINE, THE GROWTH OF FLESH, SKIN, AND BONES

298. Take a handful of red roses, spring water, the juice of celandine, honey, juice of hemlock, fennel, tutsan, burdock, a spoonful of a suckling child's urine and red wine. Mix these ingredients together, warm them a little, and then remove from the fire, strain and keep. Let this be applied to a sloughing wound, and it will cleanse and heal it.

## FOR AN ILL-CONDITIONED ULCER

299. Take good cheese, and pound it carefully, mixing with some clear honey. Anoint the ulcer frequently with this, and cover it with cabbage leaves. This will cleanse it in three days, for it is excellent.

## FOR A WHITLOW

300. Take honey, yolk of eggs, and wheaten flour. Mix together and apply as a plaster to the diseased part as may be needful. It is indeed a good application.

## FOR A DISEASE OF THE LEG, CHARACTERISED BY GATHERING AND SUPPURATING, RED GRANULATIONS, SPREADING TOWARDS THE TOES, BEING OF A VIVID REDNESS

301. Procure three pennyworth of roses, two pennyworth of olive oil, a pennyworth of oil of turpentine, a spoonful of honey, a little wax, three pennyworth of red lead*, a little mutton or stag's suet, a small quantity of sulphate of copper in powder, and a spoonful or two of the blessed distillation,** or the

distillation of red wine***. Mix and temper them in a pot on the fire till the whole is thoroughly warmed. Anoint the disease with it and this will benefit it.

* *Lead tetroxide, a bright red pigment used in medieval manuscripts;* ** *Pughe adds:* Aqua Benedicta Rolandi; *** *Pughe adds:* Brandy.

## FOR AN OFFENSIVE SORE

302. Take barberry, called in Latin boxus* boiled in ale or wine. Wash the sore therewith and it will benefit it. Alternatively take the leaves and pound well with wine or mead, straining it under a press. Keep in an earthen vessel on the fire till it is warmed thoroughly, washing the sore therewith.

* *The Welsh is 'sydd yr ysbeinwydd'. Sudd (sydd) means juice, and ysbîn is barberry. The original Welsh entry for 'bocsws' is translated by Pughe as 'boxus', and is not in the GPC. Bocs is Welsh for box tree, and buxus in the Latin. It seems that this is European Barberry, Berberis vulgaris rather than box. Some however believe this to be bearberry, rather than barberry.*

## TO PREPARE AN OINTMENT FOR SCROFULA

303. Take yellow wax, rosin, suet, elecampane, and celandine. Pound them well together and boil, then strain through a clean cloth. Anoint the part to heal it.

## FOR SCROFULA

304. Take vervain and pound it well in a mortar, filling a vessel with it to the brim. Add as much water as will fill it, let it stand overnight, and then strain. Let this be taken as the sole drink. You may add white wine to the pounded herbs instead of water, and drink of it as much as you wish, once in the twenty-four hours.

Take vervain also and pound it small, with oil of olives, boiling together and straining under a press. After this, add to it some yellow wax, honey, and stag's suet, and boil until it becomes an ointment. Keep in a vessel and anoint the diseased part with it. If you also take the roots of this herb, wash it clean, dry it well, reduce it to powder, and mix it with wheaten flour in the proportion of a third, in order to make bread. Then subsist upon this bread and goat's milk as your only food, and you will recover sooner. This is well proven.

## A PLASTER TO REDUCE THE SWELLING, AND TO EXTRACT WORMS* FROM SCROFULOUS ULCERATIONS

305. Take the milk of a single-coloured cow and oatmeal. Boil well to the consistency of a child's pap, spreading it thickly on a cloth, and adding honey on the surface. This will extract the worms and reduce the swelling, remove venom from the flesh, remove the hardness, and heal the sore. This is proven.

* *Pughe notes:* These 'worms' were generally imaginary, being only portions of disintegrated structures.

## FOR HEAT AND INFLAMMATION IN THE LIVER, HYSTERIA, PAIN IN THE LOINS, AND PAIN IN A MAN'S SHOULDERS

306. Take centaury and livergreen*, pounding them well, and filling a vessel with them. Add an equal quantity of water and wine. Let it stand covered for about six hours, then strain under a press, and drink as much as you can, while fasting night and morning. Take for food a broth made of mutton, and the following herbs:

166

borage, lettuce, fennel, parsley, and a little honey. Let this be your only food. Make also a lotion** with the ashes of wood, fern, or nettles, and boil in it two or three pennyworth of lard. Let it cool until the next day, then remove the surface and preserve in a vessel. Anoint with this your shoulders and other painful parts, then by God's help you will recover.

*Llysiau'r afu means herbs of the liver, so is possibly Liverwort, Marchantia polymorpha. However it is more likely to be Hepatica nobilis, also known as Common Hepatica, Anemone Hepatica, Liverwort or Liverleaf. It is named after its leaves, which like the human liver have three lobes. (The Greek for liver is hepar). Thus, following the Doctrine of Signatures, the plant was used for liver disorders; ** The original is leisy, from lleisy (modern lleisw), meaning a decoction, lotion or lye, which Pughe translated as 'lay'.*

## FOR A BURN

307. Mix your own urine with cow dung, and let it clear. Pour this portion into a vessel, and wash the part with it.

## FOR SWINEPOX*

308. It is an eruptive skin disease forming white vesicles, from which clear water is poured forth. Take broom seed and lard, boiling and straining them. Mix two penny-worth of black soap well with it, and anoint your whole body with the mixture. It is truly good.

*\* Swinepox is the commonest disease among pigs, caused by the suipoxvirus. Edward Jenner was told by locals that people worked around animals and who had caught swinepox or cowpox would not get smallpox. This led to the validation of the discovery of vaccination. Because cowpox and swinepox are caused by viruses from the same family as smallpox, immunity to either will give immunity to smallpox as well.*

## FOR A WOMAN AT THE CHANGE OF LIFE

309. Make gruel with oatmeal and spring water. Add a pinch of cumin, and a pinch of the stone called cryth, or in Latin creta [chalk]*. When this is not procurable, use limestone powdered as fine as possible, and sifted through a fine cloth or silk. Mix this with the gruel, and let her take a cupful of it at the end of each day for a week, and it will be useful to her.

*\* Both oats and chalk can help with bone formation, and female bone density can rapidly diminish in mid-life.*

## TO EXTRACT A TOOTH WITHOUT PAIN

310. Seek some ants with their eggs, and crush to a powder. Have this powder blown into the tooth through a quill, and be careful that it does not touch another tooth.

## FOR TREMBLING OF THE HANDS

311. Put pounded mugwort in water overnight, and wash your hands in it. It will benefit you if you wash your back and nape of the neck with this water. It will strengthen you miraculously.

## FOR HYSTERIA

312. Take feverfew, wormwood, and the inner bark of ash. Boil well in perennial spring water [i.e from a spring which does not dry up in summer]. Strain, and

drink while fasting for three mornings. This will procure you a recovery, so that you will not be afflicted ever again.

## FOR BLEEDING OF THE NOSE
313. Take a handful of nettles, and put in a cloth to your nostrils, plugging your nostrils with some of the same. It is good.

## ANOTHER FOR BLEEDING OF THE NOSE
314. Take a small sheet of iron and put it in the fire until hot, but not red hot. Drop the blood upon it, and when there is a sufficient quantity, scrape it off, and blow into the nostrils with a quill. This will restrain the bleeding from the nose, from a wound, or a cut, wherever it is upon a man's body.

## FOR A PATIENT WHO IS BURNT
315. Take a handful each of mallows, snail shells, pennywort and linseed. Pound them in a brass mortar, and mix them together, so that they are ultimately incorporated. Apply this to the swelling or sore, and retain it there continually, never leaving it uncovered. If you like, you may syringe it with soft water to wash it. In consequence of the plaster, a watery discharge will come from the nose. It is a good application.

## TO KNOW WHETHER THE PATIENT WILL LIVE OR DIE
316. Anoint the patient's heel with some hog's fat, and give the remainder to a dog to eat. If the dog will eat it, the patient will live, if not he will die.

*This is missing from Pughe:*

## I WYBOD AI BOD GWRAIG YN FEICHIOG AI NAD YW
317. Gadewch iddi wneuthur dwr mewn presen neu gopren, a dodwch ddynhaden yn y dwr, ag os bydd beichiog hi a fydd yn llanw ysblottau gwaedlyd.

## TO KNOW WHETHER A WOMAN IS PREGNANT OR NOT
Have her urinate in a brass or copper vessel. Place a nettle in the urine, and if she is pregnant it will be covered with bloody spots.

## TO CAUSE THE HAIR TO GROW
318. Take barberry*, and fill an iron pot with it. Then fill the pot with as much water as it will contain, and boil on a slow fire until reduced to half. With this water, wash your head morning and evening. Take care that the wash does not touch any part where hair should not grow.
*Berberis vulgaris. One is tempted to try this, but aged at two-thirds of a century it is probably not worth it...*

## ANOTHER WAY TO CAUSE THE HAIR TO GROW
319. Take two spoonfuls of olive oil, two spoonfuls of new honey, and an onion as large as a pigeon's egg. Pound them together in a stone mortar until it becomes an ointment, and anoint your head with it night and morning. Wear a leather cap until the hair is grown. It is best to pound the onion well before it is added to the ointment.

168

## TO REMOVE HAIR SO THAT IT DOES NOT GROW AGAIN

320. Take ants with their eggs, and reduce to powder. Mix the seed of henbane in powder with it, and apply to the place required. Rub it on well until the part is warm, twice a day. This will destroy the hair at the roots so that it will not grow in that place again. You may mix it with water so as to form a paste, and anoint the place with it night and morning.

## TO DESTROY PEDICULI [HAIR LICE]

321. Take gum resin, called olibanum, and lard. Boil them together and anoint the head, or any other part requiring it. This will destroy them.

## FOR FRECKLES OF THE FACE

322. Anoint your face with a hare or bull's blood at night, before you sleep. Wash it in the morning with some butter-milk.*

   * *The remedy 2:181 does not include butter-milk.*

## TO EXTRACT A TOOTH

323. Take ivy gum* and ivy leaves, and burn them into a powder in a new earthenware pot. Mix this powder with the juice of the herb petty spurge**, and insert the paste in the tooth so as to fill the cavity. It will cause the tooth to fall from your jaw, but have a care that it does not touch another tooth.

   * *Ivy gum exudes from the incised bark, and was sold as the gum-resin Gummiresina Hederae in yellowish or red-brown, irregular pieces by apothecaries; **Euphorbia peplus, Milkweed has a milky sap.*

## FOR STRANGURY*

324. Pound mallow leaves and garlic together with white wine. Drink it, and in any case you will pass water.

   * *Slow and painful urination caused by muscular spasms of the urethra and bladder.*

## HERE IS A METHOD OF PREPARING A STOMACHIC BEER WHICH IS USEFUL FOR PARALYSIS, SHAKING PALSY, LATENT AGUE, FULLY DEVELOPED INTERMITTENTS, COLDNESS ABOUT THE HEART, RHEUMATISM, CARDIALGIA, STRANGURY, HERNIA HUMORALIS* AND COLD IN THE NERVES AND VEINS

325. Take a handful each of rosemary, sage, agrimony, bedstraw, hyssop, both leaves and branches. Add the roots of mallows, elecampane, radish, saxifrage, a handful of each. Pound them together well in a mortar. Boil the mixture in three gallons of strong ale wort until it is reduced into one gallon, and remove it from the fire to cool. Strain through a clean linen cloth. Take a quart of pure honey and add to this wort, boiling until it is reduced to a quart, meanwhile skimming it carefully.

Remove it to cool, and take six gallons of strong new ale, dregs and yeast included, and put in a clean brewing tub, cover it and let it stand for three days and nights. Then put it in a strong cask, and take a pennyworth of cloves, a pennyworth of ginger, a pennyworth of grains of paradise, a little fennel seed, a pennyworth of caraway, a small quantity of the seed of English galingale, and as much as the whole of canelle bark. Powder them as fine as the finest wheaten meal, and put them in a small linen bag. Hang this in the cask, (a small stone being included in the bag to weigh it down) and leave it there. Drink some of this liquor the first thing in the morning, and the last thing in the evening. It is as safe for a man to drink it as spring water.

### The following are the special Virtues of these various herbs:

Rosemary is a stimulant; sage will remove fever; bedstraw is for paralysis; hyssop for the chest; agrimony for the bowels; saxifrage for the bladder; radish for the stomach; elecampane for the joints; cloves and ginger for the nerves; pink** for the kidneys; grains of paradise for the brain; and galingale and canelle for the lungs and veins. It is proper that every person should take this drink for the cure of the diseases above mentioned. If he should be the subject of any other disease, let him add the proper herbs for it, and take this drink frequently. You will in consequence have a healthy body, a more youthful look, greater elasticity of limbs, a stronger sight, a more determined will, more freedom in walking, and a sweeter breath. This is the best beer of all, and the healthiest drink in the world.

* *Inflammation of the testicles;* ** *The Welsh is Ysnoden Fair, which is English or Sweet Galingale.*

## A GENTLE APERIENT

326. Take a hen's egg, removing the embryo, and mix with some sound ale, both egg and ale together. Drink it while fasting in the morning, then fast subsequently for three hours and you will receive benefit.

## FOR NAUSEA OF STOMACH IN CONSEQUENCE OF COLDNESS IN THE SAME, THE FOOD BEING REJECTED, AND THE BOWELS CONFINED

327. Take two cupfuls of white wine, or an emetic every other day, take treacle, a quart of red wine, a pennyworth of mustard, three pennyworth of aloes, boil these ingredients together and keep in a vessel. Take two spoonfuls warm in the morning while fasting. Take a pennyworth of pepper, two pennyworth of fennel, boil them in clarified honey. The leaves of fennel are superior to the seed.

## FOR A DRY OR OBSTRUCTING COUGH, SO SEVERE THAT THE FOREHEAD BECOMES COVERED WITH PERSPIRATION, BUT WITHOUT ANY EXPECTORATION

328. Obtain these ingredients - a pennyworth of pepper, a pennyworth of fennel seed, two pennyworth of anise-seed, a pennyworth of cumin seed, two pennyworth of liquorice root, a pennyworth of canella bark and a pennyworth of grains of paradise. Powder these finely, and boil in a quart of honey upon the fire till it becomes cloudy*. Remove and keep in a clean vessel. Take a spoonful while fasting every** morning, and another spoonful the last thing before going to bed. Avoid a meat diet, and eating nothing but keep to food made of corn.

* *The Welsh is 'a thynn i lawr a dod mewn llestr glân i gadw'. The translation by Pughe is 'a clear bay colour', but there is no reference to clear in the text.*

** *Pughe translates as 'in the' instead of 'every'*

170

## FOR SPASM IN THE LEG OR ANOTHER MEMBER

329. Take a pennyworth of black soap, three pennyworth of quicksilver [*mercury*], two pennyworth of oil of olives, frankincense, four pennyworth of the vital water called the blessed distillation* and boar's lard. Compound these ingredients effectively until they become as white as a neck cloth**, let the painful part be rubbed briskly with this ointment morning and evening. It is proven.

*\* Pughe again footnotes:* Aqua Benedicta; *\*\* Cwrsi means head-dress or handkerchief.*

## FOR A COUGH

330. Take a quart of milk, and a pennyworth of garlic. Then pound together, boiling in milk and straining. Drink as you can of this, and use garlic also with your food. Let lean and fresh meat be your diet.

## FOR ARTICULAR RHEUMATISM*, AND PAIN IN THE HIPS OR THE SHOULDER BLADE WHEN WALKING

331. Take two pennyworth of black soap, three pennyworth of quicksilver [mercury, which is poisonous], three pennyworth of water of life**, and a pound of red boar's lard if this can be procured. When the lard is molten, cast in the black soap and strong water***. Mix greatly, and when cold cast in the quicksilver, and rub the ingredients together till they are as white as lawn.\*\*\*\* Rub the painful part with this ointment by the fire night and morning, as long as required.

*\*This is when the cartilage in the joints becomes worn out; \*\* Pughe notes here:* Aqua vita. *It was prepared at this time by distilling ale, small wine, and the lees of strong wine, in which anise-seed had been macerated. The same name has been also given to brandy and spirit of wine; \*\*\* The Welsh is edlyn distyll, which seems to mean distilled potion, referring to the water of life; \*\*\*\* Pughe's use of 'lawn' here refers to its meaning as fine linen or cambric.*

## FOR THE PLICA POLONICA*

332. Shave the head once a week for a year, and wash every night with a strong decoction of sage, then every morning with cold sea water, or with salt and water once a week. Anoint your head with a hen's or an eel's fat. When you have so anointed it, apply the following cataplasm as warm as possible to your head. Take the whitest fermented wheaten bread, boil in sheep's milk, and add to it a spoonful or two of honey, a large spoonful of oil of chestnuts, and the yolk of an egg. Incorporate these ingredients well together, and apply as a plaster to your head. Let it remain there twenty-four hours, and when you have removed it wash your head well with a decoction of fennel and soap, scrubbing it carefully. Let your diet be an abundance of milk, and a sparing quantity of meat; or roasted or boiled apples, with milk, as often as you can procure them.

*\* The Welsh is RHAG GWALLT YN CYNNYGLU, SEF YN TYFU'N GYMMHLETH FAL NAS GELLIR EI GRIBO. Cyngheglog means 'interlaced', and examples of its use in Geiriadur Prifysgol Cymru refer to the long hair just above the hoof of an animal. The Welsh term for this applied to human hair is 'clymu' and 'clymau', knots. The original Welsh meaning is possibly: 'For knotted hair that grows twisted together so that it cannot be combed.' Plica Neuropathica was first described in Poland in the 19th century, thus Pughe's term. It is a rare condition in which hair shafts become tangled, forming a matted*

*appearance. Often plica polonica will present as a sticky moist mass, and attempts to comb out the problem will prove impossible. Plica Polonica sufferers may well have erythema (red inflamed skin) which may be accompanied by a bad odour.*

*Missing from Pughe's translation.*

### RHAG POB GWAYW YN Y CYMALAU, A'R ESGYRN, A'R GLINIAU, A'R CEFN

333. Cais sebon du werth tair ceiniog, gwerth grôd o arian byw, gwerth grôd o eliw gliwydden, a gwerth grôd o distyll bendigaid, a bloneg twrch neu liw arall, a maedd yn dda mewn blwch pridd yn gaedig, ag ymelïa ag ef wrth y tân nos a bore.

### FOR EVERY PAIN IN THE JOINTS, BONES, KNEES AND BACK

333. Take three pence worth of black soap (coal-tar soap), a groat's worth of quicksilver, a groat's worth of ointment of lime twigs, and a groat's worth of blessed distillation and the lard of a wild boar or other oil. Mix well in a closed earthenware vessel, and daub yourself with it in front of the fire, evening and morning.

*Missing from Pughe's translation.*

### RHAG DIFANT NATTUR, SEF NATTUR DYN YN YMOLLWNG YN Y WIALEN O'I ANFODD

334. Cais ychydig o blwm a phwya'n deneu yn dewder gwenhithyn, bydded dau ddyrnfedd ei hyd, a hanner dyrnfedd lai o led, a gwna dwll y nail benn iddo, a dod linyn drwydd a chlym am dy fain gefn erwydd y llynin hwn a oera dy nattur, yna cymmer risgl nesa i'r pren o'r derw ag o'r drain duon ddyrnaid o bob un, a brew yn dda, a dod o fêl ai gwnelo yn felus, a chymmer lwyaid fechan o had anis yn byloraid, a un faint o had ffunel pyloraid, a hanner hynny o ganel pyloraid, a bwrw y rhain ar y berwyn, ai yfed yn ddiod dri bore a thair nos, ag na chymmer arall o ddiod; profedig yw.

### FOR LOSS OF NATURE, NAMELY MAN'S NATURE DROPPING IN THE PENIS AGAINST HIS WILL

334. Take a little lead and pound thinly to the thickness of a grain of wheat. Make it two handbreadths long and half a handbreadth wide, and make a hole on one side. Place a cord through and tie to the small of your back because this cord will cool your nature. Then take a handful of the bark nearest the wood from the oak and blackthorn and boil well, and add honey and make it sweet. Take a small spoonful of powdered aniseed and half that amount of powdered cinnamon, and toss these onto the foam*, and drink it for three days and three nights, and do not take any other drink. It has been proven.

*\*berwyn means foaming*

### FOR PULMONARY COUGH

335. Obtain the roots of mallows, figs, and elecampane in powder. Make it into a confection with honey, by incorporating together in a mortar. Take a large spoonful, at least morning and night, two hours before and after food, and accustom yourself to a diet of goats' milk, and apples.

## TO EXPEL THE POISON OF ERUPTIVE DISEASES FROM THE BLOOD. SCROFULA, TUBERCLES OF THE LUNGS, ALL ERUPTIONS OF THE SKIN, AND ALL PHLEGM OF THE HEAD AND STOMACH, WITH MANY OTHER DISEASES OF THE HEAD AND EYES, COME IN CONSEQUENCE OF THIS ERUPTIVE POISON

336. Take cleavers,* (which are recognised by their round seed which adhere to the clothes when ripe) and pound them well. Fill up an earthen vessel with this, and pour upon the cleavers as much boiling spring water as the vessel will admit. Let this stand for an hour and strain through a clean linen cloth. Let this be your only drink for nine days. When cleavers cannot be obtained, water-cress may be used. For food take milk, and as many roasted or boiled apples as you can, with the milk, and a slice of wheaten bread and honey. Do not take any meat except fresh mutton, or soup made of mutton, with cleavers, water-cress, and white field trefoil** being boiled in it. Boiled nettles, or water-cress and vinegar should be taken with the meat instead of bread. It is proven.

* *Pughe addends:* It is remarkable that Cleavers has again come into much credit as an anti scorbutic. The whole section is worthy of attention; ** *This is probably White Clover, Trifolium repens*

### FOR DERANGEMENT OF MIND

337. Take linseed and pound thoroughly. Make a thin gruel with it (as you would oatmeal porridge), with a cupful of pure water. Pound and mix betony with this gruel, finally removing the herbs, then boil the gruel till it has become as thick as porridge. Upon some of this porridge cast powdered betony, aloes wood*, fennel, and anise-seed. Let the patient drink three or four spoonfuls daily, and he should be put to sleep in a dark room. It is proven.

   * *Pren alwys*

### FOR COUGH AND DYSPNOEA

338. Take the root of elecampane, two pennyworth of black pepper, and the same of the roots of mallows. Let them be powdered and made into a confection with clarified honey. Take as much as a pigeon's egg the first thing in the morning, and the last at night. It is proven.

*This is missing from Pughe:*

### RHAG DŴR RHWNG CIG A CHROEN

339. Cais o'r ferllys ddau ddyrnaid, a phwya'n dda, au berwi drwy ymenyn, ag yn dwym dod ynddo ynogydfaint wer manllwyn, a gad ei doddi, ag a hwnnw ira'r lle or bor dolur yn dda da.

### FOR WATER BETWEEN FLESH AND SKIN

339. Take two handfuls of parsley and pound well and boil in butter. Place in it the same amount of warm mutton-suet and leave it to melt, and with that bathe the sore part very well.

## TO DISPERSE SWELLINGS FROM HANDS OR FEET
340. Take red nettles, hemlock, and sage, and with these make fomentation for the patient. Surround the affected part with it, and wash it with your own water* daily. It is proven.

* *The Welsh is dŵr (water), but presumably this is urine because of the possessive case.*

## TO RELIEVE CONSTIPATION
341. Take the roots of gladwyn, the inner bark of elder and the juice of house leek. Pound them well in a mortar, and mix them with old ale. Then strain through a clean cloth and give to the patient to drink when fasting. This will speedily relieve him of his constipation, and he should not take any other drink until his bowels are moved.

## FOR A HAEMATURIA [*BLOOD IN THE URINE*]
342. Take fennel seed and the seed of parsley, or the leaves when the seed cannot be obtained. Pound them well and mix with goat's whey. Strain carefully, and let the patient drink a quart of this for fifteen days, night and morning. Let him avoid salt and sour [acid diet], and take fresh food [bwyd can also mean meat as well as food], light and warm, and well-leavened wheaten bread. Also give a broth made with watercress and coarse oatmeal, boiled using spring water. Let this be used and he will recover.*

*The Welsh is 'a gweglydd hallt a sur, ag arfer o fwyd îr, ysgon, a gwresog, a bara gwenith a digon o lefain ynddo, a chawl trwy ferw'r ffynnon, a dwr ffynnon, a rhynion ceirch, ag arfer hwnnw ag iach fyddi.' Pughe's translation is 'Let him avoid salt and acid diet, and use light and hot fresh meat with well-fermented wheaten bread. Also make a broth with parsley and oatmeal, boiled in water*. Let this be used and he will recover.'*

*This is missing in Pughe:*

## I DYNNERU ARENNAU A FONT WEDI SIGO* NEU HWYDDO
343. Cymmer ychydig o floneg, a chymysg ef a dyrnaid o ruw pwyedig, a dyrnaid o'r chwerwyn pentwyn** yn bwyedig, a pheth llinhad pwyedig, ai faeddu yn blaster, a dod ar liain wrth y dolur; profedig yw.

## TO SOOTHE KIDNEYS THAT ARE BRUISED OR SWOLLEN
Take a little lard and mix with a handful of powdered rue and a handful of powdered mustard, and a little powdered linseed. Mix to a poultice, and place on a cloth on the wound. It is proven.

*sigo means strain, bruise, hurt, damage, collapse*
**chwerwyn (pen) trwyn is mustard*

## FOR UNCONSOLIDATED CANCER*
344. Take dog's dung which has become white, and glass. Powder the glass as fine as you can, mixing the two together with some oil of olives (- rancid oil is the

174

best). Heat them together on the fire, then apply to the disease, and the patient will be cured.

*This is Pughe's translation. The Welsh is 'RHAG CANGCAR A FO HEB DYFY YNGHYD' - For a Cancer that has Not Developed Fully?*

## FOR A CARBUNCLE OR CHRONIC ULCER

345. Take a portion of virgin wax*, the same quantity of frankincense, and the same again of pitch, with half as much of walnut wood. Pound these four ingredients, adding some verdigris. Grind them fine and put into a pan. Melt, and stir them well so that they do not adhere to the pan. When they have completely melted and become incorporated, remove from the fire, strain carefully and apply to the disease. It is truly useful.

*One assumes that this is wax which has never been used. This author did Google "virgin wax" but none of the results are repeatable in a family book.*

## FOR THE FRENCH CARBUNCLE* OR PLAGUE

346. In dangerous times when contagious distempers prevail, this is how the contagion can be avoided. Obtain three small branches of rue, and one of walnut**, and a fig or two. Eat them together and you will be preserved. It is proven.

*The Welsh is Y Wharren Ffrengig, but I cannot source a translation as yet for Wharren. The French Disease, or French Pox, was syphilis in later medieval times, but originally the French Disease was 'The Great Pox', the Black Death which spread across Europe (1338-1351), killing a third of the population. The last major outbreak on Britain of bubonic plague was the Great Plague of London in 1665-1666; **The original Welsh is collen ffreinig. Collen is hazel, and cneuen ffrengig is now walnut. However, in the past the walnut was either collen Ffreinig or Ffrengig (French/foreign hazel).*

## ANOTHER TO CURE THE PLAGUE

347. Take the faeces of a young child between ten and twelve years of age, and reduce into fine powder. Then put two spoonfuls at most of the powder in a cupful of white wine. Let it be administered to the patient six hours at the most after he has sickened. The sooner the better it is done. Many have proved this.

## FOR THE CRUSTED TETTER*, CALLED KING'S WORM

348. Get ivy leaves, pound and boil in mutton and the lees of stale urine. Boil them well and strain, then mix two pennyworth of black soap with the miixture, and anoint the part with it.

*Pughe footnotes this as impetigo. This is a highly contagious skin infection, often found in pre-school children. The Welsh is Y Ddarwden Fawr, meaning Great Ringworm. Crusted tetter, or impetigo, consists of mattery pimples developed on a highly inflamed skin, appearing chiefly on the extremities. It is either acute or chronic. The eruption in the acute form is preceded by a slight fever, and in about thirty-six hours red spots appear on the skin, accompanied by heat and tingling. On the second day, the centres of these spots are raised by the pus contained, to which the name of phyzacious pustule is given. This stage is accompanied by much pain. Maturation occurs from the fourth to the sixth day, and the disease usually terminates in two weeks. The chronic form is more common, and afflicts young children more often than adults. The disease was still called king's worm in early nineteenth century America. I am not sure whether this is a ringworm (tinea capitis - a fungal disease), or a form of impetigo (a bacterial deisease) treatment.*

*This was partially expurgated in the original text:*

## RHAG GWARD YN CERDDED YN EDLIF I FYNYDD AG I WARED, NEU'R BOSTWM WAED

349. Cymmer gribau sanffrêd, a'r geidwad, au crafu, au pylori, a bwrw megis crimped o'r llysiau mewn wi giar, i rostio, ai fwytta cyn bo ef called, ag arfer hyn bob dydd lawn wythnos neu ragor, ag arfer o bylor y mâs ar dy gawl a'th ddiod yn dwym bob dydd nys bych iach, a bwydau ysgawn, îr, gwresog, a bara gwenith drwyddo, a digon o lefain ynddo, a da yw. *Da hefyd yw'r feddyginiaeth hon rag yr hadred, sef traul nattur dyn o'r wialen o'i anfodd.*

FOR HAEMATEMESIS [*VOMITING OF BLOOD*]

349. Take betony and sage. Scrape and powder, then cast a pinch of this powder into a hen's egg, roast it and eat before it is hard. Do this daily for a week or more. Use some acorn powder with your soup, and drink this warm daily until you recover. Let your diet be light, fresh, and warm, with well leavened wheaten bread, as it is beneficial. This is also useful medicinal treatment for seminal weakness.*

*\* This is spermatorrhoea, or nocturnal emissions. Pughe omits the last part of this paragraph, which is here translated as 'the unwilling loss of man's nature from the penis.'*

*This is missing from Pughe:*

## RHAG YR HADRED\*, SEF TRAUL NATTUR DYN O'R WIALEN O'I ANFODD

350. Cymmer gregyn oestrys, a llosg a phylora nhwy, a phob afal a chymmer ei fywyn a dod atto'r pylor\*\*, a gwna'n belenau, a chymmer ddwy belen neu dair bob bore'n gyntaf, ag yn ddiweddaf y nos dros o naw i bymtheg diwarnod.

## FOR SPERMATORRHOEA, THAT IS UNWILLING LOSS OF MAN'S NATURE FROM THE PENIS

350. Take oyster shells, and burn them and make into a powder. Bake an apple and take its core (or pulp) and add the powder to it, and make into pellets [tablets]. Take two or three pellets first thing every morning and last thing at night, over a period of nine to fourteen days.

*\*Hadred also means gonorrhoea, but is spermatorrhoea here; \*\*Pylor can mean core or pulp.*

## FOR SPASMS

351. Take sixteen figs and sixty nine bees. Remove the heads, legs, and wings from the bees and reduce to a powder. Add the bee powder to the figs, with as much honey as may be needed. Pound the whole together, and make into pills of the size of haws [*hawthorn berries*]. Let the patient have one at the commencement of the spasm, and another smaller pill at the end. Meanwhile he should be kept walking about. This treatment should be persevered with, until the patient recovers.

## RHAG MAGL* AR LYGAID

352. Pob wi yn galed a holl e far ei hyd, a dod ynddo gymaint a chneuen o goprys gwynn yn frwd, ag erbyn y diferon mewn pottel, a dod ddiferyn yn y llygad; profedig yw.

## FOR A CATARACT ON THE EYE

352. Bake an egg hard and split it lengthwise. Put in it as much as a nut of hot white copperas**, and collect the drops in a bottle, and place a drop on the eye. It has been proven.

*\* Magl now means cataract, and albugo means stye, but the original meaning may have been stye; \*\* A 1464 cure also involves zinc sulphate, white copperas, as a cure for sore eyes.*

## A COLLYRIUM

353. Take a quart of spring water, situated in a shady place, and add to it as much in quantity as a nut or two of lime sulphate. Boil for twenty-four hours in a well-covered earthenware pot. For an hour it should boil briskly, and for an hour it should cool on the ground, then it should be strained through a fine clean linen cloth. It should be kept in a bottle, and it will be none the worse for seven years. A drop at a time should be inserted in the patient's eye.

## AN OINTMENT TO CLEAR THE EYE

354. Obtain daisy, eyebright, strawberry leaves, red fennel, betony, milfoil, field scabious, knapweed, roots of the burr-reed, honeysuckle leaves, ground ivy, and vervain. Take equal parts of each, and pound well with butter. Let them stand for a week, and on the ninth day boil them well, finally straining through a clean linen cloth. Keep the ointment in a well-covered glass vessel, and insert as much as a grain of wheat of it in the eye. It should be used for two days and nights in order to remove an opacity, web, or membrane from the eye. This ointment should be put in the eye on the third night, and it will become clear and bright. It is proved.

## TO PREVENT SPEAKING DURING SLEEP

355. Take the seed or leaves of rue, and pound with vinegar until it becomes a mass. Then mix it well in old ale, strain through a clean linen, and let the patient drink it.

## TO PREVENT DREAMING

356. Take vervain, and hang about a man's neck, or let him drink some of the juice in going to bed. Certainly he will not dream if he does so.

## TO RELIEVE THE PHLEGM IN BRONCHITIS

357. Take unsalted butter and honey in equal parts. Mix together carefully, and anoint your chest with it. It is a good remedy.

## ANOTHER FOR THE SAME THING

358. Take wild celery, and boil in good wine vinegar. Wash your chest with the hot vinegar, and apply the boiled herbs to your chest for three or four hours.

## FOR A PUNCTURED WOUND IN A JOINT FROM A THORN OR NEEDLE, THE SAME BEING HEALED OVER

359. Take the finest wheaten flour and temper it with white wine. Then boil the mixture until it becomes thick. Bind this about the injured part as hot as the patient can bear it, and this will open the puncture, extracting the corruption and poison. In the absence of wine, use good ale.

## A MEDICAMENT FOR ULCERS IN A LEG, ARM, OR OTHER PART

360. Take water cress, wash clean and boil in pure water until it becomes tender. Then pound well in a mortar. Put the pounded cress in a clean frying-pan on the fire, mixed with a stag's or buck's tallow, or with mutton suet and a quantity of the lees of wine, and wheat bran. Fry the whole together for a poultice, and apply warm to the painful part. Do this three or four times, as may be needed.

## THINGS THAT ARE USEFUL FOR THE BRAIN

361 Smelling musk and camomile, drinking wine moderately, eating the leaves of sage frequently, keeping the head warm, washing the hands frequently, walking moderately, sleeping moderately, listening frequently to a little music and singing, smelling red roses, washing the eyebrows with rose water, drinking water in going to sleep, reading a little before going to sleep, and a light diet.

## THINGS THAT ARE HURTFUL TO THE BRAIN

362. For all brains the following things are hurtful: gluttony, drunkenness, late eating, much sleeping after food, tainted air, anger, depressed spirits, much standing bare-headed, eating too much or hastily, too much warmth, excessive watching, too much cold, curds, all kinds of nuts, frequent bathing, onions, garlic, yawning, smelling a white rose, excess of venery, too much music, singing and reading, strong drink before sleeping, restless sleep, too frequent fasting, frequent wet feet.

## FOR A BURN OR SCALD

363. Take the white of an egg, lay it on a pewter plate and mix with a little frankincense*, rubbing them together into a uniform consistency. Then take some fine linen and dip in some oil of olives, the beechnut oil**, or some other oil most easily obtained. Apply the same linen to the part. Spread the ointment of white of eggs and frankincense over it.

*This is a little confusing, as the Welsh is elyf carreg, meaning rich stone, and the carreg suffix is not used elsewhere when describing frankincense; **Pughe calls this 'the oil of pinetops' and footnotes that it is turpentine. None of the trees which produce turpentine oil are native to Britain. The Welsh is eliw cnau'r ffawydd, the oil of beechnuts.

## AN OINTMENT FOR CONFUSED NOISE IN THE HEAD, HINDERING HEARING*

364. Take a head of garlic, then peel and perforate it five or six times around its middle, and dip it in new honey. Insert it in your ear, covering it over with black wool, and rest each night on the other side. Let this remain seven or eight days, and it will remove the noise from the head, and restore the hearing.

*This may be tinnitus.

*This is missing from Pughe:*

## RHAG Y FRECH FAWR*

365. Cymmer berllys yr hêl**, a thorr, a phwya nhwy yn fân, a rho mewn pot o sentdradoles*** a dŵr ffynnon, dod yndo ymenyn a halen, a gwna gawl o honynt, ag yf o hano unwaith neu ddwy yn yr wythnos.

## FOR POX, SYPHILIS

365. Take wild celery and cut and pound it small, place in a pot of sentdradoles and spring water, and add butter and salt. Make a broth and drink it once or twice a week.

    * *y frech fawr: pox, venereal disease, syphilis; **perllys yr hêl: wild celery, smallage, Apium graveolens; ***the meaning of sentdradoles is as yet unknown.*

*This is missing from Pughe:*

## ARALL RHAG YR UN PETH

366. Cymmer biod dri neu bedwar o honynt, a hollt hwynt a chyllell, a rho mewn crochan distyllydd y pluf a'r perfedd a'r cwbl o honynt, ag a'r dwr distyll, neu'r edlyn a gei o honynt golch y dolur, ag yn amgenach yr wyneb, a'r ddwy feddyginiaeth yma sydd brofedig.


## ANOTHER FOR THE SAME PURPOSE [POX]

366. Take three or four magpies and open them with a knife. Place the feathers and the entrails and everything in a distiller's pot [a still]. With the distilled liquid, or the potion taken from them wash the sore, and better still the face [surface], and both treatments are proven.

## FOR A BURN

367. Take linseed oil, and apply to the affected part with a feather. It will extract the fire, and heal the injury in as beautiful a way as any other remedy.

## FOR THE STONE OR STRANGURY

368. Take a quart of white wine and make a posset fromit. Remove the curds, and add four pennyweights of the scrapings of white soap to the whey. Boil and drink it as warm as you can. It is really useful.

## FOR RETENTION OF URINE

369. Take a flint, heat it white in the fire, and warm your drink of strong ale with it.

## A DIURETIC

370. Take the fourth part of a handful of parsley, and as much again of bronze fennel. Bruise them well and put in a cupful of old ale. Drink the ale and it will benefit you. It is proven.

## TO RESTRAIN BLEEDING FROM RECENT WOUNDS

371. Take the leaves of leeks, and pound with honey and wheaten flour. Incorporate these together carefully away from the fire, and apply cold to the wound.

## A GOOD COLLYRIUM

372. Take rotten apples, and strain with some spring water. Wash your eyelids with this, and it will cleanse and brighten your eyes.

## ANOTHER COLLYRIUM

373. Take sulphate of zinc and dissolve in spring water. When you go to bed, wash your eyelids therewith, dropping some into your eyes.

## FOR DISEASE IN THE SHOULDERBLADE, THE LIVER, AND THE BREAST

374. Habituate yourself to eat nine peppers daily*, and it will do you good.

 * This must mean peppercorns. The Welsh is pubur, now spelt as pupur or pybyr.

## FOR ALL KINDS OF HEAT AND INFLAMMATION IN THE FACE, EVEN IF IT IS ERYSIPELAS

375. Take a quart of smithy water*, a handful of sage leaves, a handful of elm leaves, or of the inner bark of elm, and a pennyworth of frankincense. Boil these together until half has evaporated, and keep in an earthenware vessel. Anoint the face with it.

* *Water was kept in a large 'slack tub', and used by a blacksmith to quench hot metal. The term slack seems to come from 'slaking' the heat of the iron.*

## FOR PAIN IN THE LIMBS, BACK, OR SHOULDERS

376. Take the blessed distillation,* or brandy, and sheep's foot oil. Put in a vessel and warm together well. Anoint the painful part with this, covering the patient with an abundance of clothes afterwards.

*Pughe yet again notes:* Aqua Benedicta Rulandi

## AN APPROVED REMEDY FOR A PAIN

377. Pound wild celery, and put in some blessed distillation, or brandy, strain and add some molten boar's lard to it. Mix it well and anoint the painful part therewith.

## FOR PAIN OR SWELLING IN THE THIGHS

378. Take a quart of sage wine, and a handful of thyme, and boil together. When half-boiled, add some fresh butter, then boil down from a quart to a pint. When you go to bed wash your feet well. Then dip a linen cloth into the liquid, and apply three or four times to the painful members as hot as you can bear it, for six or seven nights. It will do much good without doubt. If you have any brandy or blessed distillation, add a spoonful to the liquid when sufficiently boiled, mixing it well.

180

## TO RESTRAIN HAEMORRHAGE FROM A WOUND ON THE NOSE

379. Take an old linen cloth, and wet it thoroughly in red wine vinegar, or if you have none, then in any vinegar. Burn the linen and apply the resulting powder to the wound. It will restrain the bleeding quickly. If the bleeding should be from the nose, blow up some of the powder through a quill [into the nose].

## A PLASTER FOR A SORE, WOUND, OR SWELLING, NOT YET MATURE

380. Take some meal* and boil in fresh milk until it is as thick as stirabout**. Put into a pan with a portion of suet, and boil well. Mix it thoroughly for a plaster, and apply as hot as you can to the part.

*Meal is the edible part of any grain or pulse ground into powder;**The Welsh is iwd, the same as uwd, which means porridge or pottage (a thick stew or gruel).*

## FOR THE BITE OF A DOG

381. Take dittany, garlic and the white of an egg, and make it into a plaster. Apply to the wound, and it will cure it.

## TO MATURE CARBUNCLES

382. Take a pint of fresh milk, and set on the fire. Add a portion of bruised mutton suet, and a handful of oatmeal. Break it up and beat it carefully while boiling. Let it boil until it becomes thickened, so that you may spread it on a clean linen, then apply to the diseased part. When it breaks, dress it with some turpentine* on white leather, piercing it with many holes.

*The Welsh is twrpant. Twrpentein or tyrpant is turpentine, so 2.363 was wrongly translated by Pughe. Originally from the terebrinth tree of Mediterranean regions, it was later distilled from the resins of various pine trees.*

## FOR DEAFNESS

383. Take some leek juice and goat's gall, mixing them well together. Drop some of this into the ear, and cover it with wool.

## FOR BLINDNESS

384. Take some celandine seed mixed with the morning dew, and pound well in a mortar. Strain the juice and mix it with an equal part of clear honey. Boil it briskly to a third, keep in a glass vessel, and drop into your eye when needed.

## FOR THE ITCH*

385. Take dock root and butter, pound the roots and strain through linen. Purify the butter, boil the juice and butter, and keep in a pan. When needed melt it, and anoint the skin three times, i.e. every other day, and you will be cured.

*The Welsh word 'crafu' can mean psoriasis, scabies (also known as the 'seven-year itch') or prurigo, which is a general term for different types of itching eruptions of the skin.*

## FOR A SLOUGHING ULCER

386. Take black wool, soap, and the powder of baked beef. Pound them together and apply to the sloughing part. It will cure it.

## FOR PAIN IN A JOINT

387. Take the crumbs of wheaten bread, fresh from the oven, crab apples, betony, and dandelion. Pound them together well in a mortar in equal parts. Boil

them in good red wine until they become a plaster, apply to the painful part as hot as it can be borne, and it will break out in the form of boils.

## THINGS HURTFUL TO THE HEART

388. Onions, peas, cumin, garlic, sorrow, anger, too much care, too much travelling, drinking cold water after a journey, and bad news. If a man wishes health and long life, let him carefully maintain a merry heart, let him neither eat, drink, nor do what will harm it, for as the wise man says, - 'A merry heart and all is well.'*

*In this author's biography of Black Bart Roberts, the greatest pirate in history, we read that he was the first to say 'A short life and a merry one shall be my motto'.*

## FOR PAIN IN A JOINT

389. Take water chickweed, the leaves and blossoms of primrose, and a flintstone*. Pound them well together and boil with May butter. Anoint the painful part with it warm. Let it be kept in an earthenware pot.

* Pughe translates a'r gelestr as celestr, meaning flint, which is unlikely. However, the Welsh could be gellesg, meaning corn-flag, yellow iris, gladiolus or sword-grass. More likely, elestr/gelestr means the sword flag, fleur-de-lys, iris or lily.

## FOR A BOIL

390. Take mallows, boil in spring water and make into a plaster, then apply to the disease.

## ANOTHER FOR A BOIL

391. Boil pennywort* in sheep's cream, and apply to the boil.

*Dail y geinog is now dail y geiniog, also known as navelwort, formerly known as Cotyledon umbilicus but now Umbilicus rupestris, also known as kidney wort, wall pennywort and penny-pies.*

## FOR CHILBLAINS

392. Take dry dead leaves gathered from the surface of a bog*, and pound well. Take the white of an egg and pound with the herbs, adding some May butter to it. Incorporate the whole together and apply as a plaster. It will cure chilblains.

*This seems to make little sense. Cors means bog or marsh, but can also mean reeds or reed grass. The Welsh is 'Cymmer y dail sydd ar wyneb y gors yn sychion'. Perhaps he means 'take leaves gathered from the surface of dried reeds'?*

## FOR TOOTHACHE

393. Take the roots of the water flower de lys and bruise smartly*. Strain through linen, and inject through a quill into the nostril furthest from the painful tooth.

*The Welsh is ffest, which can either mean quickly or diligently.*

## FOR A BURN

394. Take fern and pound well with sheep's milk, and let it be applied to the burn with a feather. It should be stirred carefully before it is used.

## TO RESTRAIN HAEMORRHAGE FROM A WOUND

395. Take rue leaves, pound well and apply to the wound.

## ANOTHER REMEDY TO RESTRAIN HAEMORRHAGE FROM A WOUND

396. Scrape off the rind from a branch of broom, make it into a ball, insert in the wound, and bind firmly.

## FOR CUTANEOUS ERUPTIONS

397. Take the leaves of the lily and ground ivy, and pound them well together. Then take mutton suet and fry the whole combined. Express through a cloth and anoint the part with it.

## ANOTHER REMEDY FOR CUTANEOUS ERUPTIONS

398. Take oat straw and bum, cover the scald with this and rub it. It will dry and cure it.

## TO PREVENT DREAMING

399. Take the leaves of betony, and hang about your neck, or else drink the juice in going to bed.

## FOR A CANCER IN THE MOUTH, ON THE BROW, OR ANY OTHER PART

400. Take eight or nine leaves of sage, and pound well with some salt and vinegar. Apply it as a plaster to the part.

## A MEDICAMENT FOR BLINDNESS

401. Take twelve grains of fair wheat, and lay upon some cold clean polished iron. Then press another iron, red hot, upon the wheat. A substance like honey will exude from the wheat. Apply this to the painful eye with a feather.

## TO RESTRAIN HAEMORRHAGE WHEN ONE OF THE PRINCIPAL VEINS IS DIVIDED

402. Take a piece of salt beef, both fat and lean together, as much in size as will fill the wound. Lay it on the embers until it is warmed through, and insert it warm into the wound. It will staunch the bleeding.

## FOR A PAIN IN THE LIMB, WHETHER ATTENDED WITH SWELLING OR NOT

403. Take water pimpernel and mix with honey, the yolk of an egg, and the best wheaten meal. Let this be applied as a plaster to the painful part. If the part is disposed to suppurate, it will hasten that termination. If not it will remove the pain, and heal the disease.

## FOR THE KING'S EVIL

404. Take the root of lily and bake under the embers of a fire until it is dry. Reduce it then to a powder, and mix with goose grease or lard. Dress the sore with it, and it will heal it.

## TO REMOVE EXFOLIATIONS FROM THE SKULL OR ANY OTHER BONE

405. Take betony, vervain, and rue. Mix them with wheaten meal and the white of eggs, pounding the whole together till they become completely incorporated. Let it be applied as a plaster to the part.

## FOR ALL SORTS OF CUTANEOUS ERUPTIONS, INCLUDING RINGWORM*

406. Take onions, pounding them small and boiling in water or vinegar. Let the affected part be washed with this, and it will heal a scald head or any other eruption on any other part of the body.

*Pughe notes: Favus. The Welsh is penn crach, literally scabby head. Favus usually affects the scalp, caused by a fungus that was not discovered until 1839. It appears like a number of yellowish, circular, cup-shaped crusts, grouped in patches like a piece of honeycomb, each about the size of a split pea, with a hair projecting in the centre. These increase in size and become crusted over, so that a lesion can be seen round the edge of the scab. Growth continues to take place for several months, when the scab falls away, leaving a bare patch. The disease is essentially chronic, lasting from ten to twenty years. It was formerly mistaken for leprosy.*

## FOR THE ITCH*

407. Take dock roots, bruising them thoroughly in new butter. Fry the whole, mixing and compounding the mass constantly. Anoint the patient with this and he will be cured.

*See 2.385 above*

## ANOTHER REMEDY FOR THE ITCH

408. Take the roots of elecampane and clean them well, and then boil them in spring water. When boiled sufficiently, incorporate them with good thick cream, or unsalted butter, so that they may be made into an ointment. Let your flesh be anointed with this three times in nine days, that is, once every three days. Drink also a good draught of the water in which the roots were boiled, night and morning, for this is an antidote to the specific virus whose existence in the blood and fluids occasions eruptions on the skin, carbuncles, and such like.

## FOR CARBUNCLES

409. Take black wool and incorporate it with some black soap, and bind this upon the disease or carbuncle.

## FOR CANCER OF THE MOUTH

410. Take the juice of plantain, vinegar, and the distilled water of red roses. Mix and wash the mouth with this frequently.

## FOR AN ERUPTIVE VIRUS* IN THE BLOOD AND FLUIDS

411. Take water chickweed, pound well and express the juice under a press. Drink a cupful three times a day on an empty stomach. It is truly good.

*Pughe translates Y Frech as an eruptive virus, but brech means 'pox, spotted or pimpled disease of the skin, rash, eruption; syphilis, venereal disease' (GPC).*

## ANOTHER REMEDY FOR POX

412. Take chickweed, the leaves or the inner bark of elm, water cress, and scurvy grass. Pound them well and express the juice under a press. Let this be your only drink for nine days, and as a diet confine yourself to good wheaten bread prepared with yeast and goat's milk. It is proven.

This medicine and the former one will destroy the eruptive poison in the blood and humors, also that of the inveterate eruption called in Latin Scabies*, and every kind of eruptive poison in the blood. Pneumonia and numerous other diseases, more than an ignorant person would believe, are occasioned by this kind of blood poison.

* *Pughe tells us:* Scabies or itch - Scabies does not depend upon a virus, but upon the presence of an insect, - the Acarus Follicularum. *Scabies (from the Latin scabere, to scratch), is also known as the 'seven-year itch' and is a contagious skin infection in humans and animals. It is caused by a tiny and usually not directly visible parasite, the mite Sarcoptes scabiei, which burrows under the host's skin, causing intense allergic itching.*

## FOR A BURN OR SCALD
413. Take black soap or white, and bind to the injured part.

## FOR AN ERUPTION ON THE FACE
414. Take best wheaten meal, mix with vinegar and honey, and apply to your face.

## FOR CARBUNCLES AND BOILS
415. Take refined wheaten meal, lard, May butter, and sage. Pound together and make a plaster, and apply to the carbuncle until it maturates and draws out the matter.

## FOR PAIN OR SWELLING IN THE MAMMAE
416. Take the bark of the thornless holly. Pound well and mix with good old ale. Strain and administer it to the patient as a drink. It is proven that by the use of this, the gathering of the breast will be prevented.

## ANOTHER FOR ACHING OR SWOLLEN BREASTS
417. Take milfoil, and an egg (with its shell). Pound together carefully, and apply as a plaster to the breast. It will certainly cure it.

## FOR PAIN IN THE LEGS
418. Take the herb called coltsfoot, (they are like burdock in appearance). Boil them well in the milk of a cow of one colour, with oaten groats and May butter, and apply warm to the painful part.

## FOR TIGHTNESS OF THE CHEST
419. Take hyssop and centaury in equal portions. Pound them well and strain carefully. Mix the white of eggs with the strained juice, and drink for three days while fasting.

## ANOTHER REMEDY FOR TIGHTNESS IN THE CHEST
420. Take rue, and boil well in vinegar, and administer to the patient.

## FOR HYSTERIA
421. Take mugwort, red fennel, and red mint*. Boil well in old ale, and strain carefully through a cloth. Drink it warm and you will recover.

* *Gerard notes that red mint is a peppermint which grows in France. However, this appears to be Mentha Smithiana, a hybridized cross of Mentha arvensis, Mentha aquatica and Mentha spicata.*

## FOR A TERTIAN AGUE*
422. Whoever drinks the juice of betony and plantain, mixed together, will recover.

*A fever with shaking fits recurring every other day, often associated with malaria.*

## FOR PAIN OR SWELLING OF THE LEGS, FEET, OR ARMS

423. Take oatmeal, cow's milk, the juice of house leek, and mutton suet. Boil together until it becomes a thick mass. Apply as a plaster to the painful part and it will remove the pain and swelling.

## FOR AN EPIPHORA OF THE EYE

424. Take some black snails, and boil in pure water. Mix the oil which floats on the surface, and anoint the eye with the same.

## ANOTHER REMEDY FOR AN EPIPHORA OF THE EYE

425. Take lead and melt in an iron pot, remove, and pour vinegar thereon. Cover it up carefully so that the vapour may not escape. When cold and settled, let the clean liquor be decanted and kept in a glass bottle. Deposit in the bottle a fragment of elyf* as big as a large nut. When required, mix it with equal parts of decoction of mallows, and wash your eye with it, or mix the vinegar with white of eggs in equal parts, beating them together well. Let your eye be washed with the same.

* *Pughe adds:* I am not satisfied as to what is intended by Elyf, it is orally rendered aloes, but what use aloes could be of here I do not see. Tr. *However, Pughe is translating elyw, aloes, not elyf, which is the same word as alaf which means delicacy or wealth. Elsewhere he translates elyf variously as frankincense, oil and alum, so here it means alum or frankincense. Potassium aluminium sulphate has been used for millennia in medicine, and is used today to treat hepatitis, and to enhance the body's response to immunogens. Alum in powder or crystal form, or in styptic pencils, is sometimes applied to cuts to prevent or treat infection. Powdered alum has been commonly cited as a home remedy for canker sores and animal injuries. It is still used in some toothpaste, and alum powder dissolved in five parts water has been used to shrink haemorrhoids and stop them from bleeding.*

## FOR A HEADACHE

426. Take an apronful of sheep's sorrel, and boil in the milk of a single-coloured cow until it is nearly dry. Apply as a plaster to the head, the patient keeping to his bed, being covered with clothes, so as to cause him to perspire.

## FOR A COLD*

427. Take the seed of nettles and boil in honey. Anoint your feet and arms or other parts requiring it with the same, and it will remove the cold.

*The Welsh is 'rhag oerfel', which means 'for a chill', or a general feeling of coldness. Pughe translates 'for a cold in the limbs', but limbs are not referred to.*

## FOR A PARALYSIS AFFECTING A MAN'S SPEECH

428. Take sage leaves, marjoram leaves, (roots when the leaves cannot be obtained) and pound the whole together in equal parts. Strain, mix with good ale, and administer to the patient. It is well proven.

## FOR AN ULCER WHICH HAS HEALED OUTWARDLY, BUT IS INWARDLY PAINFUL

429. Take barley meal, the white of eggs, and honey. Mix them together and make a plaster, apply to the painful part and it will benefit and heal it.

186

## FOR ONE WHO HAS DRUNK POISON

430. Take fresh rue, wash and bruise well, then mix with white wine. Strain and let the patient drink a good draught of it.

## FOR SWELLING OF THE WOMB, OR HARDNESS OF STOMACH

431. Take linseed and boil in goat's milk, applying it as a plaster to the swelling.

## FOR PAIN OF THE WOMB

432. Take horse mint or tansy. Bruise well, and strain carefully, boil with old ale and drink as warm as you can.

## FOR WORMS

433. Take the juice of tansy and milk, strain and boil well until reduced to a third, drinking it warm.

## FOR A SCALD HEAD*

434. Take pitch and wax, boiling them together. Shave the scald head carefully. Apply the plaster to the same as warm as it can be borne. Leave it on for nine days.

*Pughe uses the same original 'pen crach' for favus in 2.405 above, but favus is a more severe illness. Scald head is an obsolete term for ringworm of the scalp. See 2.27 above.*

## FOR PAIN AND OPACITY OF THE EYE

435. Take the yolk of an egg, fine wheaten meal, and a little sulphate of copper. Mix briskly, applying it to the eye, and it will remove the opacity.

## FOR AN OPACITY OF THE EYE

436. Put the juice of ground ivy in the eye, and it will cure it.

## FOR RINGWORM

437. Take the white of a baked egg, and apply as a plaster on a linen cloth.

## FOR PAIN IN THE BACK

438. Take young broom, boil in spring water, and wash your back with the same.

*This is missing from Pughe:*

## I ŴR A FO WEDI EI LOSGI GAN WRAIG

439. Cymmer elyf mâl a chwrw, a chymysc, a gwlych bilin lliain ynddo, a thro beuparth y wialen.

## FOR A MAN INFLAMED* BY HIS WIFE

439. Take ground alum and beer, and mix. Soak a cloth sheet in it, and wrap twice around the penis.

*This is unfortunately not in the sense of being inflamed by desire, but having contracted some sort of burning infection in the penis.*

## FOR DYSPNOEA [SHORTNESS OF BREATH]

440. Take the strained juice of hyssop, the same amount of juice of centaury, mixing them with as much again of the white of eggs. Let this be your only drink for three days.

## FOR PAIN OF THE CHEST
441. Take parsley and sage, pound together and apply to your chest.

## FOR PAIN UNDER THE SHOULDER
442. Take the juice of sage, and warm wine, one proportion of the juice, and two of the wine. Drink it and it will benefit the pain under the shoulder, pain of the womb, and of the stomach. It is also useful for headache, paralysis or muscular weakness. It is proven.

## FOR BLACK JAUNDICE*
443. Take thyme, rue, pennyroyal, hyssop, parsley roots, fennel, the leaves of birthwort, called in Latin chamaerops** and two spoonfuls of anise-seed. Boil the whole in a quart of water containing three spoonfuls of honey. Strain through a clean cloth, and drink blood-warm.

*This is Leptospirosis, Weil's disease, which can be deadly. Known as Ratcatcher's Yellows, it is caused by a bacterium in the urine of infected animals, so can pass into a cut in rivers and streams. Severe complications can cause liver failure; ** Chamaerops is a species of palm today. The Welsh is dail yr ysgyrr, which is not noted in the GPC, and translated by Pughe as birthwort. Astrolochia clematitis is European Birthwort. Astrolochia longa is mentioned in Maud Grieve's Herbal as being used for rheumatism and removing obstructions after childbirth. She also mentions the American Astrolochia serpentaria for fevers, smallpox, typhus, pneumonia et al. Birthwort has been linked to kidney failure, but has been a herbal medicine for over two millennia. It was mentioned by Theophrastus (c.372-286bce) for disorders of the uterus, snake bites and head sores. Its main use was to induce labour, hence its name of birthwort (birth plant).*

## TO CURE A CANCER
444. Take a cupful of red wine, three or four spoonfuls of honey, and as much as a large hazel nut of frankincense. Mix and boil until reduced to a third, then strain and put in a bottle to keep. Let the affected part be washed with it frequently and this will cure it.

*445 is missing from Pughe's translation*

## I ŴR WEDI EI LOSGI GAN WRAIG
445. Cymmer linod, a llaeth geifr gwynnon, a brew yn iwd, a dod werth y wialen beuparth iddi; profedig yw.

## FOR A MAN WHO HAD INFLAMMATION (VENEREAL DISEASE) FROM A WOMAN
445. Take linseed* and the milk of white goats and stew together. Then bath the penis in it twice a day. It is very soothing.

*Iolo's word is linod, from llinod, which is the same word as llinad, meaning linseed (the seed of flax).*

## FOR A HEADACHE
446. Take a spoonful of the juice of betony, and a spoonful each of wine and honey. Mix with it nine pepper corns, and drink morning and evening for nine days.

## TO HEAL A WOUND OR SWELLING, AND TO EASE PAIN
447. Take a portion of oatmeal, the milk of a myswynog*, the juice of house leek and mutton suet. Bruise together until they become a thick mass, and apply as a warm plaster to the painful part. This will ease the pain and remove the swelling.
* *Pughe explains:* A cow which has been a year without calving. *The Welsh means 'farrow cow', i.e. a non-pregnant cow.*

## FOR HAEMOPTYSIS*
448. Take wild celery, mint, rue, and betony. Boil in fresh milk, drink it warm and it will cure you.
   * *Haemoptysis is the coughing (expectoration) of blood or blood-stained sputum from the larynx and respiratory tract. It carries the danger of asphyxiation, and the source of bleeding may be in the lungs.*

## FOR STRANGURY
449. Take red nettles and parsley, pound well together, and apply as a plaster to the stomach.

## TO STRENGTHEN THE UTERUS
450. Take acorns, roast them hard and reduce to a powder. Put a spoonful of this in a drink of good ale, and drink warm every morning for a week or nine days, lying in bed for an hour or two.

## A GOOD EYE WATER
451. Take rotten apples, strain with spring water and wash your eye therewith. This will clean and clear your eye wonderfully.
   *This same remedy is also given in 2:372

## FOR TOOTHACHE
452. Take holly leaves and boil in spring water until they are tough. Then remove the pot from the fire, and put a kerchief over your head, holding your mouth over the pot in order to inhale the vapour. It will cure you.

## A PROVEN REMEDY FOR TOOTHACHE
453. Take the roots of pellitory of Spain*. Wash clean and bruise well, and form three small balls with your hand, each about as big as a plum. Retain the first between your cheek and the painful tooth as long as you walk a mile with moderate steps, and as the saliva collects spit it away. When you think that the ball has been there as long as that, put in another and walk backwards and forwards for the same space of time. After that put in the third, then lie in bed, and warm yourself well, and when you have slept you will be free from the pain. This I have often proved and have found to be a present remedy for the toothache.
   * *Also known as Spanish Chamomile and Roman Pellitory, Anacyclus pyrethrum is a small Mediterranean plant containing a volatile oil, once used to relieve toothache.*

## TO FIND WHETHER THE SKULL IS FRACTURED
454. If the integument* is entire, shave the hair where the bruise is. Apply a thick new linen cloth doubled, spreading the white of an egg upon it. Bind this on the

part for a night. In the morning, let it be removed and see whether the linen is wet, for if the linen is moist and wet there, certainly the skull is fractured.

*The integumentary system is the organ system which protects the body from damage, made up of the skin and its appendages such as hair, nails and glands.*

## FOR FLATULENCE OF STOMACH
455. Take wild carrot seed and make into pills of the size of peas, using honey. Take four every morning and evening, for three days.

## FOR SORE LIPS
456. Take the root of the knapweed and pound well, adding some cold milk cream to it. Mix carefully, straining through a clean cloth. Anoint your lips with this salve.

## TO PROVOKE AN APPETITE
457. Boil centaury in clear spring water. Let the sick person drink nine spoonfuls of this, while fasting for three days, and it will help him.

## FOR EVERY KIND OF VENOMOUS BITE
458. Take plantain leaves and drink their juice. Take also yew* and celandine, in equal parts, and pound well together, tempering them with stale urine. Then apply to the wound and it will ease the pain, reduce the swelling, and extract the venom.

*Shakespeare called the yew 'double fatal' because not only were the berries poisonous, but the Welsh longbow (never an English invention) was the greatest killing weapon of its day.*

## FOR THE BITE OF A MAD DOG
459. Take a handful of betony, a handful of wild sage, a handful of bitter nightshade*, and a cupful of standing water. Pound the herbs well, mixed with the water, and strain. Mix a pennyworth of treacle with this, and let the patient drink it for two or three mornings. It is proven.

*This is Solanum dulcamara, also known as Bittersweet Nightshade or Woody Nightshade, with its familiar purple and yellow flowers trailing through countryside hedges. Bittersweet is so called because the bark is first bitter then sweet. It is also known as Aw'f'ood, Belladonna, Blue Bindweed, Dogwood, Fellon-wood, Fellonwort, Mad Dog's Berries, Bittersweet Nightshade, Poison-berry, Poison Flower, Poisonous Tea Plant, Pushion Berry, Robin-in-the-Hedge, Snake-berry, Snake's Poison-food, Sweet Bitter, Terrididdle or Terrydivle, Tether Devil. The name Fellonwort was explained by Coles: 'The leaves or berries stamped with musty bacon, applyed to that joynt of the finger that is troubled with a felon, hath been found to be very sucessful for the curing of the same'. In mediaeval times it was used in witches' potions as charms and spells. Ben Jonson in 'Masque of Queens' wrote: 'And I ha been plucking plants among Hemlock, Henbane, Adder's Tongue, Nightshade, Moonwort, Leopard's Bane; And twice by the dogs was like to be ta'en'. It was a plant of ill omen, of which Gerarde related: 'If you will follow my counsel, deal not with the same in any case, and banish it from your gardens, and the use of it also, being a plant so furious and deadly, for it bringeth such as have eaten thereof into a dead sleep, wherein many have died'. When dried the shoots are used for skin diseases. The berries are poisonous, causing vomiting. The roots smell like the potato, but are bitter when chewed. The leaves have been used for scurvy and rheumatism.*

## FOR AN INFLAMED EYE
460. Seek cream, and as much again of the white of eggs. Then dip a linen cloth of the size of the eye in it, and apply thereto.

## TO HINDER INEBRIATION
461. Take a handful of betony, bruise well, mix with spring water, and strain carefully. Let it be drunk while fasting, and you will not get drunk that day.

## A GOOD EMETIC FOR THE HEAD AND STOMACH
462. Take three spoonfuls of the juice of betony for three successive mornings, and inject it through a quill into the nostril.

## FOR PAIN IN THE LIMBS
463. Take a handful of the herb called colt's foot, and as much of the leaves of burdock. Pound and mix with the milk of a single-coloured cow. Add oaten groats and butter, the whole being boiled well. Apply as a plaster to the painful parts as hot as you can bear it. It will ease the pain.

## ANOTHER REMEDY FOR PAIN IN THE LIMBS
464. Procure the same herbs, and wrap them unbruised about your feet night and day. They will extract the poisonous water from your feet. At other times brown paper should be used in the same way instead of hose [*breeches/stockings/socks*]. It is proven.

## FOR CHILBLAINS OR PUSTULAR ULCERATIONS ON THE FEET AND HEELS
465. Take hot beeswax when honeycombs are strained, and immerse your feet in it, as hot as you can suffer it. Stand in this a long while, and you will be cured. It will absorb the purulent matter.

## TO REDUCE SWELLINGS OF THE WOMB
466. Take mercurial ointment, and May butter, or the lard of pigs slaughtered in that month, and also wax and rosin. Melt this with bruised orpine, in equal proportions. Mind that the butter or lard should exceed the wax and rosin in quantity. Let this be boiled well and strained. With this ointment anoint the side in which the pain is situated, by rubbing it up and down as hard as you can. It is proven.

## FOR CONSTIPATION
467. Take the roots of gladwyn, and pound them as you would garlic, with good old ale. Let it stand aside a space of time. Strain, and warm as a potion for the patient. It will certainly act as a laxative, for it is proven.

## FOR A BOIL ON THE BACK, WHEN THE SKIN IS ABRASED
468. Take a quart and a half of the best ale you can obtain, and boil it to a spoonful*. It is a good ointment for all sores of the back, being spread on new linen, and applied to it. The use of this will extract the impurity. Then dress it with a healing ointment. If there is a swelling in the leg, get the leaves of foxglove, bruise and apply thereto, covering the leaves with potter's clay. It is good.

* *This is boiling three pints down to a spoonful, which today would be an expensive remedy — over £10 a spoonful. Home brewing has much going for it.*

## ANOTHER REMEDY TO REDUCE THE SWELLING, AND EXTRACT THE POISON

469. Dress the ulcerated part with clarified honey, and it will benefit it.

## FOR MENORRHAGIA*

470. Take the inner bark of the blackthorn, rejecting the outer, and pound it well in the milk of a single- coloured cow. This mixture, being administered to the woman, will certainly be of use to her.

> * *Excessive menstrual bleeding.*

## ANOTHER REMEDY FOR EXCESSIVE MENSTRUAL BLEEDING

471. Take archangel, and pound well with strong red wine, straining it carefully. Let this be given to the woman to drink freely, night and morning. The use will be of great benefit to her. Archangel should be kept dry for winter, being taken as a powder then. Take it in a spoonful of warmed wine, as warm as it can be drunk. The root pounded with the wine and strained is also useful, or the powder may be taken with the wine. The herb should be grown in a garden apart from other plants.

## FOR A THORN

472. Take common soap, apply to the part and it will draw it well. Leave on until it is extracted.

## FOR A SICK ANIMAL

473. Take black soap* and boil in ale. Let it be given the animal and it will purge him.

> *Black soap was imported, coarser than Castile soap, and made of olive oil and ashes. However, imported soap was still expensive. During the Middle Ages, soap was made by killing an animal, removing and then cleaning the fat and heating it until all of the oils separated from the solids. This was set aside until the lye was made by burning wood, collecting the ashes, adding water to the ash and then heating it. This made the lye water. The oils (either olive oil or animal fat) were then added to the lye water and heated and stirred until it thickened. It was poured into a container to solidify. It was cut into small pieces and used. The ashes coloured the soap greyish.*

## FOR INFLAMMATION OF THE BREAST

474. Take plantain leaves and lard, pound them together and apply to the breast.

## FOR A SWELLING OF THE STOMACH

475. Take goat's whey, and pound the herbs called ramsons*, mixing together and straining. Let it be your only drink for three days.

> *Wild Garlic, or Wood Garlic, Allium Ursinum. Also known as Bears' Garlic, the Welsh is craf y geifr, Goats' Garlic.*

## FOR RETENTION OF URINE

476. Take red nettles and parsley, pound them into a plaster together, and apply to the perineum.

## A GOOD HABIT FOR THE PRESERVATION OF HEALTH

477. Whatever sex you may be, wash your face, hands, etc., with cold water every morning, scrubbing them well afterwards. Wash your back and nape of the neck once a week also, scrubbing them well afterwards with a coarse cloth.

## TO DESTROY A WORM LODGED IN A MAN'S FLESH

478. Take the lard of a red pig*, May butter, sage, and acorns. Pound them well together until they become an ointment, and apply the same to the affected part.
* *Probably the Tamworth breed, covered with ginger bristles, a hardy but slow-maturing pig.*

## ANOTHER REMEDY TO DESTROY A WORM

479. Take the juice of sage, and a little distillation of wine.* Anoint the part where the worm is lodged, and it will kill it.
   * *Pughe reminds us:* Spirit of Wine or Brandy.

## FOR BLEEDING OF THE NOSE*

480. Take an egg shell and receive the blood in the same. Then set on the fire to bake until it becomes a powder. Blow this powder into the nostrils, and it will stop the bleeding. It is proven.

## FOR INFLAMMATION OF THE MAMMAE

481. Take the bark of thornless holly, and pound well, mixing it with good old ale, and strain. Let this be administered to the patient and no doubt she will be cured. It is an approved remedy, and will prevent the formation of an abscess in the breast.

## ANOTHER REMEDY FOR INFLAMMATION OF THE BREASTS

482. Take yarrow, and an egg, shell and all, pounding them together. Apply to the breast. It will not fail to cure it.

## FOR AN ACUTE PAIN IN ANY PART OF THE BODY

483. Take half a gallon of the lees of wine in the cask, the same quantity of the lees of good old ale, a ffiol* full of wheat bran, and the roots of the cinquefoil. Boil well, pound the herbs carefully, then boil the whole together till the mass becomes tough. The more it is boiled, the better the plaster will be. Let this be applied to the painful part, and with God's help you will certainly be cured. It is proven.
* *Pughe adds:* See about this measure at the end of the Volume. Lit. a cupful.

## FOR GASTRODYNIA [*STOMACH ACHE*]

484. Take camomile, bruise well, and boil in a pint of wine till it is reduced to half. Let it be given to the patient, and he will certainly recover.

## ANOTHER REMEDY FOR STOMACH ACHE

485. Take wild carrots, and infuse in as much as will cover them of water, using it for drink. It is proven.

## TO HEAL A BRUISE, AND TO DRAW WATER FROM THE INJURED PART, OR FROM BRUISED BONES, AND DISPERSE THE SWELLING RESULTING FROM THE SUPERABUNDANCE OF HUMOR, TAINTED BLOOD, OR CORRUPTED FLESH

486. Take half a pound of mutton suet, and half a pennyworth of black soap, and melt together. Add six well-beaten eggs, yolk and white together, the whole being well mixed. Remove the mass from the fire to cool, mix it well and spread on a cloth carefully. Let this be applied to the injury daily, or every other day until it is cured.

## TO DRAW HUMOR OR TAINTED BLOOD FROM A BRUISE ON THE SCALP

487. Wash your mouth clean, and anoint your head with oil of olives, letting some of it drop into the ears. Let this plan be followed for eight days, and you will be cured.

## FOR HAZE* OF THE EYE CALLED ONGLE**

488. Take pepper and reduce to powder, mix with the marrow of the wing bones of an old goose, and bind up in a linen cloth. Burn it upon a bakestone***, until it can be reduced into fine powder. Let this be blown into the eye until it is cured.

*This is Pughe's translation. The Welsh is Yr Haw – haw means ripe, full or sluggish (GPC), so can mean fullness; ** Pughe explains: Onyx. Onyx was a name for a collection of pus in the anterior chamber of the eye. Lasocki in 2008 noted that in the fourteenth century ongle meant a 'Kind of sickness of the eye: the layer which is thick, large, and strongly attached to the conjunctiva is difficult to cure'; and also an 'Ache of the fingers' ends in extremity of cold weather; also, a painful slipping of the flesh, or swelling of it over, the nail.'; *** Many Welsh readers will remember their mothers' round, flat, cast-iron bakestones, used for making Welsh Cakes.*

## ANOTHER REMEDY FOR HAZY EYES

489. Take the flowers of hawthorn and willow, making a distillation of them. Use this night and morning, for it is useful for inflamed, painful, and watery eyes.

## ANOTHER REMEDY FOR HAZY EYES

490. Inject the juice of the celandine into your eye through a quill, twice a day.

## FOR THE ITCH*

491. Take the leaves of betony, pound and strain the juice. Rub the skin well with the same night and morning for nine days. It will cure it.

*Here, the Welsh term is y cossi. Cosi is a word used around 1400 for irritation or an itching. It is outside the remit of this volume to prove that Iolo Morganwg did not make up these remedies in Book 2, but gathered them from old sources. However, this author is for many reasons convinced that they are genuine.*

## FOR A CONTUSION OF THE HEAD, OR A FALL, FRACTURING THE SKULL, AND LACERATING THE BRAIN

492. Take betony and pound briskly in a mortar, then boil well in the lees of red wine. Let this be applied as a plaster to the head. This will cool the head, and bind the bones together.

## FOR A PAIN OF THE NATURE OF CARDIALGIA OR STRANGURY
493. Take clean oats, and fry in unsalted butter until they are browned. Apply to the painful part upon a cloth, and it will be most certainly cured.

## FOR ERYSIPELAS
494. Take the dung of geese feeding on grass, hartwort, daisy, betony, and unsalted May butter. Pound together, and then boil on the fire and strain. Let it be kept in a clean vessel, and the patient anointed with it. It will cure him.

## TO STRENGTHEN THE LUNGS, THROAT, AND CHEST
495. Obtain red fennel, and the bruised tops of hyssop, also mallows, and boil in perennial* spring water. Let the patient drink this and he will certainly recover.
* *Water from a source which does not dry up during the year.*

## FOR THE BITE OF A MAD DOG
496. Boil wild sage in as much as will cover it of ale or water. Let it be used as ordinary drink for nine days.

## FOR ALL KINDS OF HURTFUL ACHES IN WHATEVER WAY THEY COME
497. Obtain parsley, plantain, daisy, garlic, and grains of paradise. Pound well in a mortar, strain and take the juice in ale. If the patient can obtain beef, he should not eat it when he recovers.

## FOR HOARSENESS
498. Take mugwort, red nettles, and plantain, and boil them well in goat's whey. Let a cupful of this be drunk every morning, and it will cure you.

## FOR WHOOPING COUGH AND BRONCHITIS
499. Take ground ivy in milk and water, and administer to the patient every morning while he is fasting, and also in the evening. It will cure him.

## FOR A COUGH
500. Take a handful of white sage, pounding it well in a mortar, mixing with good old ale, and straining carefully under a press. Make a posset of this ale, using the clear part, and you will be cured.

## ANOTHER REMEDY FOR A COUGH
501. Take powder of orpiment, and hard boiled eggs, twice a day for thirteen days, and you will recover.

## ANOTHER REMEDY FOR A COUGH
502. Take the foot of a duck and the foot of a hen, with the marrow of a fresh bone. Make them into an ointment, and anoint your chest therewith, but not your stomach, then you will be cured.

*This entry is added in Welsh to illustrate the problems of translation:*

## RHAG PEN TARDDEDIG O WAITH TES
503. Cais y gyntaf waddod cwrw da cadarn, a rhwain, a blawd rhyg, a gwna **is** **3** plaster o dod wrth y pen, a wythnos o yspaid i bob un o honynt, ai olch drwy drwnc sur, ai grafu yn dda, a thyn y blew marw yn llwyr, a gellwng waed, lle bo

gwrid, a hynny rhwng pob pryd o'r tri uchod, ag oddyna cais wynn wiau, a fflwr rhyg, a gwna **g**, 3 plaster y 3 phryd, ai olchi bob gwaith y lân, ag yna cais wraidd y marchalan, a gwraidd y tafol, a mwg y ddaiar, a'r droedrudd, au pwyo 'nghyd yn dda, au berwi trwy wer eidion yn dda, au hidlo yn lân, a phan fo oer cais goprys glâs, amcan fach of swlffwr a gwna'n bylor mân mân a chymysg ar ei hidlaid, *pŷn yn gwbwl ag y **selí5** yn dda o'i fonn, fel y bo mêl tew, ag a hwnnw elia'r pen yn dda, ag oddyna cais ymenyn ar unrhyw lysiau daiar a enwyd uchod ond peidio a'r pylor, a gwna eli o honynt, ag alia a hwnnw ag iach y bydd.
*Oeddiwrth pwno

## FOR AN ERUPTION OF THE HEAD IN CONSEQUENCE OF SUMMER HEAT

*503. First get the lees of good strong ale, rosin, and rye meal. Make three plasters from it, and apply a plaster to your head, each one for a period of a week. Then wash your head with stale urine, scrape it well, and remove all the loose hair. Bleed where there is redness, between each application. Then obtain the white of eggs and rye meal, and make three plasters, three times, washing the head clean each use. After this, obtain elecampane root, dock root, fumitory, and herb Robert. Pound well together, and boil them with ox tallow, and strain carefully. When cold, obtain copper sulphate and a small portion of sulphur. Reduce these to a very fine powder and mix with the strained ointment. Incorporate the whole well with a spatula, stirring it from the base until it becomes like thick honey. Anoint the head well with this, then get butter and any of the above mentioned herbs, but not the powder [of the minerals]. Make an ointment from them, and anoint with it. And he will be cured.*

## HERE IS A MEDICAMENT FOR A MAN WHO HAS AN ERUPTION OF THE HEAD, WHICH HAS PROVED INTRACTABLE

504. Get pitch and fresh wax, melt together, and apply as a plaster, as warm as can be borne. Leave it unchanged for nine days.

## ANOTHER REMEDY FOR AN ERUPTION OF THE HEAD

505. Take sulphur and mercury. Incorporate together with roasted garlic and fresh lard, mixing them well. With this anoint your head.

## ANOTHER REMEDY FOR AN ERUPTION OF THE HEAD

506. Take two handfuls of crown imperial (called petilius in Latin)*, before it is in flower. Boil in a pot of strong whey until it is reduced to half. Then wash your head with it warm, scrubbing the scabs away. Again make a plaster of crown imperial, and apply to your head warm, leaving it there a night and a day, when it should be re moved. A plaster should be afterwards prepared with rye meal and spring water, and applied on a linen cloth over the diseased part. Leave it on three days and nights. Then it should be removed and the head washed with stale urine, the head being scraped to the flesh. Then take a red onion and make into a plaster, boiling and tempering with the juice of mountain mint and the lard of an old boar. This practice will cure it.

*\* Fritillaria imperialis is a large erect type of lily.*

## ANOTHER REMEDY FOR AN ERUPTION OF THE HEAD

507. Take pitch and wax in equal parts. Melt them together and pour into a box, letting it stand in water until cold. Scrub the head, and wash as directed

above. Then take a piece of linen, apply to the head, and then apply another upon that. Then take a portion from the box, reduce to powder and spread upon the linen. After this apply another linen, and then a bandage about the forehead and all, so that the powder is not lost. Let it remain there for seven or eight days. Each time you change it, the head should be washed as before. When you perceive that this process is no longer needed, take the fat which is obtained from the feet of rredres* when boiled. Blow it from the surface of the water in which they are boiled into another vessel, preserving it in a box. Anoint the head with it until it is well. It is proven.

* *This unknown word is in heavy Gothic script in the original text.*

## TO PROMOTE THE GROWTH OF HAIR

508. Shave the head clean with a razor, and take honey with the juice of onions in equal parts. Anoint and scrub the head well with this every morning and night. The head should be washed with the distilled water of honey. It is proven.

## ANOTHER REMEDY FOR HAIR GROWTH

509. Shave the head carefully, anoint with honey, and sprinkle the powder of mollipuffs upon it.*

* *Called by Pughe Lycoperdon Bovista, now known as the Warted Puffball fungus, Bovista officinalis*

## TO CURE BILIOUSNESS, OTHERWISE CALLED HYPOCHONDRIASIS, OR DISEASE OF THE BILE

510. Take male fern, (the best is that which grows upon the oak*), boiling it in strong ale wort. Drink a hearty draught of this every other day, for eight days, subsisting meanwhile upon a corresponding diet consisting of fresh meat. Avoid vegetables, and prefer well-baked wheaten bread, your drink being good wine, or ale, and milk mixed in equal quantity, partaken of temperately. Take also caraway seed in powder, fennel seed, wild carrot seed, anise seed, canella, and such dry herbs mixed with your drink. Walk hard daily, and amuse yourself with song and harp, with another being the performer, not you. By following this plan you will (by God's help) recover.

* *This is probably Polypody of the Oak, Polypodium vulgare.*

## TO RELIEVE NAUSEA OF THE STOMACH [OR HEART?]*

511. Take an infusion of the blood-red pink, called in Latin cariophilum major.** Mix with honey, and sprinkle upon it the powder of anise seed and the powder of fennel. A good draught should be taken night and morning, and the flowers should be kept dry so that they may be at hand at all times.

* *The Welsh is 'rhag mwyth y galon'. Mwyth can mean fever, ague or the first signs of illness. Calon can mean heart as well as womb or belly. Thus this may be a remedy for a heart ailment. In 2.566 Pughe uses cylla for stomach, so this may well be a heart remedy;* ** *Pughe notes:* Dianthus Caryophylus or Clove Pink.

## A PLASTER TO REDUCE A SWELLING THE RESULT OF A WOUND, BLOW OR OTHER INJURY TO A MAN'S BODY, OR ON A MEMBER WHERE THE SWELLING CONCEALS THE INJURY

512. Take a handful of the leaves of smallage (called in Latin oleoselinon), fine wheaten meal, and the white of four eggs. Pound them well in a mortar, beating the white of eggs until it becomes thin, then add the meal to the beaten egg whites and smallage. Let the whole be mixed for a plaster, and applied to the affected part, and it will reduce the swelling completely, until the nature of the injury can be plainly discovered.

## FOR DROPSY, IN LATIN CALLED HYDROPS

513. Take fresh dough, and make a large pie so that a goose or two capons at least may lie within it*. Fill the pie with the following salutary herbs: two handfuls of sage, two handfuls of dwarf elder, one handful of betony, a handful of water cress, a handful of hart's tongue, a handful of parsley or bruised smallage roots, half a handful of hyssop, and half a handful of columbine (called in Latin aquilegia). Let all these herbs except the parsley be put in the cavity of the pie. Then get an ounce of the powdered rootlets of leeks, an ounce of powdered anise seed, two ounces of powdered marsh mallows, and put the whole in the above cavity. Cover them well with dough.

This pie is put in a hot oven for the same time required to cook bread, and baked well. It should then be taken out, divided into four parts, and put in an earthenware pot of sufficient capacity while still hot. Pour upon it two gallons of strong old ale, racked carefully from the lees. Cover the vessel carefully, and leave it to macerate for a night. From then on, drink a fair quantity of the same three times a day - morning, noon, and night. This potion will prove a more effective diuretic than anything else, a little broom ash being mixed therewith. Let it be drunk as directed, and it will preserve you from the dropsy, for it is proven.

*This seems a large pie, but fowl, like livestock were much smaller in the past. A capon is a cockerel castrated when young to improve its flavour. The pie recipe seems to be mixed with another for a diuretic drink.*

## THE WAY TO PREPARE BROOM ASH, WHICH IS EXCEEDINGLY USEFUL FOR DROPSY AND STRANGURY, BEING MIXED WITH DRINK OF LIKE NATURE, OR MADE INTO A CONFECTION WITH HONEY, OR INTO BOLUSES*; NO LESS THAN FOUR OF THE BOLUSES, OR AN EQUAL QUANTITY OF CONFECTION BEING TAKEN NIGHT AND MORNING

514. Take a large sheet of iron, or a bake-stone, heat it to a red heat, and put fresh broom (in full seed is best) upon it. Turn the broom about well, that it may bum, so as to give you a sixpenny cupful of ashes. The vessel in which it is then kept should be covered carefully, so that no air can get into it or from it. When it is required, let a spoonful of it be taken, mixed with a good draught of strong old ale, good old mead, or good white wine.

*A bolus is a large pill*

## FOR ACUTE ERYSIPELAS ATTENDED WITH SWELLING, HEAT, AND BURNING IN A JOINT OR OTHER MEMBER

515. Take barley meal, and well made butter, moderately salted as if for eating. Mix them together gradually in equal portions, and keep in a clean well-covered vessel as long as you wish. Let some of this be spread on a cloth or linen and applied to the affected part. Should it ferment, it ought to be worked with a wooden spatula, or if it becomes hard, tempered with the white of eggs. From the use of it you will recover through God's help. It is proven.

## FOR A MALIGNANT ERUPTION

516. Take glass, powder it and mix with black soap, then apply frequently to the affected part. It will certainly heal it.

## FOR ANY STIFF OR SWOLLEN ERYSIPELAS OF AN ACUTE NATURE BEGINNING IN A MAN'S LIMBS OR BACK

517. Take hemlock, mudwort*, marsh mallows, red fennel, and the flowers of the water lily if you can obtain them, or if not the common mallow. Bruise them between your hands, and boil for a long time in the urine of the sick person. Then put some unsalted butter in the mixture, and boil briskly. Remove from the fire and wash the affected part with the liquid, while hot. Apply the herbs also as a plaster on a cloth, leaving this a night on the affected part. Then warm again and apply a second time, and continue this application until cured. The patient's own water is better than that of another man, less he should be diseased, and the use of it will certainly cure him.

*The Geiriadur Prifysgol Cymru of 2002 is the first complete historical dictionary of Welsh, but named lledlys as an unknown plant. Pughe notes it as mudwort, Limosella aquatica, which is a small herbaceous plant growing on mud and in moist areas. This 'Water Mudwort' is not noted in Grieve's Modern Herbal of 1931 nor in Culpeper's 17th century writings. Limosella australis is Welsh Mudwort. The Welsh plant is not present in England, Scotland or Ireland, but can be found with some difficulty in grassy marshes on estuaries in North and South Wales. It forms perennial semi-aquatic mats of plants. We do not know which variety of mudwort to choose here.*

## FOR THE ITCH ON A MAN, BEING A WATER THAT WILL CURB IT ON WHATEVER PART OF THE BODY IT IS

518. Take a bottle full of pure water, and put in a clean vessel on the fire. Then take some aloes* and an ounce of sulphate of copper, adding it to the water, boiling well. Remove it from the fire to clear. Afterwards put it in an earthenware pot and cover it well. When wanted, warm some of it, and wash the part with a cloth. It will cure you and dry the eruption, so that it will fade away.

*This is the word elyf that Pughe sometimes also translates as frankincense, alum or oil.*

## FOR PARALYSIS

519. Take a few bay leaves, wild sage, wild strawberries, brookweed*, the leaves of honeysuckle, and rosemary, and pound them in a mortar separately. Mix with lard, divide into small balls, put in an earthenware pot for ten days, then in a pan, bruising them well. Warm them over the fire, mixed with May butter or animal oil, and strain while hot through a cloth. This should be kept in a glass vessel and

warmed by the fire when about to be used, which should be night and morning. By God's help it will cure the patient. It is proven.

*The Welsh is 'a dail neu wreiddiau y sammwl' – 'and leaves or roots of sammwl'. 'Samwl' is brookweed or water pimpernel, both names for Samolus valerandi, according to Geiriadur Prifysgol Cymru.*

## FOR GOUT, CHARACTERIZED BY SWELLING AND AGONISING PAIN IN THE JOINTS, FEET, HANDS, AS WELL AS THE STOMACH, THIGHS AND THE HEAD, INDUCED BY THE DESICCATION ON THE HUMORS INTO A CALCAREOUS EARTH. THIS COMPLAINT IS CALLED ARTHRITIS* IN LATIN

520. Take equal parts of the juice of tansy and clarified honey. If the complaint is hot, fry the ingredients in a pan, keep carefully (but if cold, then let the remedy be also cold) and spread on a fine flannel. Let it be applied to the painful part. It is a good and proven remedy, as I can witness, for a woman lay bedridden for four years with this disease, and she was restored in a month by the use of this remedy.

* *Pughe footnotes:* 'Gout (remarks Good) is one of the maladies which seems to have been common to England in its earliest ages of barbarism. It is frequently noticed by the Anglo Saxon historians, and the name signed it is fot adl, (foot ail.) In the Cottonian MSS. at the British Museum, lib. Vitel c. 3, we have the following prescription, which was once regarded as a specific. "Take the herb datulus ortulosa, which we call greata cranleac (a species of iris or flag flower), take the heads of it, and dry them very much, and take thereof a pennyweight and a half, and the pear tree, and the Roman bark, and cumin, and a fourth part of laurel berries; and of the other herbs half a pennyweight of each, and six pepper corns, and grind all to dust, and put two egg shells full of wine; this is a true leach craft*. Give it to the man to drink till he be well."'

*Leechcraft was the skill of a physician, the doctor's craft, the art or science of healing.*

### ANOTHER REMEDY FOR GOUT

521. Take a portion of rue, of coarse salt, of the white and yolk of an egg, and a little black soap. Let the rue and salt be bruised together in a mortar. Add the egg and black soap, mixing the whole together well. Apply it as a plaster to the affected part, and it will be cured.

### ANOTHER REMEDY FOR THE SAME DISEASE

522. Get one or two onions, and roast thoroughly before the fire, then get some blessed distillation* and put it over the fire in a retort**. Then bruise the onions small, and boil in the blessed distillation for a while, then straining them into a dish through a clean cloth. With this let the painful part be anointed night and morning until it is well. Many physicians state that this is a proven remedy, though such a cheap one.

*Pughe yet again reminds us: Aqua Benedicta Rulanda; **A retort is a closed vessel with an outlet tube, used for distillation, or decomposition by heat.*

### ANOTHER REMEDY FOR GOUT

523. Take equal parts of linseed, the lees of wine, and quick lime. Let this have a prolonged boiling, and apply as a plaster to the painful part. If the affected part is

hot, let pennywort be bruised fine, and apply to it. It will reduce the swelling and the heat. It is proven.

## ANOTHER REMEDY FOR GOUT

524. Take a handful of sage, a handful of liverwort, and a handful of honeysuckle, and boil in a gallon of standing water until it becomes a quart. Wash the painful part with this, and when you have finished washing it, apply the herbs to it, and by God's help it will be cured.

## ANOTHER REMEDY FOR GOUT

525. Take the yolks of three hard-baked eggs, and reduce to a powder in a pan on the fire. Strain them carefully. This is a useful ointment for the gout, and for many other diseases.

## ANOTHER REMEDY FOR GOUT

526. Take the juice of pennywort, a little frankincense, the juice of plantain (if in season) and two spoonfuls of the powder of madder. Boil them well together in a gallon of spring water, but do not let it be over-boiled. Anoint the affected member with this as hot as it can be borne. Let a linen cloth be also dipped in the decoction and applied to the gout. It will cure it.

## A NOBLE PLASTER FOR GOUT IN THE HEAD*

527. Take two handfuls of barley bruised in a mortar, a handful of betony, bruised separately, viii** of wine, and half as much of wort. Mix these with the barley and betony until it becomes a thick plaster. Spread it on linen, and apply to the painful head as hot as can be borne, from the temporal bones to the middle of the forehead. It will cure it.

* This is also called cephalagra (lit. headache) or seizure in old medical books. William Pitt the Elder (1708-1778) had attacks of 'gout in the head' which led to 'frequent fits of insanity.' It was a chronic disease with a boring pain and causing the sufferer to scream and vomit. The London Medical Dictionary of 1809 tells us that there are several varieties of 'misplaced gout', in the head, lungs, stomach, intestines, kidneys or bladder. For 'gouty phrenitis' it recommended camphor. However, the Boston Weekly Magazine of 1803-1804, Vol. 2 recommended that the sufferer be immersed in a 'hogshead of steam'.; ** Pughe tells us. See Weights and Measures at the end of the Volume.

## ANOTHER REMEDY FOR THE SAME PAIN IN THE HEAD

528. Take rose water, vervain water, a woman's milk, and the white of an egg. Mix together and apply to the head. If there is pain in the eye, drop some of the lotion in and this will cure it.

## FOR GOUT

529. Take half a measure each of white wine and stag's tallow, or when that is not procurable, mutton suet with moderately coarse ground wheat. Boil these ingredients until they become thick. Take a quantity of garlic, peel carefully, pound well, and add to the former. Beware however that it is not hot, or the garlic will lose its effect. Mix the whole together, and apply as a plaster between the affected part and the healthy, so that it may attract it until it is cured.

## FOR EVERY KIND OF ACHE

530. Take tender brambles, sprigs of broom and rue. Wash, and pound well. Temper with oil of olives to prepare an ointment, with which treat the affected part.

## FOR A COLD OR HOT DROPSY

531. Take anise seed, and the seed of lovage, called in Latin Levisticum Vulgaris*. Powder and mix these with your food and drink. Spikenard of Spain** may also be carefully added to this, and to any other kind of drink.

* Pughe adds: Ligusticum levisticum. *It is now Levisticum officinale, indicating that it was sold by pharmacists;* ** *The Welsh is 'ysbignardd o yspain'. Spicnard can either mean the Spikenard – Nardostachys grandiflora, or Lavender. Spikenard, or nard, was widely used in herbal medicine, but comes from India, China or Nepal. There are hundreds of varieties of Lavender, Lavandula, with English Lavender being Lavandula angustifolia. Lavandula stoechas is also common in gardens and known as French or Spanish lavender, so this may be the correct herb.*

## A FOMENTATION FOR EITHER A COLD OR HOT DROPSY

532. Take some sprigs of white bryony, roots of red fennel and herb bennet. Boil together in a pot until the herbs settle in the bottom, and then pour it into a convenient vessel so that the patient may wash and foment himself with it.

Make also a soup with water cresses, and pork or mutton boiled together, giving it colour with saffron. This is useful through Jesus for all kinds of dropsies, whether hot or cold.

## FOR BLEEDING PILES*

533. Get some blessed distillation of the best sort**. Dip a piece of fine soft linen in it, and push it up the rectum as far as you can, if the piles are internal. If external, let them be washed with this distillation for three or four days, at bedtime.

* *The Welsh heading is 'Rhag Gwaedling yr Eisteddfa, a Elwir Chwyf y Marchogion, a'r Lledewig'. This literally translates as 'For Flow of Blood from the Seat, called Disease of the Horsemen, and Piles';* ** *Pughe notes:* Spirit of wine.

## FOR THE SAME ILLNESS

534. Take viper's bugloss, and the leaves of the barberry tree, and pound together, forming them into small balls. Put a pan containing burning charcoal under a commode, casting the balls thereon, and let the patient sit well-covered, over the commode.

## ANOTHER REMEDY FOR BLEEDING PILES

535. Let the patient sit in a chair over a hot fomentation, composed of mallows, marsh pennywort*, and cow's milk.

*Hydrocotyle vulgaris*

## FOR COLIC

536. Boil mugwort, spearmint, dill seed and fennel seed, in equal parts of milk and water. Then drink a good draught of this as hot as you can. Drink another draught when quite cold, taking no other drink but water, and living by rule, rejecting butter, fat meat, and good ale. Dine upon mutton, and sup and breakfast

upon the milk of cows or goats, with well baked wheaten bread. A good potion for this disease is finely powdered unburnt lime, a small spoonful of this being taken at a time in milk and water.

## THE FOLLOWING IS A GOOD METHOD OF TREATMENT FOR A PERSON SUBJECT TO FREQUENT ATTACKS OF COLIC

537. Two hours before breakfast every morning, take a good slice of wheaten bread, made with the best barm. Toast it brown and crisp before the fire, but be careful not to burn it. Eat this by itself, and do not drink anything after it. If you eat meat, reject the fat, and prefer mutton to any other meat, with well-baked oven barm bread being used with it.* You should only drink water, or milk and water, with your meals, habituating yourself to oaten cakes and gruels, with milk or honey, wine or cider. Avoid all garden vegetables. Insist upon** fennel seed, caraway seed, and dill seed, ground also with your wheat bread, avoiding butter, pork, (particularly if old), rich cheese, goose flesh and duck.

*People used to use bread as a plate. Only the upper classes possessed crockery or pewter plates; **The Welsh is 'mynn falu' which seems to mean obtain, or insist upon. Pughe translates this as 'house'.

## FOR AN ABSCESS OR IMPOSTUME

538. Take cows' milk, linseed, and a little pounded garlic. Boil them together, make into a plaster, and apply to the affected part.

## WATER FOR ALL SORTS OF GOUT*

539. Procure the seed of eryngo, fill an earthenware pot with it, covering it very carefully, and bury it fully half-a-yard in the earth. [18 inches under the surface] It should be left from the first Lady-Day** in harvest time, until the last Lady-day in spring. It should then be opened, and you will find some clear water in the pot. Keep this carefully in a glass vial, for it is most useful for all sorts of gout.

* The Welsh is gwst mawr, or great ache; ** In September 1752, Great Britain switched from the Julian Calendar to the Gregorian Calendar. In order to achieve the change, 11 days were 'omitted' from the calendar - i.e. the day after 2 September 1752 was 14 September 1752. Prior to 1752, the year began on 25 March (Lady Day). Lady Day is one of the Quarter Days, which are still used in legal circles. The Quarter Days divide the year in quarters - Lady Day (25 March), Midsummer's Day (24 June), Michaelmas Day (29 September), and Christmas Day (25 December). Lady Day was the major day when farm rents and taxes were traditionally due. With the 'loss' of 11 days in September 1752, some people believed that they had 'lost' 11 days of their lives. They also were required to pay full taxes on 25 March, New Year's Day, but had worked for 11 days fewer. As a result, the Government altered the tax year to 11 days later. 25 March 1753 was a Sunday and taxes were due on Monday 26 March 1753. It was decreed that taxes were due on 6 April 1753. To this day, the UK tax year starts upon 6 April.

## TO CLEAR THE EYE

540. Obtain some fresh sprats* and lay them in the sun, or at such a distance from a fire as will subject them to a heat when oil exudes from the sprats. Mix this oil with honey, and anoint your eye with it.

*The European sprat, sprattus sprattus, is a small fish formerly found in huge numbers in the Celtic Sea, and comprising 12% fat. The source of many vitamins, when used for food it can be canned, salted, fried, grilled, baked, marinated, etc.*

## FOR A WATERY EYE

541. Take the leaves of red cabbage, and hen's fat, and compound together thoroughly. Cover the eye with this lotion at night, securing it with a bandage.

## FOR PAIN IN THE EYE

542. Procure some of the juices of centaury and celandine, boil them together, and apply this to the eye.

## TO REMOVE EXFOLIATIONS OF BONE FROM THE SKULL

543. Drink the juice of betony three times a day while fasting, the dose being three spoonfuls each time, and they will come away.

## FOR A CANCER

544. Take knapweed and goat's feet*, calcine in furnace, reduce to a powder, and apply to the cancer.

    * *Traed geifr translates as the above, but one wonders whether it could be a herb or plant. Coltsfoot is troed yr ebol or troed y tarw (bull's foot), horseradish is troed y march, cowslip is troed y fuwch (cow's foot) etc., etc. However, the plural possibly denotes that the translation is correct. Ipomoea pes-caprae is known as Goat's Foot, as is Oxalis pes-caprae, but both are non-European species and unlikely to be known in Western herbal medicine. Goat's Rue, Galega officinalis was used, however, and mentioned in Grieve and Culpeper, so possibly this is the herb referred to.*

## FOR A GOUT ATTENDED BY AN OFFENSIVE SUPPURATION

545. Procure the juice of bugle, and the juice of ribwort plantain, the white of an egg, mouse ear chickweed, and fine rye meal. Make into a plaster, let this be applied upon the part daily, being secured by a linen cloth, and it will cure it.

## FOR A BOIL

546. Obtain some plantain, make a plaster and apply to the part. It will cure it.

## FOR AN ABSCESS OR IMPOSTUME OF THE HEAD, WITH DEAFNESS

547. Take well pounded wood sage and oil of almonds. Boil and mix well in a silver spoon on the embers of a fire. Then take some clean linen, give it a twist, dip in the ointment and insert in the painful ear, binding it until the matter is discharged. It is proven.

## TO EXTRACT A TOOTH BY MEANS OF A POWDER

548. Take the roots of nightshade with black berries.* Pound the roots well in goat's milk. Then add the separately pounded black berries. Incorporate the whole into a pulp, and macerate in vinegar for thirteen days. Renew the vinegar three times**, then powder the residue and add vinegar to it for three days*** more. When this has cleared, decant the vinegar, and dry the sediment in the sun or near the fire in the like heat. Let the powder be put in the tooth if there is a cavity in it, and it will extract it without pain, and without delay.

*Pughe notes. Solanum nigrum. *This is European Black Nightshade or Garden Nightshade;* ** *The Welsh is 'y gwin egr dair gwaith', meaning 'the sour wine three times', but*

204

*Pughe translates as three 'days.';\*\*\* Equally, here the word is tridiau, or three days, not three 'times' as Pughe translates.*

## FOR HEADACHE AND WHOOPING COUGH

549. Take a red onion, and pound small with a little bile, adding some honey. Let this be boiled. When boiled, secure the patient, belly up, and pour some into his nostrils. Then let him get up and sneeze, when he will be cured and eased.

## TO MAKE A CERECLOTH*

550. Take two ounces of cod oil, two ounces of pitch, two and a quarter ounces of mastic, and an ounce of frankincense. Mix them well together, and set on the fire, taking a quantity of plantain juice, and mixing with it. Put the cloth in this molten fluid, so that it may absorb as much as possible of the wax. Then set it aside to cool, warming it by the fire, when required, for a bruise or other injury on a man's body.

*\* This was a cloth coated with wax, formerly used for wrapping the dead. Cere is Latin for wax, and it was also used as an altar cloth to protect the altar from being stained with wine.*

## A METHOD OF MAKING A PLASTER ACCORDING TO ART, ALTHOUGH TOO CRUDE FOR INFLAMED ULCERS

551. Take smallage, senna, roots of lily, roots of nightshade (called morel)\*, and roots of plantain. Let these be pounded very small, with honey, clarified white of eggs, and fine meal being added. Let them be carefully compounded, and mashed together, (but not on the fire) until they become thick as porridge. Spread on a cloth, and apply to the wound. It will remove the anguish, and restore the wound to its natural condition. This is the most excellent of plasters for all sorts of injuries.

*\* This should be translated as the roots of llysiau'r moch, pig's herb. This can mean black nightshade, Solanum nigrum, mentioned in 2:548, or Atropa belladonna, Deadly Nightshade. However, the latter is also known as Devil's Cherries or Great Morel, so it is Deadly Nightshade. Atropa is from the Greek Atropos, one of the Fates who cut the thread of life, in reference to its deadly poisonous nature; and Belladonna means beautiful lady. It is called Banewort, Belladonna, Naughty Man's Cherry, Daft-berries, Death's-herb, Dwale, Deadly Dwale, Dway-berries, Jacob's Ladder, Mad, Manicon, Mekilwort, Great Morel and Sleeping Nightshade. It is called Daft-berries because the berries cause giddiness. Around 1370 Langland, in 'Piers Plowman' related: 'The friar with his physic, this folk hath enchanted, And doth men drink dwale that men dreadeth no sin'. Dwale means opiate, that which dulls. Manicon is so referred to in Hudibras: 'Bewitch Hermetic men to run Stark staring mad with manicon'. It used to be called Solanum somniferum, or Sleeping Nightshade. In Italy it was used by women to give lustre to the eyes, thus bella donna. The berries are sweet and poisonous. The leaves are dried and used as a drug. It is an anodyne for neuralgia, enlarges the pupil of the eye, and is used for ophthalmic complaints. The plant is narcotic, but goats feed on it seemingly without effect.*

## TO PREPARE A GOOD RESOLVENT APPLICATION TO REMOVE BLOOD OR BRUISE FROM AN INJURY

552. Take old bacon, melt in a pan, and let it stand until the salt settles in the bottom. Then take virgin wax in equal quantity as frankincense in powder, melting and mixing them well with the lard. When it has somewhat cooled, take a moderate quantity of mastic and frankincense, setting it on the fire again, and mixing well. When cold, add as much again of flour of sulphur* to the frankincense, and mastic, mixing them well and diligently, until the whole resembles honey. Let it be kept in a box until required.

*In 1869, Dr William Cook wrote in the Physiomedical Dispensary of the many herbal uses of flour of sulphur, but noted that: 'The only worthy use to which it can be put, is in the treatment of itch; and it effectually destroys the itch animalcule. For this purpose, it is best applied as an ointment...'

## TO PREVENT TEETH BECOMING YELLOW AND ILL-SMELLING

553. Take the leaves of sage*, powder with as much again of salt, and make it into balls. Bake them until they are burnt, and make into powder. Let your teeth be rubbed frequently with this. It will render the teeth clean, white, and sweet.

*Sage and peppermint feature in many non-fluoridised and natural toothpastes, and is said to prevent plaque. A website called makingyourown.co.uk states: 'Sage is known to be a natural cleanser. As with baking soda, all you need is a penny size worth of sage powder poured into your hand, and press a damp toothbrush into the powder before brushing.' It also recommends sage as a mouthwash: 'sage, rosemary and myrrh can all be infused into water and used as a deodorising or mild cleansing mouthwash.' Hundreds of the herbs and plants noted in this book feature, with their medical properties, in 'Breverton's Complete Herbal'.

## FOR CANCER

554. Take equal parts of quicklime, pepper, horse mint, strong bile, honey and barley meal. Boil this well in an earthenware vessel, powder, and apply to the cancer. It will destroy it.

## ANOTHER REMEDY FOR CANCER

555. Take powdered quicklime, red precipitate of mercury*, equal to a fourth part of the lime in quantity, and mix with as much honey as will make it into a mass. Put it in an earthenware crucible, in a furnace, heated as for bread. When it is cold, keep it carefully covered in a glass vial, and apply as much as may be required upon the cancer. It will completely destroy it. Then apply a detergent plaster to the ulcer. When quite clean, dress it with healing salve or lint, and it will cure the patient.

* This is mercuric oxide (HgO), a heavy red crystalline powder obtained by heating mercuric nitrate, or by heating mercury in the air.

## FOR DROPSY BETWEEN THE FLESH AND SKIN*

556. Take the parings of white sheepskins, and boil until they become a glutinous mass. Apply to the dropsy, on linen.

* Pughe footnotes: Ascites. This is excess fluid in the space between the tissues lining the abdomen and abdominal organs (the peritoneal cavity).

## TO BREAK OR RE-OPEN ANY GATHERING

557. Take a portion of black soap, another of honey, and a third of fine wheaten meal. Incorporate them together, and apply to the part. If you wish it to break quickly, add more soap.

## FOR MALIGNANT ST. ANTHONY'S FIRE, OF WHICH, IF A MAN SICKENS, HE WILL MOST PROBABLY DIE*

558. Take a pound each of the warm dung of a pigeon** and rye meal, and pound together. Add half a pound of vinegar, mix well, and apply cold to the diseased part. Cover it with cabbage leaves, and bind the same carefully with a linen cloth. Let it not be removed for three days, and what is covered with the plaster, will at any rate be cured.

* *Pughe notes:* Erysipelas Phlegmonoides. *Eryisipelas is also known as Holy Fire, an acute streptococcus bacterial infection of the deep epidermis, with lymphatic spread. Queen Anne, Charles Lamb, John Dryden and John Stuart Mill all died from the disease. A fungus in rye bread can cause Ergotism, however, which was known as St Anthony's Fire. It is caused by eating grain, usually rye bread, contaminated by a fungus. Convulsive symptoms include painful seizures, spasms, diarrhoea, itching, mania, psychosis, headaches, nausea, vomiting and hallucinations. There have been epidemics throughout history, and not until 1834 did Fuchs separate ergotism from erysipelas and other afflictions. The Annales Xantenses for the year 857 record: 'a great plague of swollen blisters consumed the people by a loathsome rot, so that their limbs were loosened and fell off before death.' In the Middle Ages, the gangrenous poisoning was known as ignis sacer (holy fire) or St Anthony's Fire, after the monks of the Order of St Anthony who had some success in treating it. 'Ergotism' was not recorded as a disease until 1853, which explains Pughe's misattribution.*

** *Pughe notes:* Just killed. *The rich, and monasteries, kept pigeons in dovecotes as medieval 'fast food'. One idly wonders how many pigeons would have to be killed to procure a pound of their faeces, and whether it was gathered internally or externally. This could have been a very expensive remedy.*

## FOR GOUT

559. Take equal parts of wood sorrel, rue, agrimony, tansy, pimpernel, celandine, avens, ivy leaves, and ground liverwort. Pound together well, strain, and drink the strained liquor. It is good.

## TO PREPARE AN OINTMENT FOR GOUT

560. Take the lard of a young pig, a horse's fat, a boar's lard, and the herb called feverfew, or in Latin febrifuga, pounded well. Mix them well together, and set on the fire until they boil. When boiled until the virtue of the herbs is extracted, strain. Keep the ointment in a well-covered glass, and anoint the painful part near the heat of a fire.

## ANOTHER OINTMENT FOR GOUT

561. Take wall cress, southernwood, sage, and as much as an egg of sugar. Half-fill a glass vessel with this, and then fill up to the top with salt. The herbs should have been pounded well in old ale, and the vessel should be left in the sun for a week or near the fire in a similar heat. You will obtain an ointment which should be kept carefully. Anoint the painful part with this.

Then obtain wheat bran, white wine, and boar's lard. Boil them together, and make into a plaster, applying this as warm as it can be suffered to the swelling. This application will disperse it.

## ANOTHER OINTMENT FOR GOUT

562. Take black snails, and bake them before the fire in an earthenware vessel. Keep the oil in a clean vessel, and anoint the painful part with it. It is beneficial for hot and cold gout.*

* It may be that cold gout is in the toes and hot gout in the fingers. In the 1722 'Memoirs of Literature', edited by Michael de la Roche, we learn that: 'If the Application of hot Medicaments upon the tender Part gives some ease, 'tis a sign that the gout is cold; to which one must add the Whiteness of the Skin, the Softness of the Flesh, and a lingering Pain. If, on the contrary, the application of cold Remedies eases the Pain, 'tis a sign that the Gout is hot; which appears more clearly from the Redness of that Part, and the sharp and violent Pain. Not that but a cold Gout is often attended with a sharp Pain and Redness; but that Pain and that Redness are much more sensible in the hot Gout.' Cold and hot gout cures were given in Culpeper's 'The English Physitian', and it seems that cold gout was supposed to be caused by cold winters.

## ANOTHER OINTMENT FOR GOUT

563. Take pitch, virgin wax, frankincense, mutton suet, and boar's lard. Fry well together, strain, and keep in a pot. With this anoint the painful part.

## A USEFUL OINTMENT FOR ERUPTIONS AND WOUNDS

564. Take the fat of bacon, melt and let the salt settle in the bottom. Then take the fat, and add pitch and frankincense, making an ointment. Let it be applied as may be required.

## AN OINTMENT FOR A HEADACHE

565. Take the juice of dwarf elder, honey, wax, salt and frankincense and boil them together. With this anoint your head and brows.

## FOR GOUT IN THE STOMACH*

566. Take a handful of tansy and pound it. Pour a quart of bottled wine upon it, and let it stand well, covered for a night in an oaken vessel. Then put it in an unglazed earthenware vessel, boil gently, and strain. Let three draughts be taken of this, one each night for three nights, the patient being covered well in bed afterwards, so that he may perspire. This will cure him. It is well to sleep in flannel sheets or blankets.

* Here Pughe uses cylla for stomach, whereas in 511 he uses calon.

## ANOTHER FOR GOUT OF THE STOMACH

567. Take an armful each of tansy, mallows, wormwood, and half an armful each of garden sage and rosemary. Boil these well in a pot, put a pound of salt in the water, and pour out the decoction into a vessel large enough to bathe in. Get in, and sit therein so that it may cover your ankles, then cover yourself with blankets, so that you may be kept in a full perspiration for two or three hours. Add more hot liquid as may be required, so as to keep up the heat. Drink three tablespoonfuls of good old mead, mixed with powdered fennel seed, every half hour. Then at the end of the time specified, let the bath cool, and when it is no

warmer than new milk, get out. Go to bed and cover yourself well with blankets. Take a spoonful every hour of the decoction of blessed thistle, for six hours, carefully avoiding cold for some days.

## PAIN IN THE JOINTS FROM COLD, WEARINESS, OR SPRAIN
568. Take seaweed, boil in seawater, and anoint the painful part with this, as hot as you can bear it. Then apply the boiled seaweed to the pain, well pounded in the manner of a plaster, as warm as it can be borne easily. This is a good remedy for every painful swelling resulting from a fall or blow.

## FOR WHOOPING COUGH
569. Take pig's lard, powdered garlic, and a little honey. Boil well, and anoint the feet of the patient with the mixture. Then cover the feet with a flannel, and the bed in which the patient must lie with an abundance of blankets. The blankets should be removed when he has perspired freely, and the patient will certainly recover.

## FOR CANCER
570. Apply the juice of red onions to the ulcer, and make a plaster of the leaves of cow parsnip, stalks, flowers, and seed included. Compound the same with honey, vinegar, and a little frankincense.

## FOR INFLAMMATION OF THE LUNGS*
571. Take elder flowers, or in their absence, eryngo flowers, or the leaves, or the green inner bark, and wood sorrel. Boil in the whey of goat or cow milk, and let it be your only drink for nine weeks. So that you may not be in want of the flowers, let them be gathered in their season, and dried in the sun. Keep them and boil them in the whey as required. When wood sorrel cannot be obtained, boil bruised apples with the flowers in the whey. This is useful for all sorts of fevers in the blood and humors.
* *Pughe notes*: Lit. Lung Pock. *The Welsh is 'brech yr ysgyfaint.' Ysgyfaint can either mean lungs, pulmonary disease or pneumonia. Brech means pox, or a skin rash.*

## FOR A COLD
572. Take a pound of garlic, and pound well, adding to it a quart of good bottled wine, or in its absence good old ale* or strong mead. Let it macerate while well-covered, strain under a press, and drink it lukewarm. If the cold affects a joint, warm the remains of the garlic and apply to the part as warm as it can be borne. It is proven.
   * *Pughe omits good old ale.*

## FOR A WEB OF THE EYE
573. Take the juice of celandine, and a little honey. Mix well and apply to the eye with a feather night and morning. It is proven.

## FOR BLACK FEVER*
*574. Take anise-seed, fennel seed, and rue well powdered, to which add good white or bottled wine. Let it stand six hours, and when given to the patient, give it a slight boiling, so that no time is lost. Then strain and let it be given to the sick person as his only drink. * Typhus.*

## ANOTHER FOR TYPHUS

575. Take the surface of new ale in the wort, and administer a good draught to the sick person every three hours, for twenty-four hours. Then let him have a slice of wheaten barm bread toasted by the fire, wine being poured upon it while hot. This bread and wine should be taken in small portions during four hours. It is proven.

## FOR A BRUISE OF THE EYE

576. Take parsley and pound well with unsalted butter, then apply it as a warm plaster to the eye.

## FOR SPECKS ON THE CORNEA

577. Take the juice of celandine, of fennel, and a little honey. Let some be dropped into the eye morning, noon, and night, the eye being covered in the mean time so that the light might not affect it. Proven.

## FOR VERTIGO

578. Take the roots of cowslips and sage leaves, in equal quantities. Boil well, the roots being first pounded. The boiling should be carried on until the herbs are hardly covered, when they should be strained under a press. A good draught of this should be taken two hours before and two hours after food.

## FOR SUNBURN

579. Take the leaves of marsh pennywort*, rudely pounded with cream. Boil them together on a gentle fire so as to form into an ointment, and anoint the affected part with it.

*This was also used to remove freckles and pimples, but it seems that only the Myddfai doctors recommended it for sunburn. It is today formulated into hydroctyle extract, or Kotu Kola containing l-asiatic acid, a powerful wound-healer and contributor to collagen growth. As with many other entries, modern medicine is revisiting earlier remedies based upon plants.*

## A GOOD EYE SALVE

580. Take vinegar, white wine, the juice of celandine, and plantain. Mix them together in a pan, cover over and let them stand in it for three days and three nights. Take the salve out, keep in a box, and anoint your eye.

## THE TREATMENT OF BOILS AND BLEEDING SORES

581. Take the fat of an old boar, half as much of virgin wax*, frankincense and mastic, and boil together. When nearly cold, add as much flour of sulphur, as of the frankincense, then mix for an ointment and keep in a box.

* *Pughe adds:* The wax of honeycombs not brood combs.

## FOR AN INDOLENT ULCER

582. Obtain frankincense and arnamentum,* grind together in powder, and apply to the ulcer.

**Pughe explains:* A corruption of 'Auripigmentum' or yellow sulphate of arsenic. It should be used with great caution.

## A USEFUL UNGUENT*

583. Take plantain, pimpernel, and wild tansy. Pound well in a mortar with fresh lard, and let it ferment for nine days. Then it should be boiled and strained

210

through linen. Add wax, frankincense, and pure rosin.** When all are molten together, the poultice is ready.

*The Welsh heading is 'Tred Da'. Tred is the same word as entrêd, meaning a poultice or plaster, so the meaning is a good plaster; ** A note in Welsh reads: 'Rhosin mae'n debyg', which means the same as rosin.*

## AN OINTMENT FOR THE HEADACHE
584. Take the juice of dwarf elder, new wax, and rosin. Boil together, and anoint your temple with the ointment.

## TO PREPARE A GOOD OINTMENT
585. Obtain equal parts of the juice of wild celery, tansy, nightshade, plantain, and marsh pennywort. Also add honey, fine wheaten meal, boar's lard, and sheep's suet. Let the mixture be boiled on the fire until the mass becomes thick. Then strain through linen. It is useful.

## FOR DEFECTIVE SIGHT
586. Take the juice of ground ivy, fennel, celandine, sow's lard, honey, a little vinegar, and an eel's blood. Put the whole in a vessel until it ferments. Anoint your eyes with this, it will restore lost sight. Proven.

## FOR PAIN IN THE EYES
587. Fill an egg shell with the juice of fennel, rue, clarified honey, wine, and the urine of a child. Anoint your eye with this.

## AN EYE OINTMENT
588. Obtain a black snail in the month of May and roast on the embers of the fire, preserving the oil until required. Anoint your eye with this, with a feather.

## FOR A STYE IN THE EYE, OR AN INFLAMMATION
589. Obtain the yolk of an egg, wheaten meal, and a little sulphate of copper. Let the mixture be applied to the eye when going to sleep, and it will produce perspiration during the night. Do this for three days and it will cure it.

## FOR DEAFNESS
590. Obtain a sow's gall, goat's milk, and clear honey, and drop it warm into your ears. It is an unfailing remedy.

## FOR A SLOUGH, BEFORE AND AFTER IT HAS SUPPURATED
591. Take a good handful of sage, half a handful of plantain, and the same quantity of red fennel. Let these be boiled in a quart of water, a quart of honey, (or two quarts of water would be better so that it may stand a longer boiling), and a pound weight of white frankincense*. Let it be boiled long and well, so that it is reduced to a third. Let it be kept in a vessel, with the herbs simply bruised between your hands left in it. It is a good water to foment any cancer, dead flesh, (doughy) painful swelling, or blistered, inflamed, or painful part. By God's help it will cure it.

*Frankincense or olibanum is produced from the trunk of the Boswellia tree. The more opaque, the higher the quality. This would be another expensive remedy.*

## FOR AN INDOLENT ULCER* OF RECENT STANDING, WHEN YOU WISH TO DESTROY THE UNHEALTHY GRANULATIONS

592. Obtain honey, treacle, frankincense, sulphur, white-lead**, and mercury, and make them into a plaster. Apply to the part frequently and it will heal it. If not, let a plaster of honey and black soot be applied to the ulcer, and this by the help of God will cure it.

*An indolent ulcer is one that is inactive or slow to heal or grow. It can likewise pertain to an organic disorder accompanied by little or no pain; ** White lead is basically lead carbonate, a heavy white poisonous powder used as a paint pigment in the past. It was responsible for many deaths during and after the Industrial Revolution.*

## A SLEEPING POTION

593. Take the juice of opium (poppy) and eryngo, or the seed of the latter. Compound them into pills with milk, and let these be administered to the patient. One will induce sleep in general, but if not let him take another, and another again if required. Take care that two or three hours should intervene between each dose, in order to watch their effect before another is given.

## FOR AN ERUPTION OF TETTERS*

594. Take lard, black soap, and mercury, rub them together into an ointment, anointing the affected part therewith, and it will be healed.

* *Pughe notes: Herpes. The Welsh is tardd afrifed, which means intolerable eruption. This viral disease can be oral or genital.*

## FOR RINGWORM*

595. Take toadstool** or (when not to be had) agaric***, red alder leaves**** and clarified butter. Boil them together in sheep's milk and strain through new linen. Anoint the part frequently with this, and with God's help you will be cured.

* *Pughe notes: Favus. This is a fungal disease affecting the scalp. The Welsh is 'rhag y clefri neu'r ddarwyden fawr'. Clefri can mean mange, scabby disease, leprosy, scurf etc.; **However, 'madarch' translates as either mushroom or toadstool, and there are hundreds of varieties, many poisonous; *** Pughe notes: Boletus. However, there are over 100 species of the Boletus genus of mushroom alone. The Welsh is 'ffwng y ddaiar a elwir bwyd llyffaint' (- earth fungus also named toadstool). This makes little sense at present; **** Pughe notes: When changing their hue in Autumn. The Red Alder, Alnus rubra, is native to North America. The native British Alder is Alnus glutinosa, the Black Alder, to which he is probably referring.*

## FOR CRUSTED* OR HUMID** TETTER

596. Take the roots of red dock, and boil in sheep's milk for two hours at least. Remove from the fire and add some clarified butter, straining it through new linen. Anoint the diseased part with this ointment, and it will heal it.

* *Pughe notes: Impetigo; ** Pughe notes: Eczema*

## FOR SCABIES

597. Take the white of an egg, strained rapidly through linen, the juice of red fennel and celandine, clear honey, a child's urine, and white wine in equal parts. Mix briskly and anoint your body therewith, even your eyes if needful.

## FOR LEPRA*

598. Take the roots of red dock, the roots of elecampane, honeysuckle leaves, wild hyacinth [bluebell], broom sprigs, bugle, violet, heath shieldfem**, and avens. Pound them well together in a mortar with unsalted butter, then boil them well. Remove from the fire and strain through new linen. Add to this a portion of flour of brimstone and verdigris. Anoint the diseased part frequently with this ointment, and by God's help it will cure it.

*The Welsh is 'rhag tardd gwahanol, a elwir y gwahanglwyf' – 'for leprous illness, called gwahanglwyf.'; *Variously known as Aspidium, Polypodium or Lastraea oreopteris. The Welsh is rhedyn Mair, Mary's fern, which has several interpretations. In 1420, this was the male fern, Dryopteris filix-mas. It was also the mountain fern, Oreopteris limbosperma. It is also the lady-fern, Athyrium filix-femina and the royal fern, Osmunda regalis, although these are later attributions. In 1515 rhedyn Mair was noted as Polypodium vulgare. To make matters even more complicated, the name is also given to sweet cicely, Myrrhis odorata.*

## FOR RINGWORM*, A DISEASE SOMEWHAT LIKE HUMID TETTER, ATTENDED WITH MUCH IRRITATION

599. Take crude honey, a fox's marrow, and rosin. Mix well together by pounding them in a mortar until they become an ointment, and anoint the disease with this.
* Dermaphytosis, often caught from sheep and cattle.

## FOR BOILS

600. Take the juice of nightshade,* and of plantain, barley meal, and the white of eggs. Make a plaster thereof and apply thereto.
* Pughe adds: Moriel in the text must be intended for morella, i. e. nightshade. This is probably black nightshade, as mentioned above, which has also been known as petty morel and morella. Morella has been superceded by Myrica as a plant genus, and could also refer to sweet gale (bog myrtle)

## ANOTHER FOR BOILS

601. Take feverfew, knapweed, mugwort, bugle, deyil's bit, and daisy. Wash clean, and pound with old ale. A spoonful at a time should be given to the patient, and if given in time it will preserve him from the complaint. This is an excellent potion.

## FOR AN INTRACTABLE PAIN

602. Drink the juice of tansy, pounded carefully with strong old ale, and strained.

## FOR A PAIN OF THE THROAT WHEN THERE IS AN ERUPTION*, OR SUPPURATION IN THE PHARYNX, ATTENDED WITH A FEVER

603. Boil sage and rue in water. When it has boiled a little while, add vinegar and honey so that it may be somewhat sweet. Then gargle your mouth and throat with it warm, ejecting the same carefully, so that none is swallowed. When you have gargled well, drink a good draught of the same as a potion. Do this for three or four times in the day and night. Take also equal parts of mallows, sage and rue, pounding these well, and adding to sheep's milk, or any other milk convenient, as much as may be needed to give it the consistency of a cataplasm. Let this be applied warm to the throat, changing it as it dries. Keep dissolving in your mouth

also as much twice in quantity as a nut of pure old honey boiled hard. Do this for three days, and by God's help you will recover.

* *Pughe notes:* Diptheria. *However, this could be quinsy, a peritonsillar abscess. In Lynn Hughes' 'A Carmarthenshire Anthology' there is a remedy attributed to the Physicians of Myddfai, which this author cannot find in this original text, so must be from an untranslated ms. It is: "Quinsy: In case of quinsy, let blood from beneath your tongue or beneath your two arms and from the vein of the head and put a plaster of mallow, linseed and a little butter without salt around your neck and at the base of your tongue."' This author almost died of a double quinsy, while at university.*

## ANOTHER FOR THE THROAT OR PHARYNX

604. Take sage, rue, and the berries* or flowers of the elder tree (or inner bark when neither can be obtained), mallows and feverfew. Put them in a mortar and mix with a little honey and white wine, or vinegar. Pound them well together. Let a portion of the pounded ingredients be applied warm to the throat as a plaster on a flannel, the other portion being strained, and two tablespoonfuls of the same being taken every two hours. Use a spoonful as a gargle before each dose, this being afterwards carefully ejected. Ensure that none is swallowed, as it would be charged with the poison of the disease. Instead of using the plaster you may foment your throat with the liquid each time you drink. Do this for three days, keeping a flannel about your throat, and with God's help you will recover.

* *Pughe footnotes:* Lit., 'Gems' a beautiful term for these ruby-like berries.

## ANOTHER FOR THE THROAT OR PHARYNX

605. Boil rue in white wine, strain and drink four spoonfuls of this every three hours, fomenting the throat (covering it afterwards with a flannel) at every dose. Before each dose, gargle your mouth and throat carefully with the decoction and vinegar, half and half, ejecting the same afterwards. By God's help you will recover in consequence.

## ANOTHER FOR THE THROAT OR PHARYNX

606. Take a large apple, extract the eye and core as well as some of the pulp. Then take rue, bruise small, filling the apple with it, and cover it over. Roast the apple before the fire. When sufficiently roasted, pound the whole together, mixing a little honey with it, and also a spoonful of white wine, making a confection. Take a spoonful of this every two hours until you have recovered. Before you take it, however, you should wash the mouth and throat with a decoction of rue and vinegar in equal proportions.

## THE FOLLOWING IS A GOOD GARGLE

607. Take sage, rue, mallows, and elder flowers, either fresh or dry. Boil them well in water. When you have done so for a while, add a spoonful of vinegar, and as much of honey, continuing the boiling some time longer. Then strain carefully through a linen cloth and keep. When required for use, warm from two to four spoonfuls. Take a mouthful and gargle well as long as you can, taking care not to swallow any, then finally eject it. Do this from twice to four times with a spoonful at a time. It is useful for every affection of the mouth and throat, and should be

used in all dangerous seasons, when epidemic sore throats prevail. This, with God's blessing will preserve you. When you have a sore throat, after gargling, take a draught of the potion, and by God's help it will benefit you.

## FOR INFLAMMATORY FEVER IN A CHILD

608. Boil a handful of cinquefoil in cow's milk, and administer a spoonful to the child every hour for three days. By God's help it will cure him.

## TO DESTROY UNHEALTHY GRANULATIONS IN AN ULCER, RESULTING FROM A WOUND OR BLOW

609. Take old tallow, stale gander's dung, a crust of rye bread, egg shells, and salt, in equal parts. Put them into a pot, calcine and reduce into fine powder, and apply.

## ANOTHER TO DESTROY UNHEALTHY GRANULATIONS IN AN ULCER

610. Take a pound in weight of burnt lime, and the same quantity of orpiment. Boil in water in a porringer [a shallow bowl] for a great length of time. Then remove from the fire and set aside to dry where no dirt can come to it. When it is perfectly dry let it be reduced to a powder. If some of this is applied to the unhealthy granulations it will destroy them. It should be left upon the part from one to three hours, and then washed away with sheep's milk, or with cow or goat's milk, when sheep's milk cannot be procured. This should be done once a day until you see that the cancer is destroyed.

Then dress the part with healing ointment, the patient all the time taking no other drink than a decoction of cleavers* and betony, restricting himself to a milk diet, preferring that of goat's milk. Twice a week he should partake of mutton of mature age.

* *Pughe notes:* This is admirable practice so far as this diet drink is concerned at any rate.

## FOR A WOUND

611. Take a nettle, roots and all. Wash the roots clean, pound it well, then boil in unsalted butter. Make an ointment, apply to the wound and it will cure it.

## THE TREATMENT OF WOUNDS

612. Take lard, honey, wine, and rye meal. Boil these ingredients together, and apply to the wound on a cloth. It will clear and heal the wound, but should it do so too soon, procure the herb called wild nep.* Make a plaster with this, apply it to the part and it will re-open it.

* *Pughe adds:* Nep wyllt - *Rape, or brassica napus. Rapeseed, or Oilseed Rape, seems a newish addition to the British countryside with its bright yellow fields which cause asthmatic allergies, but is an ancient plant. The original Welsh text calls this 'llysewyn a elwir y nep wyllt' – 'llysewyn also named wild nep.'*

## ERYSIPELAS

[This entry is not numbered, and the heading absent from the Welsh text, but the entry and text has been inserted here by Pughe]

[612.5] Erysipelas has divers constitutions, even hot and cold, the hot being the most dangerous of the two, and is attended with more extensive ardency,* the cold being less so. In consequence of this they must be treated differently, the hot requiring cold remedies, and the cold hot ones. Thus the cold form is treated, this disease being lancole** Take the white of eggs, and rye meal, make dough of them and leave it on the part till it falls away by itself. Let this be done till the part is healed.

* *Pughe notes:* i. e. Inflammatory. It may be a question what sense "ffroenau" has in the text, I have assumed it to be derived from "ffro" - ardent, as erysipelas never exhibits any character to which the term "nostrils" (ffroenau) could be applied in any way; ** *Pughe places lancole in brackets with a question mark. It is not presently known what lancole signifies.*

## A MEDICAMENT FOR PUTRID FLESH, WHICH HAS LOCAL INFLAMMATION IN AND ABOUT THE ULCERS

613. Take fine rye meal and clear honey. Make a dough and apply to the ulceration. When required let it be renewed, and this will restore the patient to health and activity.

## A GENERAL REMEDY FOR ALL KINDS OF ERYSIPELAS

614. Take tow* and cut it fine. Wash in lees procured from wheat ale, boil well and apply to the affected part for one night and half a day. Let it then be removed, and the part washed with male urine. Afterwards cover it with a powder prepared as follows. Take some wings of geese, pluck off the feathers, calcine them, powder and apply to the disease. This again should be covered with the fat of a wild cat, or pig's lard and a cabbage leaf. Then obtain some good old ale, made with wheat unmixed with barley. Fill a pitcher with this, add salt, arfemeint** and pitch in equal parts, with more beeswax than either of these Boil the mixture until it becomes thick, then remove from the fire and let it cool. This should be applied as a plaster: first the above mentioned powder; then the plaster of fat; and the cabbage leaf upon that. It should be renewed morning and night. Let an infusion or decoction of avens be given the patient, and in the day he drinks it, the progress of the disease will be arrested.

*This is Pughe's translation of 'carth'. It means the coarse and broken fibres of hemp or flax before spinning. The GPC gives a definition of 'hemp, hards, tow, oakum.'; ** Pughe adds: A popular corruption of "orpiment", I believe. The word is missing from the Geiriadur Prifysgol Cymru. It is arsenic sulphide.*

## ANOTHER REMEDY FOR ALL KINDS OF ERYSIPELAS

615. Take the juice of avens, mallows, and linseed. Mix with honey and the milk of a single-coloured cow. Put in a pitcher, boil it well and apply to the disease as hot as the patient can bear it.

## ANOTHER REMEDY FOR ALL KINDS OF ERYSIPELAS

616. Powder pepper and boil in vinegar until it is quite dried up. Then mix powdered frankincense, rosin, verdigris, and honey with it. Incorporate it well in a mortar, and apply on a cloth to the affected part.

## A MEDICINE FOR PAIN IN THE BONES, SOMETIMES ATTENDING ERYSIPELAS

617. Put the seed of eryngo in an earthenware pitcher. Cover it over with embers so that it may roast thoroughly. Express carefully through a linen cloth, and with this strained liquid anoint the disease. If you can not get eryngo seed take the entire plant, roots and all, and treat in the same way.

## ANOTHER MEDICINE FOR PAIN IN THE BONES, SOMETIMES ATTENDING ERYSIPELAS

618. Obtain oil of roses* and anoint the affected part with it. Then infuse sage and hyssop in wine, or mix the juice of these herbs with wine. Let the patient drink this until he recovers.

*Oil of roses is tremendously expensive today. Whether this could be obtained from a pharmacy, or was made by the medical men, is unclear.*

## ANOTHER MEDICINE FOR PAIN IN THE BONES, SOMETIMES ATTENDING ERYSIPELAS

619. Take white peas* and roast them well on the fire. Then powder the peas, anoint the painful part with clear honey, and sprinkle the powder upon the part. Let this remain until it falls off spontaneously. Let this be repeated until the affected part heals.

*These may well be Haricot Beans, Cannellini Beans or somesuch, rather than peas.*

## FOR A PAINFUL ERYSIPELAS ATTENDED WITH SWELLING

620. Take the roots of fern, and pound them well in a mortar. Mix carefully with a little warm water. Then express through a cloth, and make it into a poultice with barley meal, mixing the white of an egg with it. Spread it thinly on a cloth, and apply it to the affected part.

## AN APPLICATION TO A PAIN, WHICH WILL SHOW WHETHER IT PROCEEDS FROM BRUISED FLESH OR CONTUSION

621. Anoint the whole of the affected part with honey. Obtain fresh cheese and rye meal. Put these ingredients in the earth for a night, then apply them to the openings in the painful part. When you remove this plaster next day, if there are holes in it, know that there is a worm in the ulcer.

## ANOTHER APPLICATION TO A PAIN, WHICH WILL SHOW WHETHER IT PROCEEDS FROM BRUISED FLESH OR CONTUSION

622. Take a black snail and apply to the pain. If you find a portion of the snail eaten next day, know that there is a worm inside.

## THE WAY IN WHICH THE WORM MAY BE DESTROYED

623. Take the root of the gladwyn, and bruise in honey and wine. Apply a black snail to the affected part, and cover it with the above plaster, and it will destroy the worm.

## ANOTHER WAY IN WHICH THE WORM MAY BE DESTROYED

624. Take pepper, rue, linseed, and feverfew. Dry these last three, powder the four elements and apply to the part. It will destroy the worm.

## AN APPLICATION FOR A BITE, OR A SUPPURATING ULCER, EVEN WHEN IT IS A CANCER

625. Take marsh pennywort, powder and cover the part with it.

## ANOTHER APPLICATION FOR A BITE, OR A SUPPURATING ULCER, EVEN WHEN IT IS A CANCER

626. Take old lard, quicksilver, frankincense, mastic, and a little pepper. Bruise these ingredients separately. Then mix and incorporate with the lard when cold. Then rub the quicksilver with the mixture until it is killed. Anoint the part with this by the fire.

## ANOTHER APPLICATION FOR A BITE, OR A SUPPURATING ULCER, EVEN WHEN IT IS A CANCER

627. Take a little of the juice of the roots of bloody veined dock*, the juice of avens, the juice of field mint, a little of the juice of marsh mallow, and the juice of plantain. Put them in a pan on the fire with lard, and form an ointment of this. Anoint the diseased part therewith, and it will cure it. Amongst all dangerous diseases which are to be dreaded, mortified flesh and cancer are the worst, and by careful treatment only can they be cured, not otherwise.

*Pughe omits 'roots', and the original Welsh here is 'y taf * as', with the asterisk being footnoted by Pughe as 'Ystyr as ydyw dippyn bach'. Tipyn bach means a little bit or a little while.*

## FOR ALL KINDS OF MORBID FLESH OR EVEN ERYSIPELAS

628. Take wheat grain, hen's dung, black beans, garlic, salt, goat's dung, horse bones and fragments of blue cloth*. Put them in a pot, cover carefully, set on the fire and leave there until all is calcined.** Mix it with as much as there is of pepper, and of powder of white glass and garlic. Wash the part with vinegar and stale urine night and morning, covering it with the powder afterwards. It will heal it.

Also cover the powder with goats' dung and butter, and take water-flag iris and new wax. Cover the affected parts with the powder, and apply the wax over it. When the venom is extracted, dress it with the juice of plantain, honey, white of eggs, and rye meal. Drink the juice of plantain, avens, and agrimony. Let the patient avoid cheese, nuts and women, and then he will recover.

*'Of blue rags' is perhaps a better translation of 'o frattaiu gleision', but why they must be blue is a mystery. Also, gleision is the plural of glas, which can either mean blue, green, grey or silver; **To calcine is to heat (a substance) to a high temperature but below the melting or fusing point, causing loss of moisture, reduction or oxidation, and the decomposition of carbonates and other compounds.*

## FOR THE SAME KINDS OF MORBID FLESH OR EVEN ERYSIPELAS

629. Take a mole and burn it in an earthenware pot until it is reduced to powder. Powder finely, and cover the part where the mortified flesh is with this powder. Take hart-wort* and knapweed, and carefully ground in a mortar, adding some honey and butter. Make the whole into a plaster and apply it to the part. It will destroy the dead flesh and the disease. Sprinkle sage powder upon it. This will bind it and cure it.

*Tordylium maximum, probably*

## FOR THE SAME KINDS OF MORBID FLESH OR EVEN ERYSIPELAS

630. Take sandarach gum*, frankincense, copperas, natron, and verdigris. Powder carefully and sprinkle upon the morbid flesh. Leave it there two or three days, then cover the part well with agrimony carefully pounded with honey. Clean and dress carefully twice daily and it will cure it. If you cannot obtain the above, seek some soot, the ashes of old shoes, and stale urine. Mix well and apply so that it may remove the disease, then treat it with agrimony and honey as above.

*Sandarac (or sandarach) is a resin taken from a small cypress-like tree, Tetraclinis articulata.*

## FOR CANCER

631. Take copperas and pepper. Bruise them together, and temper with white of eggs and honey. When it has cleared on the fire, anoint the cancerous part well with it.

## FOR CANCER

632. Powder white frankincense, and apply.

## FOR FOUL BREATH

633. Take the juice of orpine, feverfew, angelica, and pennyroyal. Mix with honey, and administer a spoonful to the patient night and morning while fasting, and he will recover.

## FOR A PERSON WHO HAS LOST CONSCIOUSNESS OR SPEECH, IN CONSEQUENCE OF ILLNESS

634. Take pennyroyal gathered on Whit-Sunday or on the eve of St. John the Baptist. Boil, dry the decoction, and make a powder of it. Let this powder be administered to the patient in some drink, and it will be of benefit.

## FOR AN OFFENSIVE ULCER ON THE LEG

635. Boil oak leaves in white or red wine, and apply the wine and leaves to the part, and it will be of use.

## ANOTHER FOR AN OFFENSIVE ULCER ON THE LEG

636. Take oil of olives, and white wine. Mix well, anoint the ulcer with it. It will remove the evil smell, and heal the disease.

## TO HASTEN A TEDIOUS LABOUR

637. Take the juice of savory, and administer it in water.

## TO RESTRAIN HAEMORRHAGE FROM AN ULCER OR WOUND, OR FROM WHATEVER OTHER CAUSE

638. Take nettles, pound well, and pour vinegar upon them. Apply this to the wound, but beware less the patient should faint. If he does so, anoint his eyebrows with vinegar, and give him some drink.

## FOR UTERINE HAEMORRHAGE

639. Take nut shells*, and powder finely. Then make a decoction of the inner bark of blackthorn, adding a little honey. Mix the powder with it, and let it be the only drink for a month or two if required.

* *Coccwyon cnau*

## FOR A PAINFUL CONDITION OF THE MOUTH

640. Take a spoonful each of the juice of sage, the juice of rue, white wine or vinegar, and honey, and mix them. Let the patient first wash his mouth with salt and water, then let him take a spoonful at a time when the above mentioned salt water is in his mouth, and gargle it well. However, let him have a care not to swallow it, but eject it. Then he should take another mouthful and swallow it, and it will cure him. Let him repeat this proceeding again and again until he recovers. It is a valuable remedy for dangerous affections of the mouth and throat.

## TO PRESERVE FROM DANGEROUS EPIDEMICS

641. When dangerous epidemics prevail, take the juice of rue, and white wine, or strong old mead in equal parts. Drink a spoonful or two, morning, noon, and night in going to rest, at least an hour before or after food.

## ANOTHER TO PRESERVE FROM DANGEROUS EPIDEMICS

642. Take a handful of rue, four heads of garlic, and a handful of sage. Pound them together with wine or strong mead, and strain carefully. Drink four spoonfuls of this every morning, while fasting as long as the epidemic prevails.

## A GOOD CATHARTIC

643. Take a spoonful of the juice of spurge, mixed with powdered frankincense. It is beneficial to the chest and stomach.

## ANOTHER GOOD CATHARTIC

644. Take a spoonful of the juice of hyssop, and boil in a quart of red wine until it is reduced to half. Let the patient drink it warm at night, and cold in the morning.

## PRO MORBO CADENDO, OR EPILEPTIC DISEASE

645. Take mistletoe from the oak*, and put in an unglazed earthenware pot. Cover it well and set it on a slow fire, but not too near. Dry the herb until it can be powdered, being careful that it does not burn. Reduce to powder and give to the patient in every drink and food he partakes of. Make also a mass as big as a pigeon's egg thereof with honey, and give to the patient between his meals, and continue this practice for nine weeks. It is proven.

*The Welsh is actually 'y gwisglys a elwir uchelfar y derw' which seems to mean 'mistletoe known as mistletoe of the oak'.*

## ANOTHER FOR EPILEPTIC DISEASE

646. Gather branches, leaves and berries of mistletoe at Christmas. Make a confection of the berries with honey in equal parts. Keep well-covered. The other portion of the plant should be powdered as above mentioned. And whenever a person is subject to this disease, mix as much of the powder with the confection as you can, carefully preserving both from mouldiness. Let the sick person eat a good mouthful thereof fasting morning, noon, and night. It is proven.

220

## ARALL

647. Cymmer fustl ci, a chrog ef yn y tŷ y bo'r claf, lle caffo wynt dridiau, yna bwrw mewn cwrw amcan o chwart, a brew hyn el yn beint a dyro i'r claf pan gotto o'i syrth, cyn y delo'r clwyf yr ail waith arno.

## ANOTHER FOR EPILEPTIC DISEASE

Take a dog's bile and hang it in the patient's house, in a place where he can smell it for three days. Then place it in about a quart of beer and boil till it becomes a pint. Give it to the patient when he recovers from his lethargy, before the illness affects him once more.

## FOR CARDIALGIA

648. Take ash keys*, linseed, and a pear. Pound together well with white wine, and administer the whole lukewarm to the patient, mixed with as much wine as will make it drinkable.

   * *These are the winged seeds of the Ash tree, so called because they resemble a bunch of keys.*

## FOR SWELLING OF THE STOMACH

649. Take the roots of fennel, and the roots of ash. Pound them well, and temper with wine and honey. Let the expressed liquor be given to the patient to drink, and he will recover.

## TO KNOW WHETHER A WOUNDED PERSON WILL LIVE OR DIE

650. Obtain pimpernel, milkwort, or trefoil. The herbs should be pounded with water, and strained. Administer to the patient, and if he vomits he will die.

## TO HEAL WOUNDS

651. Obtain hog's lard, and melt it with honey, wine, and rye meal. Boil carefully, spread on linen, and apply to the wound. It will draw and cleanse the wound, and heal it effectually.

## TO OPEN A WOUND

652. Take wild turnips, pound to a plaster, and apply to the wound. It will open the wound and heal it. Proven.

## TO HEAL A WOUND

653. Take the herb called centaury, powder it and cast into the wound. By God's help it will cure it.

## TO RESTRAIN BLEEDING FROM THE NOSE

654. Obtain periwinkle and hang in a bag about the neck of the patient. Proven.

**Many diseases and fevers of all kinds are bred, and affect the body of man in consequence of the scrophulous diathesis, and they can only be avoided by the use of effective remedies.**

## FOR SCROFULA*

655. Take daisy and plantain. Mix with strong drink until it is thickened, and cast some powdered sulphate of copper on the potion. If this is habitually given the patient before he sleeps, it will cure him.

*A tuberculous condition causing swelling of the lymph nodes of the neck, known as King's Evil. This in a less serious form is known as swollen glands.*

## FOR SCROFULA BEFORE SLEEP

656. Bruise daisy, yellow stone crop, and plantain, and apply it as a plaster to the complaint. Drink the juice also.

## ANOTHER FOR SCROFULA

657. Take the flowers or leaves of knapweed. Bruise with the yolk of an egg and fine salt. Apply to the part.

## ANOTHER FOR SCROFULA

658. Take the roots of red nettle and the roots of mugwort, when it is in bud*. Boil in milk and water, and add butter to it. Drink this night, morning, and noon, and take no other drink until you are well. Proven.

* In Pughe's translation *'ar ei emdawd'* is inserted here, and its asterisked footnote reads: *'Endawd, blodau a gemma Gwydd. D.G'*

## FOR A SCROFULOUS ULCER WHEN IT HAS DISCHARGED ITS CONTENTS, AND INFLAMMATION

659. Take chamomile, and prepared sulphur in powder. Boil in goats' milk and water, until all moisture has evaporated. Dry, and reduce to fine powder, sprinkling it on the ulcer. This will contract all manner of sores.

## FOR SCROFULOUS SWELLINGS

660. Take honey and white rosin. Iincorporate them together, and apply to the part.

## FOR FRACTURED BONES

661. To promote the union of fractured bones, take celandine, and boil with wine, pepper, and honey. Use it nine days as drink, and they will unite.

## MEDICINE FOR FRACTURED BONES

662. First bind the limb, then take roasted acorns, and powder them. Put four spoonfuls of the powder in a quart of half milk and half water. Boil well, and add as much clarified honey as will render it sweetish. Let the patient have it as his only drink until he recovers. Also take wine, honey, salt, and rye meal in equal parts. Mix together for a plaster, and apply to the part. This will unite the bones. Whoever drinks a decoction of the violet, will greatly promote the extraction of broken bones.

## TO KNOW WHETHER THERE ARE LOOSE FRAGMENTS OF BONE IN A MAN'S LIMB OR NOT

663. Take the white of eggs, linseed, and a woman's milk. Make a plaster of this, and apply to the wound. If the plaster does not dry, know that there is a bone therein. If there is not a piece of bone, it will dry crisp.

## FOR MEN WHO HAVE LOST THEIR REASON
664. Take daisy, field southernwood*, and sage. Pound well, and mix with wine. Put it aside, well covered, for three hours. Then strain, and let the patient drink it.
*Artemisia campestris. One wonders whether this remedy refers to those with age-related dementia.

## TO RESTORE SPEECH WHEN LOST FROM DISEASE
665. Take sage or pimpernel, extract the juice, and pour it into the patient's mouth. It will restore his speech.

## TO PROCURE SLEEP
666. Take corn poppy, for it is better than the foreign poppy* and eryngo, or the seed of these. Pound them well in a mortar, and mix with wine. Wash the nostrils, eyes, and ears of the patient frequently with this, and he will sleep.
  * In the Welsh this is French poppy, bwlwg Ffrengig. Corn poppy is our familiar red poppy, Papaver rhoeas. French poppy may be Papaver somniferum, the Opium Poppy, which would seem to be better suited as a remedy.

## ANOTHER REMEDY TO PROCURE SLEEP
667. Take the seed of eryngo, and henbane, and pound them well in a mortar. Mix with enough milk to make them into small pills. Let the patient have one every half-hour, until he has taken six or eight if need be, and he will sleep without fail.

## ANOTHER REMEDY TO PROCURE SLEEP
668. Boil poppy heads in ale. Let the patient drink this, and he will sleep.

## ANOTHER REMEDY TO PROCURE SLEEP
669. Boil a goat's horn in water. Wash your head with this when cold, and you will sleep. You should also place the boiled horn under your pillow.

## FOR INFLAMMATION OF THE MAMMAE
670. Pound plantain and lard well together, and apply it to the part until it is well.

## FOR A PAINFUL BREAST
671. Take the roots of wild rape, and scrape the outer rind. Make a cavity in the top of what you scrape, and put a fragment of sulphate of copper in there. Put it in the earth for four or five days, then remove. Take what juice there may exist, and keep in a glass vessel. Anoint the painful breast with this.

## FOR AN ABSCESS OF THE MAMMAE
672. Take virgin wax, spread before the fire*, and make a mask to cover the breast. This, used to cover the breast, will extract the poison from it.
* There is an asterisk in the Welsh, reading 'a * them wrth dân'. The footnote reads *Qu. a theis, â tannu?

## FOR THE SAME ABSCESS OF THE MAMMAE
673. Take the roots of hemlock. Pound finely with barley meal and the milk of a single-coloured cow. Make a warm plaster with it, and apply to the affected part.

## ANOTHER FOR AN ABSCESS OF THE MAMMAE

674. Take the sediment of verjuice and new wax. Make a plaster from it, and apply. You should make the plaster by boiling.

## PAIN IN THE MAMMAE

675. Pound mint into a plaster, and apply to the mammae.

## A WORM IN THE MAMMAE

676. Burn crow's eggs and powder the residue. Mix with the juice of wood sage, and administer as a drink.

## A MEDICINE TO PRESERVE FROM EPIDEMICS

677. Take mutton suet and fresh hog's lard in equal parts. Melt and strain carefully. Then put on the fire again, and add some well pounded rue. Boil briskly for a time, strain, and anoint your whole body with it, rubbing it well and soundly for as long as the plague continues.

## ANOTHER MEDICINE TO PRESERVE FROM EPIDEMICS

678. Take a spoonful of the juice of rue, and a spoonful of honey every morning while fasting, as long as the epidemic lasts. This, as well as the remedy mentioned above, is a good preservative against all sorts of dangerous epidemics, whether the sweating sickness,* eruptive fevers, typhus, or yellow fever.

* *Pughe adds:* A remarkable epidemic which prevailed in England in the 16th century, and to which those of the English race were said to be subject at home or abroad, and only they. This doubtless was an exaggeration, and we may infer from our text that it was not quite unknown in Wales, though Willan states that it did not affect the Cymry [*Welsh*] or the Scottish. This authority thinks that some unsoundness in the wheat of the period must have been the cause. *'English Sweating Sickness' first struck in 1485 and death could often occur within hours. There were more epidemics, spreading across the Continent, but it appears to have disappeared after the last outbreak in 1551. It may have been typhus, and was not plague, but its cause is still a mystery. The outbreak may well have been ergotism – see 2.558 above.*

## A POTION PREPARED BY DIVINE AUTHORITY, FOR THE HELP OF A WOUNDED MAN, WHICH WILL BE DISCHARGED BY THE WOUND, AND HEAL IT FROM WITHIN, WITHOUT FAIL

679. Take tansy, and a sprig each of hemp*, red nettle, raspberry**, red cabbage, plantain and avens. Add as much madder as all of the rest. Pound them well in a mortar, boil in strong ale, strain, and let this be drunk in the night warm, and in the morning cold. A red cabbage leaf should be applied to the wound, and nothing more, in order to cure the patient. If you collect the above ingredients in the month of May, or at furthest at Midsummer, pounding in a mortar, making into small pills, and drying without much wind, or sun, you will be able to have them at hand, when they could not otherwise be had. It is better even to keep what is needful, and then they may be bruised in ale. Use as directed above.

*Pughe footnotes:* * Cywarch, forsan, and ** Drysi, forsan

## THIS IS A MODE OF PREPARING MEDICINES FOR FLATULENT DYSPEPSIA

680. Take spirits of wine, and pour upon a powder composed of the following dry herbs: dry juniper berries, fennel seed, the seed of wild carrots, parsley seed, and dill seed. Keep them in a well-stoppered glass bottle, less the liquor should evaporate. Let a spoonful or two be taken when the pain is present.

## THE OIL CALLED IN LATIN OLEUM FOENUM, OR HAY OIL

681. Obtain fresh-mown grass, the finest you can get. Cut it small, and fill a two gallon vessel with it. Then add as much wine as will fill the vessel. Let it putrefy for three days and nights, and boil. Then add hog's lard, boil until half is evaporated, and strain carefully. When this is done, boil it again until another half is evaporated, and remove it to cool. Let it be kept carefully and clean. It is useful for all sorts of internal complaints, attended with shivering, and also colics. It is called oleum foenum.*

*There is also a footnote in the Welsh ms: 'Oleum foenum, sef yw hynny olew gwair. – IOLO MORGANWG.' Iolo is informing us that today, olew gwair is hay oil. Searching oleum foenum upon the internet, the fifth hit was fullbosom.com. Aqua oleum was fenugreek oil, and fenugreek was foenum Graecum. The site promises 'natural' breast augmentation tablets. Hay oil is a pale amber or pale yellow liquid with a sweet herbaceous, tea like fragrance, reminiscent of clary sage, wet tea leaves and hay.*

## Many dangerous diseases exist, and here are exhibited a variety of medicines to cure them.

### FOR THE ITCH AND SCABIES

682. Take sulphur, and unbumt lime. Put them in a vessel, and pour on them a quart of decoction of sage. Cover it well, and set aside for six hours, then decant the clear liquor. Wash your body with it before you go to a dangerous house or bed, and you will be preserved from contagion.

### ANOTHER FOR THE ITCH AND SCABIES

683. Take the leaves of sage, pound well with vinegar, and strain under a press. Wash your body with this.

### ANOTHER FOR THE ITCH AND SCABIES

684. Take spirits of wine, and pour it on powdered sage. Cover it carefully so that the spirits should not evaporate. Let this stand for three hours, and wash your body with it.

### A PROTECTION AGAINST FEVER IN SPRING

685. Take the inner bark of oak, sage leaves and valerian. Boil in good ale, and drink a good draught of this in the morning while fasting, three times a week. It will preserve you from disease.

### FOR TYPHUS FEVER

686. Take a handful of rue, sage, and a portion of fennel seed, and pound them together. Pour two quarts of good bottled wine upon the mixture. Let it stand

well covered for three hours, so that the spirits may not evaporate. Drink four spoonfuls in the morning while fasting. It is good for all pestilent diseases.

## ANOTHER FOR TYPHUS FEVER

687. Take a handful each of rue, sage, rosemary, and the inner bark of the mountain ash. Take vinegar, mix the lees, and pour upon the herbs in a distilling vessel, so as to extract the spirits by distillation. Drink a spoonful night and morning. Pour some also into your nostrils, and wash your brows, perineum, loins, wrists, soles, pit of stomach, chest, and neck with the same. This will preserve you from every pestilence.

## ANOTHER FOR TYPHUS FEVER

688. Boil some vinegar, put in an earthenware jar, and add a portion of spirits. Inhale the vapour into your mouth and nostrils. Then drink some of the liquid the first thing in the morning.

## ANOTHER FOR TYPHUS FEVER

689. Bruise the leaves of sage and rue, a handful of each, and put in a glass bottle, with spirits of wine. Let it be carefully stoppered, so that the spirits may not evaporate. Let a spoonful be drunk every morning.

## ANOTHER FOR TYPHUS FEVER

690. Take a good handful of rue, sage, and wood sage. Bruise carefully, and put into an unglazed earthenware vessel. Pour two quarts of white wine vinegar upon this, cover carefully, and let it stand for six hours. Then wash your whole body with this in the morning when you get up, and drink a spoonful of it. This by God's help will preserve you. It is an excellent protection against a pestilence.

## ANOTHER FOR TYPHUS FEVER

691. Wash in sea water, and scrub your whole body well, daily. In addition to this, wash your whole body with wine or vinegar once a day, and drink a spoonful of sea water every hour.

## ANOTHER FOR TYPHUS FEVER

692. Take marigold, and pound well with good wine, vinegar, strong mead, or strong old ale. Strain carefully, and drink a good draught in the morning fasting, whilst the pestilence lasts. If you are taken ill you need no other than this as your only drink. It is a good preservative against the foreign pestilence, called the plague.

## ANOTHER FOR TYPHUS FEVER

693. Gather wood sage, rosemary, sage, red mint, and southernwood. Dry thoroughly, and fill a mattress with the herbs. Sleep on this mattress for an hour every morning, where there may be a person at hand to awake you. Take care not to sleep upon it for more than an hour, less the sleep becomes too heavy. Having risen, wash your hands and face with vinegar, drinking a mouthful of vinegar also. You should drink some good wine once a day, avoiding meat, except for mutton two or three times a week, with well-baked wheaten bread.

## ANOTHER FOR TYPHUS FEVER

694. Take a portion of rue, mint, sage, and rosemary. Pound them well, sprinkling with vinegar or white wine meanwhile. Then strain under a press, and boil until it becomes thick. Add a little honey and marigold seed. When cold, make this extract into pills the size of peas. Take one every two hours of the day, as long as the pestilence continues. If the disease is the sweating sickness, then incorporate as much as you can * instead of the marigold seed, with the extract, when making it into pills.

*Pughe here places three asterisks, footnoting: 'Text does not state what.' The Welsh is difficult to translate as there seems – 'ag os y chwysaint y dolur dod yn lle had rhuddos, neu am ei ben ef, a ellych ei doesi am ben y tewych a wnelech yn belenau'. This literally means: 'if the sickness is sweating-sickness place instead of marigold seed, or on top of it (in addition to it), what you can knead (in addition to) on top of the concentrate that you make into pills'*

## FOR PARALYSIS

695. Rub your whole body with oil of olives once a day, and scrub it well. Then anoint the nape of the neck and spine as far as the sacrum, with warm honey, scrubbing well. The whole body should then be rubbed soundly, and the patient should go to bed, and cover himself well, until he perspires. When the perspiration has ceased, go to the seaside, and wear flannel about your back and chest. This plan, with God's help, will cure you.

## FOR MEASLES

696. Take apples, and cut small. Add also the same weight of honey, and put in an unglazed earthenware pot upon the fire, or before the fire, until it is sufficiently baked. Then mix well, and add some fine scrapings of new wax. Boil it so that the whole may be made into a confection. Take a spoonful each day while fasting.

## FOR PAIN IN THE JOINTS FROM COLD, SPRAIN, OR INJURY

697. Take a cupful of good old ale, and some scrapings of wax or honey. Boil together until it becomes thick. Spread upon a cloth, and apply to the painful part.

## A CONFECTION FOR A PESTILENCE

698. Take rue, sage, and betony. Pound well with honey and some vinegar, until they are so thoroughly incorporated, that one cannot be distinguished from another. Take as much as an acorn of this every two hours, and an hour afterwards take three spoonfuls of strong wine. Also take honey and suet. Incorporate them thoroughly in a mortar, and keep as much as an acorn of this confection in your mouth to dissolve gradually. Anoint your whole body also with this once a week at least.

## COMMON AND ERUPTIVE FEVERS

699. Take ground ivy, pound well with wine, and strain under a press. Drink a spoonful or two every hour. Drink an infusion of the same herb when thirsty.

## FOR HOARSENESS

700. Take wood sorrel, or garden sorrel, and garlic. Pound them well until they are thoroughly incorporated. Then take mutton suet. Melt the suet, strain, and mix with honey in equal parts. Let this mixture be incorporated carefully with the pounded herbs, and take a portion of the confection into your mouth, so that it

may dissolve gradually, and swallow as it dissolves. When it is done, take some again and again, till the hoarseness is removed.

## ANOTHER FOR HOARSENESS

701. Take the roots of nettles, dry thoroughly, and powder. Let this powder be incorporated with honey and unsalted butter. A spoonful should be taken night and morning.

## SQUAMOUS ERUPTION*

702. Take the leaves of burdock, pound them well with a little wine, and strain. Take three spoonfuls, night, morning, and noon, and let a decoction of burdock be your only drink. The affected part should be fomented with the decoction also, as hot as you can bear it, and anoint it afterwards with an unguent composed of wine, olive oil, and honey. Proven.

\* *Pughe explains:* Lepra, psoriasis, and pityriasis. *Pityriasis rosea is a skin rash. The Welsh 'tardd cennog' means a scaly eruption.*

**There are two kinds of painful and dangerous affections: wounds inflicted by poisonous reptiles; and poison. To these the human body is subject, and it is needful to avoid them. Thus are they treated.**

## FOR THE BITE OF AN ADDER

703. Take plantain, and knapweed, mix them with water, and let them be your only drink. By God's help it will cure yon.

## ANOTHER FOR THE BITE OF AN ADDER

704. Take the juice of plantain, and oil of olives. Drink a portion, and anoint the part with the remainder.

## ANOTHER FOR THE BITE OF AN ADDER

705. Drink decoction of mugwort, and foment the bite with it as well.

## ANOTHER FOR THE BITE OF AN ADDER

706. Take the brains of a red cock, the juice of rue, and sweet milk, or butter milk. Apply it to the bite. Or you may apply a raven* warm to the part, milk being your only drink or food until you are cured.

*The Welsh is cigfran, literally flesh crow, as the raven used to scavenge battlefields and features in the earliest Welsh heroic poetry of the sixth and centuries. Similarly, morfran, or sea crow is a cormorant. Brân is crow; brân dyddyn (smallholding), syddyn (dwelling-place) or fawr (great) is carrion crow; brân Arthur, goesgoch (red legs) or gochbig (red beak) is chough; brân lwyd (grey) or Iwerddon (Irish) is hooded crow; brân bigwen (white beak) is rook.*

## ANOTHER FOR THE BITE OF AN ADDER

707. If the patient is a man, hold a red cock by the anus to the wound, until the cock dies. If a woman, let the same be done with a hen.

## ANOTHER FOR THE BITE OF AN ADDER

708. Take a thong of buckskin, and bind the limb each side of the wound. Then procure a living hen. Remove the feathers from its rump, and hold the rump to the wound, until you find it swelling. Then apply another hen's rump in the same way, until the poison is extracted, and let the patient drink a decoction of the

following herbs: elder and knapweed, or centaury. Or he may take a decoction of feverfew, and subsist upon milk. This will cure the afflicted, whether man or beast.

## FOR THE BITE OF AN ASP [APE]*

709. Take bull's dung, and apply warm to the bite.

*As the asp is not a British snake, this remedy has been taken from the Greek or Arab medical manuals. Pughe translates as asp. However, the Welsh original is 'Rhag Brath Ab'. Âb is an ape, and apes were imported or traded as pets from early medival times.*

## FOR THE BITE OF A DISEASED DOG*

710. Take plantain, and agrimony, and pound them with the white of eggs, honey, and old lard. Prepare an ointment of them, and anoint the bite.

* *Pughe explains:* A mad [rabid] dog.

## ANOTHER FOR THE BITE OF A DISEASED DOG

711. Take leeks, vinegar, the seed of red fennel, and honey. Mi x well, and apply as a plaster to the bite.

## FOR POISON

712. Take two nuts, and three dry figs, rue leaves, and thirty-five grains of salt. Let this be administered to the patient while fasting, and let him subsist upon milk alone for forty-eight hours.

## ANOTHER FOR POISON

713. Take centaury, betony, sage, *wood-sage*\*, fennel, and scentless dame's violet**. Pound them well, mix with wine, and express the juice. Let an eggshellful be taken of this every hour. This is useful for the bite of a mad dog, or an adder, applying also mallow leaves to the bitten part.

* *Sage is ceidwad, Salvia officinalis, but Pughe omits this following herb 'chwerwyn y twyn', which is wood-sage, also known as woodland germander, Teucrium scorodonia; ** Probably Hesperis inodora or subsinuata, a crucifer and not a violet. Also possibly dog violet, Viola canina because that has no scent. The Welsh word used is 'tis' which means a sneeze or rejoicing, or 'dis' which means dice. Pughe translated 'ar dis' as 'and scentless dame's violet.'*

## ANOTHER FOR POISON

714. Take betony, dry and powder it. Then take twice as much as you can raise up between your two fingers of this powder, and mix with **LL**\* of wine. Boil until it is reduced to a third. This being drunk while fasting will be of service.

* *Two ounces?*

## FOR DISEASE AND PAIN OF THE FEET*

715. Boil the roots of tutsan, and pour upon curds. Pound the same** with old lard, and apply as a plaster. By God's help it will cure it.

* *Pughe notes in the English text:* Chilblains; ** *Pughe footnotes in Welsh 'Qu. berwedd?' against 'y perwedd,' which he translates as 'the same'. Berwedd means a boiling, or ebullition, so the lard must presumably be added to the boiling mixture.*

## FOR A CONTUSION OF THE NAIL

716. Apply a mixture of wheaten meal and honey to it.

## FOR WEARINESS IN WALKING

717. Drink an eggshellful of the juice of mugwort, and it will remove your weariness.

## TO REDUCE SWELLING IN THE FEET

718. Take violet, wild campion, sorrel, agrimony, plantain, marigold, daisy, barley meal, unsalted butter, lard, and the white of eggs. Make them into a plaster, and apply to the swelling, and if it is hot it will reduce it. But if the disease is cold, take water cress, radish, plantain, rue, dittany, and red nettles, all boiled in red wine, and apply.

**As the nature of many diseases is unknown, and the way in which they should be treated uncertain, unless the internal character of the same be demonstrated, it is herein stated in what way a man's flesh may be laid open while the diseases are being relieved.**

## THE FOLLOWING IS A POTION WHICH WILL INDUCE SLEEP, WHILE ANY DISEASED PART IS BEING OPENED UP*

719. Take equal parts of the juice of orpine, eryngo [*sea holly*], poppy, mandrake, ground ivy [*also translatable as rood ivy*], hemlock and lettuce. Let these be mixed in a clean earthenware dish** and left in it. Let this potion be prepared during the Dog days***, and then without doubt the patient will sleep. When you are prepared to operate upon the patient, direct that he should avoid sleep as long as he can, and then let some of the potion be poured into his nostrils, and he will sleep without fail.

When you wish to awake him, let a sponge be pressed in vinegar, and push it into his nostrils.

If you wish that he should not awake for four days, get a pennyweight of the wax from a dog's ear, and the same quantity of pitch. Administer it to the patient, and he will sleep.

When you wish that he should waken, take an onion, compounded with vinegar, and pour some into his mouth, and he will awake. Take care that you keep him quiet, and warned of the operation, lest he should be disturbed.

*A general anaesthetic; **Pughe translates this as mixing the ingredients with earth; ***Pughe omits Dog days. These were the days in July and August which seemed the hottest in the year, and the ancients believed it was because the Dog Star, Sirius was at its closest to the Sun. Sirius is the brightest star in the night sky, and the brightest star in the constellation Canis Major (Large Dog). In the Old Farmers Alamanac of 1792 'dog days' are the 40 days from July 3 – August 11, but for the Romans the period was July 23(24) to August 23(24).*

## SOME PRECIOUS UNGUENTS

720. As to bites and contusions, noxious potions and all medicaments, other than precious unguents being excepted, that wise man, Tholomews* testifies thus:

When the moon is in the ascendant in **Scorpio**, or **Cancer**, or **Pisces** [*23 Oct-21 Nov., 21 June-22 Jul., 19 Feb-20 Mar.*] , they are influenced by the sign of the Sun, and the Moon is obscured by the Earth. These are then favourable aspects for administering fluid medicines. If the Moon is high in the sky, it is said that such medicaments will turn aside excessive oppression and anger. On which account, see that you order those who take a fluid medicine to walk, and inhale the eastern air. But when the patient is confined to his room, let him prefer a western aspect, and use it. The lord of this sign will not continue to govern the signs, save for the first two days in each of the twelve. And when those two days are passed, let the physician exercise his craft and skill as may be most proper.

The following is a most notable unguent, useful for a variety of bodily disturbances. It is useful for all abscesses, impostumes and diseases, every kind of erysipelas, and cancer, even when extending from one rib to another. It will cleanse every part within and without man's body, whether a child or a man, so that he will not require a second remedy, whatever be the nature or extent of the wound, or the amount of constitutional irritation present.

Take a handful of each of the following herbs: common bugle, hound's tongue, brookweed, eyebright, agrimony, scurvy grass, ribwort, plantain, chamomile, wild clary**, strawberry leaves, white ox eye, daisy, wood sorrel, avens, herb Robert,. Add honeywort, as much as all other the herbs together, and half as much as the weight of the herbs of clarified butter. Then pound the butter and the herbs together, and let it stand for five days. In five days boil the mass, and strain through a just washed fine linen cloth. Keep it in a safe vessel, and when you desire to cure some patient of the above disease, let him swallow or eat as much as a nut of the above unguent, with some white wine, and the same should be done at night until he is well. This is termed edible ointment.

The following is an infallible remedy, called The Grace of God and this name it obtained in consequence of its unfailing effects, upon any wound, old or recent. In one night it will heal more safely and perfectly than all other ointments and plasters in a month; by doing more to cleanse ulcers, all intractable diseases, or morbid granulations, unaided, wherever it is used. It will restore any ruptured or swollen tendons, veins, or joints, into as sound a condition as they ever were in. It is a powerful remedy for any great swelling, whether an inflamed or a white swelling.

It should be prepared in the following manner. Take a pound weight of tormentil, four drams of fine rosin, as much of virgin wax, and of a certain shrub, similar to the broom, called maglys and in Latin maglisse*** three handfuls. Take as much also of the following herbs, betony, brookweed, wild clary, vervain****, calamint, the blessed rosin***** or strepuledium and a product or sort of wine, called balm babami.****** Boil them together in a gallon of white wine, till they are reduced to the half; then incorporate and mix them again, when mastic, virgin wax, and a small quantity of woman's milk, who suckles a boy, should be added. And thus should it be mixed and stirred without ceasing. Then remove from the fire again, the tormentil, fine rosin, and balsam being added previously. When cooled, it should be kept in a clean vessel. Thus is the 'Grace of God' prepared. The weight of the strepuledium should be that of two wheat grains.

*This is Ptolemaeus, Claudius Ptolemy (c.60-168 ce), the Greek geographer, astrologer, astronomer and mathematician. His astrological writings were followed for over 1500 years.*

*** The fourth herb in the list is 'torfagl' which he translates as 'cleere eye' or clary. In this context it is figwort, Euphrasia officinalis, and eyebright is a common name for this herb. He then translates 'y ffraig sef dail y syfi' as wild clary. Neither of these two names for wild clary are*

*in the GPC. Wild clary (clear eye) is Salvia verbenaca, Eurasian sage. In the last paragraph of the above, he translates torrfagl (with a double r this time) as wild clary again, when it may be eyebright.*
*\*\*\* Pughe notes: Medicago. This is probably Purple Medick but there is a Spotted and a Black Medick. Medicago sativa is a lucerne. However, it is supposed to have come to notice in Britain only in 1757 according to Margaret Grieve. It may be that it was used in Wales before England.*
*\*\*\*\* Verbena is footnoted for this in the original Welsh, and the herb is briw'r march, common vervain, Verbena officinalis.*
*\*\*\*\*\* Pughe notes: Frankincense in all probability.*
*\*\*\*\*\*\* Pughe notes: Balm of Gilead, or Balsamum Gileadense.*

## THUS IS A STIMULATING UNGUENT PREPARED
721. Take the plant called chaste tree\* or red vitex, agrimony, and dwarf elder. Pound them well, and set them on the fire with butter, and + + + + + + + +\*\* and strain through a linen cloth. Apply it to the head warm, as a plaster.
*\* There are two Welsh words given for the Chaste Tree, Gwarchwydd and Gwarchlys. Vitex agnus-castus is also known as Monks' Pepper and is native to the Mediterranean countries; \*\* Pughe notes: Corner of MSS. torn.*

## AN EFFECTIVE OINTMENT FOR ANY PAIN OF A COLD NATURE
722. Take sage, birthwort, ambrosia\*, wood sage, broom flowers, agrimony, the roots of cinquefoil, dwarf elder, and heath. Pound them well in a mortar, and put them in a little wine and a quantity of oil of olives, then let them infuse for seven days, After that let them be boiled, mixed with lard, goat's suet, unsalted butter, mutton suet, and wax. Strain well through a cloth, and add godarsin\*\* and rosin to the ointment.
*\* Pughe notes: Atriplex olida. This may be Garden Orache (Arrach), Atriplex hortensis. 'Ambros' also means wood sage, and 'chwerywn y twyn' means wood sage, but the same ingredient would not be repeated; \*\* Pughe notes: Goudron de Bordeaux, French tar prepared from the Pinus maritimus. He took this definition from S.F. Gray's 1836 supplement to his Treatise of Pharmacology. The great French finance minister Colbert (1619-1683) was pleased to discover that Canada had an unlimited supply for French ships.*

## A PRECIOUS OINTMENT FOR ANY KIND OF SORE
723. Take mutton suet, a he-goat's suet, old lard, bitter ladies' smock\*, avens, wood sage, and brookweed, or when brookweed is not to be had, privet. Pound, and boil together, straining through linen. Keep it carefully, as it is truly useful.
*\* The Welsh is chwyr. Lady's Smock is Cuckoo Flower, Cardamine pratensis, and its Welsh name is Blodyn Llaeth, Milk Flower. Chwyr does not appear in the Geiriadur Prifysgol Cymru. I assume that the plant is simply Lady's Smock.*

## THE FOLLOWING IS AN OINTMENT PREPARED BY HIPPOCRATES. FOR PARALYSIS, OR SUCH ACHES
724. Get a fat gander, and extract the fat. Also obtain twice as much of the fat of a tom cat, and as much of that of a wild cat, the fat of a fox, a quantity of pepper, a hen's fat, rosin, two onions, a pennyweight of new wax, bitter ladies' smock\*, avens, hyssop, privet, and hemp agrimony. Pound them all, and stuff the gander with this mixture, roasting it before the fire for as long as anything exudes. Take

the mixture from the gander, and boil afterwards in butter and rosin, olibanum being added. Strain through linen, and keep well and carefully. Anoint any such cold ache well, by the fire.

*Here the Welsh for Lady's Smock is berwr, meaning cress. It seems that Pughe is mistaken in his translation. See 723 above.*

## AN OINTMENT TO HEAL WOUNDS
725. Take old lard, frankincense, and wax. Put them on the fire to melt, and strain through linen, then when cold, spread with a spatula on linen. Remove it from the wound twice a day, then warm the linen and re-apply. Each time it is warmed, run the spatula all over it.

## ANOTHER OINTMENT TO HEAL WOUNDS
726. Take the juice of nettles, the juice or powder of valerian, the juice of dwarf elder, clear honey, the white of an egg, and wine in equal parts. Add some wheat flour, and incorporate them as a plaster. It should be spread on linen, and applied to the wound night and morning, until it is cured.

## FOR SCROFULA
727. Take plantain, clary, elder leaves, agrimony, cudweed*, knapweed, strawberry leaves and orpine, with unsalted batter. Express through clean linen, and keep for the purpose of fomenting the part. Prepare a potion for the patient also, with strawberry leaves, orpine, and vervain, pounding them with wine or ale, or boiling them in water. Let the patient have this for his only drink, for it is truly useful.

*Edafeddog is Cudweed, Cotton Weed which grows in marshes, Gnaphalium uliginosum.*

## THE FOLLOWING IS A HEALING SALVE
728. Take equal parts of male speedwell*, violet, borage**, ribwort, plantain, betony, pimpernel and hyssop. Pound, and add butter which has first been thoroughly clarified before it is added to the herbs. Boil the herbs with the butter as long as you would boil lamb, or salmon, straining it through a new cloth, and keeping.

*Veronica officinalis. However, Gwrnerth can also mean Carpenter's Herb, Figwort or Common Self-Heal.*

**'Cordial' flowers are those that 'cheer the heart'. Of the cordial plants, 'All four of the cardinal flowers go into metheglin, the traditional drink of Wales. The rose "take of sweet-bryar and great handful", violet flowers, violet leaves, bugloss and borage. Added to these are rosemary and strawberry leaves, and a great many other herbs and spices, including a trace of ginger. The herbs are boiled in water which is then strained; a quantity of honey is added, and the mixture is fermented with ale-barm (a sort of yeast). They say it is heady stuff, and I am sure that it will warm the heart.' -Elizabeth Lawrence 'Through the Garden Gate' 1957*

## ANOTHER HEALING SALVE
729. Take two pennyworth of rosin, a cupful of mutton suet, and twice as much of new wax. Melt them together, remove from the fire, and strain. Divide the molten matter into two parts. Colour one part with three obolus* weight of verdigris, leaving the other simply coloured by the herbs.

*An obolus was a unit of weight in Greece equivalent to a sixth of a drachma.*

## THUS IS A YELLOW SALVE PREPARED

730. Obtain a couple* of rosin, twice as much of tallow, half as much of wax, and half a cupful of clarified butter. Boil and strain through linen. Colour half with verdigris, and boil a little honey with the remainder, leaving it yellow.

* *Pughe tells us:* Cwpl in Cardiganshire [Ceredigion] signifies a small quantity.

## TO PREPARE A YELLOW UNGUENT

731. Take new wax, yellow rosin, clarified butter, and more mutton suet than the whole together. Boil them together for a while, remove from the fire, and strain through linen.

## TO PREPARE A GREEN HEALING SALVE

732. Take wax, rosin, clarified honey, betony, violet, borage, and ribwort plantain. Let the meltable articles be molten, and the herbs pounded well and then boiled with them. Let them be on the fire for a short while, then remove. Strain through a clean cloth, and let it cool, when it should be kept.

## TO DESTROY A CANCER

733. Take mastic,* camphor and frankincense, in equal parts. Bruise, and incorporate in a clean vessel, then keep it in a clean bladder. When you proceed to treat the disease, get a shovelful of burning oak. Cast a silver spoonful of the powder upon the oak, and hold the cancer over it. This, if continued, will destroy it.

* *Pughe notes:* 'Tastic' must be a corruption of mastic.

## TO PREPARE A ROLL OF PLASTER*

734. Take six eggshellfuls of oil of olives, and twice as much red lead. Grind the lead with the oil, and put on the fire in a brass vessel, mixing it well with a stick. Take a pewter plate in your hand, and strike the stick upon it from time to time, until you find the plaster becoming black. Then remove it, and let it stand until it begins to cool, when you should make it in rolls, covering it with paper before it is quite cool. Let it cool fully, then keep.

* *This is difficult to read, as the repeated word roliwm is in Gothic bold script, but the Welsh heading appears to be 'I WNEUTHUR Roliwm NEU Roliwm'.*

## TO PREPARE A DRAWING PLASTER*

735. Take wax, rosin, tar, and lard, and place them on the fire. There should be equal parts of the wax and rosin, the proportion of the tar being a pennyweight. Let the whole be boiled to the hardness of wax.

* *The Welsh is 'tred sugn', with tred being an old form of entrêd (a plaster or poultice), so this means a sucking plaster or poultice.*

## TO PREPARE A CATAPLASM FOR A SPRAIN, SWELLING OR THORN

736. Take biting stonecrop and butter. Pound them together, warm a short while by the fire, and apply three or four times to the swelling.

## TO PREPARE A DRY PLASTER

737. Take the roots of elecampane, bruise and boil well. Add the milk of a single-coloured cow. Mix well, then reject the roots, and mix fine wheat meal, or barley meal with the decoction. Honey and a little rosin should also be added, the whole

being boiled until thick. Then remove from the fire, and keep in a clean vessel. When you apply it to the diseased part, mix some lard with it, so that it might not be too dry.

## TO MAKE A POWDER OF THE WHITE OF EGGS
738. Take a broad baking stone, and lay on the fire. Place the white of eggs upon it until they blacken, then scrape off, and keep carefully.

## FOR PHAGEDENIC* ULCERATION. THIS IS A DISEASED OR CANCER-LIKE CONDITION OF THE FLESH, SOMETIMES SPREADING INTO THE THROAT, AND ABOUT THE LIPS, PHARYNX, OR ROOT OF THE TONGUE
739. Take a cupful of vinegar, the same of the juice of parsley, half a cupful of honey, and as much of treacle. Mix powdered frankincense with it, until it is of the thickness of pap. Let it be applied until a cure takes place. It is the best application, if continued without interruption until the sore is well.
* *This is a rapidly spreading ulcer, accompanied by sloughing, or the separation of dead tissue.*

## A HEALING OINTMENT
740. Take avens, violet, daisy, bugle, ribwort plantain, and feverfew. Pound, and boil them well with fresh butter, and strain. Keep it, for it is useful.

## AN UNGUENT FOR SCROFULOUS SORES
741. Take bay leaves, violet, daisy, knapweed, milfoil, the powder of marsh mallows, and the marrow of an aged ox. Compound, boil and strain.

## A HEALING SALVE WHEN THE SKIN IS WOUNDED
742. Take unsalted butter, and set on the fire, skimming the surface as it forms. Then take male speedwell and bugle, in equal parts, (or milfoil, if bugle is not at hand). Boil them well with the butter. If you add bur-reed*, the ointment will be no worse. Let this stay on the fire, adding a portion of the above herbs, so that the ointment may be of adequate thickness. Let it boil as long as lamb. Add a little new wax, mixing it thoroughly. Boil a while again. When removing from the fire, add a spoonful of clarified honey, carefully mixing the whole, and warming it thoroughly. Remove, stir well, strain through a coarse linen, and keep. If you wish to prepare some that will act as an escharotic, obtain some alum or sulphate of copper in powder. Sprinkle some of this on the surface of the salve in a box, or a wide shallow dish, and stir it well until it cools. This is useful as an escharotic for the destruction of proud flesh.
* *The Welsh is 'ychydig o gawn', which means a little straw, or a few reeds. Sparganium is bur-reed, first noted in the English language by William Turner in 1562, who noted that there were no names for the plant in English. Pughe may well have used the Welsh for bur-reed, but it is unknown in the Geiriadur Prifysgol Cymru.*

## THUS IS A YELLOW SALVE PREPARED
743. Take a bottle of rosin, twice as much of mutton suet, as much of wax, and half a cupful of clarified butter. Boil, and then remove from the fire, and strain. Colour half of this salve with verdigris, and mix a little honey with the other salve, boiling it longer, so that it may retain its yellow colour. It should be kept carefully in a clean vessel for use.

## A LOTION TO HEAL A WOUND OF THE INTEGUMENTS, BONES, OR WHATEVER OTHER PARTS MAY REQUIRE THE USE OF AN ESCHAROTIC

744. Take plantain, daisy, ribwort plantain, and a gallon of cold spring water. Pound the herbs, and boil in water. Add a pound of alum, and let it boil down to a third. The lotion is then ready.

## A FOMENTATION OR WASH FOR A BURNING OR RED INFLAMMATION, THE RESULT OF DROPSY, FIRE, OR SUN HEAT, A BRUISE, OR HURTFUL DISEASE AFFECTING THE PART

745. Take equal parts of milk and water, mallow flowers, the berries or middle bark of elder, pennywort, and (when obtainable) wood sorrel, common sorrel, or French (garden) sorrel. Boil in the milk and water and anoint the part with this somewhat briskly. Then apply as much as may be required of the boiled herbs to the affected part, as a poultice, changing it every six hours.

## FOR ERYSIPELAS

746. Take fumitory*, stonecrop, house leek, yellow stonecrop, Jew's ear** grown on the elder, a gloveful of each, or of as many as you can obtain. Pound well in a mortar, boil in unsalted butter, and strain through a cloth. This will quench erysipelas, and cause it to fade away, so that it will cure it, if it is applied in the morning frequently.

*Pughe footnotes in the Welsh version 'Qu. Fwg y ddaiar?' Ffwgws, or ffwg is long coarse grass, dry leaves or tobacco. In his list of plants, mwg y ddaiar is 'capnonia', but capnonia is unknown. Mwg y ddaear literally means smoke of the earth, and is common fumitory, fumaria officinalis, used by herbalists for centuries; ** This a jelly-like fungus, Auricularia auricular-judae. It often grows on Elders, and its former name was Judas' Ear. Judas was supposed to have hung himself on an elder.

## FOR AN ABSCESS

747. Take mutton suet, oatmeal, foxglove*, and maiden hair [fern]**. Boil them till they become a thick mass. Apply it to the abscess, and it will draw it.

* Pughe footnotes: 'Dail ffiol ffrwyth y gelwir dail ffion ffrith mewn rhai mannau yn Neheubarth.' This refers to an alternative name for the foxglove in some hilly areas (bannau = peaks) of Deheubarth; ** However, diwlith can mean either True Maidenhair or Greater Celandine.

## FOR WEAK WATERY EYES

748. Take an earthenware vessel and melt brimstone in it, until two or three times the thickness of your nail covers it. When you go to bed at night, pass water into the same vessel, and in the morning wash your eyes with the liquid. Then pour it off, and pass your morning water into the vessel. Let this stand until night, washing your eyes with it in going to bed. The morning water is best, being stronger than the evening one. If your hearing is hard, dip some black wool in the liquid, and put it in your ears at night in going to bed.

## FOR STOMACH ACHE OR COLIC

749. Take mugwort, plantain, and red nettle. Boil in goat's whey, strain through linen, and administer to the patient.

## FOR A SWELLING FROM A BLOW

750. Take water pimpernel, plantain, and fennel, in equal parts. Pound them with rye meal, honey, and the white of eggs. Apply it as a plaster, and the swelling will be healed.

## FOR IRRITATION AND CLOUDINESS OF THE EYE

751. Take the juice of celandine. Pound the herb well with breast milk, upon which a male child is being nursed, or the urine of a yearling child. Strain through a press, and apply the juice on a feather to your eye.

## ANOTHER FOR IRRITATION AND CLOUDINESS OF THE EYE

752. Pound celandine with goat's milk, and strain through a press. Mix with a little honey, and apply to your eye with a feather, three times a day.

## FOR JAUNDICE

753. Take dandelion, corn bluebottle, and garden parsley. Then pound them well with good strong old ale, and keep it carefully in a narrow-mouthed water bottle. Let it be used the first thing in the morning an hour before food, and the last thing an hour at night after food. The dose should be from four eggshellfuls to a pint.

## ANOTHER FOR JAUNDICE

754. Take sprigs of barbary, and the living leaves if obtainable *. Bruise, and boil well in sound strong ale, until it is reduced to a third, and let it be your only drink.

*This is Berberis vulgaris, called both pren melyn and pren ysbîn here. Pughe calls barberry 'y pren melyn, sef y pren ysbîn', 'yellow wood, namely spiny wood.' Historically, yellow dye was extracted from the stem, root and bark.*

## FOR EXANTHEMATOUS* CONTAMINATION OF THE HUMORS

755. Take the roots and seed of nettles. Pound well, then boil in good cider which is half-a-year or a year old. Let this be your only drink. The best cider is that made with good sour winter apples.

*This is a skin eruption accompanying an infection.*

## ANOTHER FOR A SKIN ERUPTION [AND SCROFULA]

756. Take apples, and bake or boil them. Mix them with cow or goat milk, and let it be your only food or drink for a month or nine weeks, according to the strength of the disease. This food is exceedingly good for lung pock,* or blood pock**, and it will also neutralize the poison of scrofula.

It was by means of this treatment that Hywel Feddyg, of Llangynwyd, cured Edward the Confessor***, when there was not a physician in Christendom who would promise him an hour of life in consequence of the violence of the lung disease. The Emperor Antonius also made use of it at every spring, and the fall of the leaf [autumn], and was thereby preserved from every emptive poison of the blood and humors, which is the active cause of all eruptive and suppurative diseases incident to a man's body.

*Inflammation or tubercles of the lung; ** Scurvy; *** The penultimate Saxon King of England (ruled 1042-1066) was for very obscure reasons the only English king canonised by the Roman Church. Edward the Confessor personally ordered the assassination of Rhys ap Rhydderch, a prince of Deheubarth, whose head was delivered to the saintly king in 1053.*

## FOR NOSE BLEEDS
757. Take a nettle, pound it well, and fill your nostrils with it.

## TO DESTROY PARASITES
758. Take milfoil, pound them well, and apply to the affected part.

## FOR PAIN IN THE EYE
759. Apply the yolk of eggs and wheatmeal over each brow. It will heal the pain.

## FOR HAEMORRHOIDS
760. Take limestone and the roots of fern. Pound them together, apply to the part, and they will cure it.

## ANOTHER FOR HAEMORRHOIDS
761. Boil the roots of fern in spring water until it is reduced to half. Pour it upon a small lump of quicklime*. When it has settled, pour off the clean liquor, and wash the piles.

  * *This is burnt limestone, calcium oxide, and extremely caustic.*

## TO KNOW WHETHER THE PATIENT WILL LIVE OR DIE
762. Bruise violets, and apply to the patient's eyebrows. If he sleeps, he will live. If not, he will die.

## TO DESTROY WARTS
763. Pound willow bark with verjuice or vinegar, and apply.

## TO EASE HEAT AND PAIN IN WOUNDS
764. Take the roots of marsh mallows, and the middle bark of elder, equal parts of each. Add an equal quantity of white wine, and boil well until it becomes thick. Then spread this on a well-stretched linen cloth as a poultice, and apply to the wound. If the wound closes prematurely, obtain the herb called white bryony, make it into a plaster, apply to the wound, and it will open it. *Whoever drinks the juice of the violet will (grow out of?) be healed of bone fractures, if they are present in a man's limbs*

  *This sentence is omitted by Pughe and seems out of place. The Welsh is 'Pwy bynnag a yfo sudd y wiolydd ef a deifi allan escryn twn, o byddnant mewn aelod dyn.'*

## FOR DIARRHOEA
765. Take the yolk of seven eggs, twice as much of clarified honey, the middle of a wheaten loaf reduced to fine crumbs, and a pennyworth of powdered pepper. Boil them together, and eat warm, refraining from drinking subsequently as long as you can. Use this food until you recover, for it is the most salutary article of diet in the world.

**There is a variety of chronic diseases which oppress the heart of man, producing faintness, difficulty of breathing, and heat in the cardiac region. It is only by much studious and diligent science, aided by effective medicines that they can be cured.**

## FOR DISEASE OF THE HEART
766. Take the centaury, boil in good old ale, then pound the herbs, and boil again in the same liquor. After this strain it through a clean cloth, add a spoonful of clarified honey, and boil again. Let it be kept in a covered pot, and three spoonfuls given daily to the patient whilst fasting. This will indeed remove the oppression from the heart, and restore the desire for food and drink, if God will.

## FOR OPPRESSION OF THE HEART*
767. Take the juice of fennel and honey. Boil together until they become hard, and eat a portion of the same the first thing in the morning before food, and the last thing in the evening after food. It will cure you by God's help.

*The Welsh is 'rhag mogfa ynghylch calon'. Mogfa is shortness of breath, or asthma, and 'ynghylch calon' seems to mean 'centred upon the heart'

## TO PREPARE A GARGLE
768. Take rosemary, sage, hyssop, alum, and good ale. Place in a pot on the fire. Boil until a quart is reduced to a pint. Having boiled the gargle, let it be used warm, and daily for a week

## THE FOLLOWING IS THE TREATMENT EMPLOYED BY RHIWALLON FEDDYG FOR THE RELIEF OF CONSTIPATION
769. Take small beer*, unsalted butter, and wheat bran. Boil them well and strain. Pour into a bladder, into which insert a quill, firmly binding the bladder about it. This pipe should be passed into the patient's rectum, his head being as low, and his pelvis as high as can conveniently be. The bladder should then be compressed, and the fluid forced into the body.

*Small beer was brewed at about only 2-3% alcohol, and drunk by the masses instead of water, which was generally polluted. The water in small beer had been boiled. After about 1860, bottled beer became available, but tea became the national drink, even among the working class. Again, the boiling of water made the beverage safer.

## AN EMETIC*
770. Take the seed of asarabacca**, boil in good ale, and strain. Let this be given to the patient.

* The Welsh heading is 'i beri cyfod, sef bwrw allan a fo yn y cynlla' – to let vomiting flow, namely to cast it from the stomach.

**This is Pughe's translation, the plant known as Asarumeuopaeum. However, llysiau'r cyfog can also be translated as spurge, Euphorpia.

## A SALVE TO RELIEVE PAIN, AND CURE A CONTUSED WOUND
771. Take the flesh of a fat sow of ripe age, and melt the fat. Let it stand until the salt falls to the bottom. Take as much again of new wax, and boil with the fat, adding powdered mastic and frankincense. Incorporate them well, until the mass becomes as thick as honey. It should be spread with a spatula, upon cloth or leather, and applied to the affected part twice daily. It will heal the wound, and remove the pain.

## FOR COLIC

772. Pound watercress well, adding soft spring water to it, and oat groats. Boil both to a gruel*, straining carefully. Let it be taken an hour before or after food, being the first and last thing to eat for three successive days.

*The Welsh is gwiscon, which Pughe translates as gwysgon, which means decoction or gruel.*

## TO PROCURE SLEEP

773. Cut the lily whilst the sun is in Leo, and mix with the juice of the shrub called laurel, or in Latin laurus. Put these in a heap of manure, covering with plentymore manure, and they will generate worms. Take these worms and powder them, then put the powder about the patient's throat, or in his clothes, and he will sleep until it is removed.

## TO KNOW WHETHER A MAN WHO HAS BEEN SEVERELY BEATEN WILL RECOVER OR NOT

774. Take the juice of mouse-ear hawkweed*, mixed with white wine, and let the patient drink it. If he vomits, he will live, if not, he will die.

*Pilosella officinarium. However, the Welsh is torllwyd, which could be any of goosegrass, silverweed, wild tansy, agrimony or mouse-ear hawkweed. Earlier, in 2.221, we see cat's ear (melenydd) being a hawkweed, possibly mouse-ear hawkweed.*

*This is missing from Pughe:*

## ARALL ER YR UN GWYBOD

775. Cymmer laeth bronnau y bo mab yn sugno, a dod ychydig o'r llaeth ar dorr dy law, a chymmer drwnc y claf ag edifera y llaeth ar benn dy fys i'r trwngc, od i'r gwaelod yr âir trwngc, marw a fydd, os ar yr wyneb y trig, byw a fydd.

## ANOTHER FOR INFORMATION

Take milk from breasts being sucked by a boy child. Place a little of the milk on your hand, and take the patient's urine and drip the milk from the top of your finger into the urine. If it sinks to the bottom of the urine, the man will die, but if it stays on the surface, he will live.

## ANOTHER METHOD OF PROGNOSIS [*the same method as 2:762*]

776. Bruise some violets, and apply to the eyebrows of the patient. If he sleeps, he will live; if not, he will die.

## ANOTHER PROGNOSIS

777. Take violet, bruise and bind about the forefinger. If he sleeps, he will live; if not, he will die. You should ascertain this before you interfere with the case.

## FOR THE CARBUNCLE*

778. Take the roots of lily, wash carefully and bruise well. Boil in white wine, until it is reduced to the half, straining through new linen. Let it be administered to the patient. It will cure the him.

* *Pughe adds:* Plague. *However, the Welsh 'chwarren' has many meanings, including plague, pestilence, ulcer, enlarged gland and hard swelling.*

240

## FOR BOILS

779. Take musk mallow, lard, and earthworms. Bruise together, and apply to the affected part.

## ANOTHER FOR BOILS

780. Take the yolk of an egg, and salt. Pound into a plaster, and apply to the boils.

## WHEN A MAN IS AFFECTED WITH PLAGUE, OR BLACK POCK*

781. Take white ox eye daisy (when the centre has become black), tormentil, rue, and if you like add a leaf of bay. Wash these carefully, bruise with water, and administer to the patient in strong ale, as hot as he can drink it. Let this be done whilst the patient is in bed between sheets, and near a good fire, so that he may perspire freely. By God's help, the eruption will be transferred to the sheets.

* *Pughe adds: Malignant small pox, mostly in cachectic subjects, the pustules being black from effused blood. Cachexis is physical wasting with loss of weight and muscle owing to disease. The Welsh is bannau duon, black tips. Black Pox (i.e. black pockmarks) is a symptom of smallpox, caused by bleeding under the skin, making it look black or charred. It was almost always fatal, whether of the flat or haemorrhagic variety.*

## FOR A THORN WOUND

782. Take lard, and the roots of red nettles. Pound well, and apply to the wound nine times. With God's help it will cure it.

## FOR SEMINAL WEAKNESS*

783. Take powdered pennyroyal, and powdered anise-seed, and administer them to the patient in soup, or sauce. This will prevent the flux by God's help.

* *The Welsh is 'rhag traul a rhedeg nattur' – for consumption (or wear) and a natural flow? Seminal weakness now means a nocturnal emission of semen when asleep. It is strange that John Williams did not expurgate this, as he did with similar entries.*

## FOR SCABIES

784. Take the roots of archangel, and boil well. Also boil a portion of garlic, using different water. Take a good draught of the decoction, and wash your whole body with it every morning. Boil the residue of the archangel and garlic in unsalted butter, make into an ointment, and anoint your whole body with this for nine mornings.

## PART 6

## BOOK 2B - INFORMATION FOR MEDICINERS

THE VIRTUES OF VARIOUS MEDICINAL HERBS*

*\* It is important to note that 'herbs', to a botanist or chef are plants with no woody tissue, and therefore no persisten aerial parts. However, herbalists define herbs as any plant material that is of medical use – including roots, bark, tubers, bulbs, pith, stalks, leaves, sap etc. 'The library of the Assyrian King Assurbanipal contained a clay tabler, dated about 2500bce, enumerating 250 vegetable drugs, many of which are used today.' Every culture in the world developed its own herbal pharmacopaeia, with the mediciners of Myddfai building upon Celtic tradition, adding to it information from Arab, Egyptian, Greek and Roman sources.*

**The following are the virtues and properties of various medicinal herbs useful to man.**

### THE VIRTUES OF SAGE*

785. It is useful when boiled to strengthen the nerves. If an infusion sweetened with honey is drunk, it is useful for the lungs. If the foetus in utero is dead, let the woman boil sage with white wine, strain it carefully, and she will be delivered of the dead foetus with safety to her life. Also pound this herb, apply to a poisoned wound, and it will extract the venom. Although the wound may be full of corruption, it will be cleansed to the very bottom, if dressed with this herb.

Let some be taken, pounded small, and the juice mixed with white wine, or the pounded herb macerated in white wine, strong wort, or old mead for a night and strained. Drink while fasting. By God's help it will cure the patient. It is a good thing for those in health to drink half a draught of this potion in the morning while fasting, in order to preserve healthy and prolong life.

*\* This legendary herb has been long held to be guardian over all other herbs, and has been in use in various traditional European and Chinese medicines for millennia. It contains essential oils, minerals and vitamins that are known to have disease preventing and health promoting properties. The primary biologically active component of common sage appears to be its essential oil which contains mainly ketone a- and β-thujone. In addition, sage leaf contains numerous other compounds known to have counter-irritant, rubefacient, anti-inflammatory, anti-allergic, anti-fungal and anti-septic properties. It enhances concentration, attention span and quickens the senses; hence sage infusion has long been recognised as 'thinker's tea'. Its effects also help deal with grief and depression. This herb is exceptionally very rich source of many B-complex groups of vitamins, such as folic acid, thiamine, pyridoxine and riboflavin.*

*The herb contains very good amounts of vitamin A and beta carotene levels. Vitamin A is a powerful natural antioxidant and is essential for vision. It is also required for maintaining healthy mucus membranes and skin. Consumption of natural foods rich in vitamin A known to helps body protect from lung and oral cavity cancers. Fresh sage leaves are good source of antioxidant vitamin C. This helps in the synthesis of structural proteins like collagen. Adequate levels in the body help maintain integrity of blood vessels, skin, organs, and bones. Regular consumption of foods rich in vitamin C helps body protect from scurvy; develop resistance against infectious agents (boosts immunity) and scavenge harmful, pro-inflammatory free radicals from the body. Sage herb parts, whether fresh or dried, are rich source of minerals like potassium, zinc, calcium, iron, manganese, copper, and magnesium. Potassium is an important component of cell and body fluids which helps control heart rate and blood pressure. Manganese is used by the body as a co-factor for the antioxidant enzyme superoxide dismutase. It is small wonder that sage is first in the list of useful herbs. All of the following are also used today by herbalists.*

## THE VIRTUES OF IRIS

786. The iris is a herb, having a white flower. Its virtues are that its juice, mixed with honey and wine will dissolve urinary calculus. It will also cure ague and jaundice, as well as nervousness. When you have no wine, take the juice in strong sound mead\*, or strong malt wort. It is hot and dry.

\* *Metheglin is traditional mead with herbs and/or spices added. Some common metheglins are tea, ginger, orange peel, coriander, cinnamon, nutmeg, cloves or vanilla. The name indicates that many metheglins were originally employed as folk medicine in Wales. The Welsh for mead is medd, and metheglin derives from meddyglyn, a compound of meddyg, healing and llyn meaning liquor or drink.*

## THE FOLLOWING ARE THE VIRTUES OF NETTLE

787. Take the juice of this herb mixed with white wine, strain carefully, and let it cool. Drink some night and morning. It will cure you of jaundice, renovate the blood, and remove any disease existing in it. If the juice is taken, mixed half and half with barley wort, it will cure pleurisy in the side, and will renovate and invigorate a man who is aged in body and mind. If the seed of the nettle in powder is taken, mixed with wine, it is very useful for wind colic, strangury, or a chronic cough, and will reduce a swelling, producing a flow of urine\* without harm to the bladder.

\**Nettle is a well-known diuretic.*

## THESE ARE THE VIRTUES OF BETONY

788. He who will habituate himself to drink betony juice, will escape strangury. If it is boiled in white wine, and drunk, it will cure colic, and swelling of the stomach. Pounding it small, expressing the juice and applying it with a feather to the eye of a man, will clear and strengthen his sight, and remove specks from the eye. The juice is a good thing to drop into the ears of those who are deaf. The powder mixed with honey is useful for those who cough.

It will remove a cough and benefit many diseases of the lungs. It is good for the ague when it comes, and if taken in its absence, iague will not attack a man that year. If boiled with leek seed, it will cure the eye, and brighten as well as strengthen the sight. And a wise man has said that if reduced to powder, a snake would rather be broken to pieces, than pass through the powder. Should there be swelling in the stomach, betony will reduce it, if boiled with wine and figs, and then given the patient in bed. It is a good thing to mix it with the juice of red fennel, and clear honey, for it will certainly clear the eyes, curing them if diseased, and strengthening the five senses wonderfully.

## THE FOLLOWING ARE THE VIRTUES OF PARSLEY, CALLED PETROSILIWM* IN LATIN

789. Parsley is a good herb of a warm, hot nature, and moist in the third degree. It is useful in all food as a generator of blood. It will remove obstructions of the veins and arteries in a man's body, so that the humors may circulate properly as they should. This it will certainly do.

It is also well to employ parsley for the relief of fainting, tertian ague, pleurisy, and dropsy, the juice being taken for three days successively, without any other drink. It will stimulate the spirits greatly, and strengthen the stomach.

There is a kind of parsley called in Welsh perllys yr hel**, because it grows in such places as are occasionally overflowed by the tide, and is of a salt nature. In Latin it is called petroselinwm marinwm, and is good in all obstructions of the urine and humors of the body, as well as colic and strangury, the juice being taken. The juice is useful to destroy unhealthy granulations in a wound. It will grow in gardens, where it should be kept wherever the sea is distant.

* *Pughe adds*: Petroselinum; ** *This is Apium graveolens subsp. dulce, Wild Celery*

## THE VIRTUES OF FENNEL, GALLED FUNICULWM* IN LATIN

790. Fennel is warm and dry in the second degree, and is useful for diseases of the eye. It is good for every kind of poison in a man's body, being drunk in the form of powder mixed with white wine or strong old mead. It is useful for tertian ague, and inflammatory fever. If the seed or herb is boiled in water, until it is strong of the virtues of the herb, and the head, when subject to the headache, is washed with this, it will greatly benefit and cure the same, when the headache is occasioned by cold or fever. It will remove a headache very quickly.

* *Pughe adds*: Funiculum.

## THE FOLLOWING ARE THE VIRTUES OF ROSEMARY, GALLED YSBWYNWYDD, AND ROSA MARINA* IN LATIN

791. Rosemary is warm and dry in the third degree, and it is termed a shrub, because it is a kind of plant between a herb and a tree. Take the flowers of rosemary, mix with honey, and eat them daily while fasting. You will not suffer from nausea, or any other noxious condition, as long as you use this remedy.

The flowers also are especially useful, being boiled with honey, or white wine to the half, and strained carefully. A spoonful or two should be drunk cold in the morning, a little honey being taken with it. A small quantity taken when one is attacked by the colic, will remove it in three hours. If you wish to apply it to your stomach externally, no honey should be added to it.

Take also the leaves of rosemary, and wood sage. Make them into a potion, and add honey in the same way. It is an excellent remedy for strangury, stone, and catarrh. It will disintegrate and expel it in the water.

Also, put their flowers or leaves under your head in bed, and you will not be troubled with disagreeable dreams, or oppressed with anxiety of mind.

Also, if you carry a stick or fragment of this shrub, no evil spirit can come near you, or anyone do you any harm.

The rosemary has all the virtues of the stone called jet.

Also, if you procure a spoon made of the stock or root of this shrub, in the day you drink some broth with it, you will not receive harm from poison. You will be also be preserved all that day from thunder and lightning, as well as all injurious assaults.

Also, gather the leaves of the rosemary, pound them small, strain, and drink the juice. It will remove all phlegm from the head and lungs, curing it with all certainty.

Also, if a man has an urinary obstruction, let him seek the flower or leaves, boiling them with white wine. Drink this as a potion, the first thing in the morning, and the last at night.

Also, if the flowers are put with white wine in a distilling vessel, and distilled, the product will be equal to spirits of wine, and will prove a fit substitute in all cases. It is useful as a lotion for the head when affected with a headache from cold or fever, or when a man is threatened with insanity. A spoonful of this liquid with a spoonful of honey, and a spoonful of melted butter (or thick fresh cream) is useful for a cough, or the expulsion of phlegm from the lungs.

Also, a decoction is helpful to an insane person, or one threatened with delirium. Indeed it is good for every disorder which can exist in the human body.

It is also well to boil the flowers and leaves in water, and to wash yourself well with it every morning, omitting to dry with a cloth, but leaving yourself to dry naturally. By washing thus with perseverance, the aged will retain a youthful look as long as they live. This water will expel phlegm from the brain, and restrain griping in the use of purgatives. It will expel dropsy, cure the liver, bring warmth to the nerves and veins, disperse an impostume, elevate the spirits, strengthen the bones, and increase the quantity, and improve the quality of the marrow in the bones. It improves the sight, and constipates the bowels, when boiled in vinegar, and applied to the stomach of the patient. It will promote the formation of blood, and cure the tertian ague. Should a man have debilitated himself by venery, he will be restored to his usual strength, if he confines himself to this as his only drink for nine days.

It will also cure impotence, in either sex, if used with food. When a couple are childless, let the wife, if young, use rosemary.

Also, if a man has a cold attended with fever, let him take rosemary, burn it, and convey the smoke into his nostrils. It will cure him perfectly.

Let him also take the water in which the flowers and leaves shall have been boiled, adding a little honey and pepper, drinking it warm. It is useful for all kinds of coughs; this is true. Also, take the roots of the shrub, roast them till they become a powder, then put in truth

ᵭᵽu ६ ᵭ६ ᵭᵭpᵤᵵ

ᵭᵤ⁶⁷⁶ᵽ ᵽᵶ zᵽ ᵭᵶᵽᵭᵶz⁶ (ᵄzᵤᵎ

The bark is useful for intolerable cutaneous irritation, in consequence of a deteriorated condition of the blood.

Its root also boiled in vinegar is good to foment painful joints with. Also rosemary and betony pounded and mixed with pure water, is a good wash for all

246

venomous bites, whether animal or reptile. It will cure them without the help of any other ointment.

* *Pughe footnotes*: Rosa Maria.

## THE FOLLOWING ARE THE VIRTUES OF SAGE, WHICH IS CALLED SALVIA* IN LATIN

792. Sage is a herb of a hot and dry nature. Boiled in all kinds of food and drink it is useful in nervous cases. It is well to take a decoction as the sole drink. Honey being added renders it more useful for the stomach. If a woman has a dead foetus in utero, let her boil sage in white wine, and drink it cold. She will be safely delivered of her burden. When carefully bruised, and applied to a poisoned wound, it will extract the poison, and heal the wound.

If a wound also is full of blood, let it be applied well bruised to the same, and it will cleanse it.

When a man also has pain under his rib, let him obtain some sage, boil it on the fire as hot as he can drink it, and it will cure him.

Also the decoction in water, or a potion prepared with wine, mead, or ale, is a very excellent drink for the cure of dropsy, whooping cough, or headache.

* *Pughe notes*: Saluis. *This is the second entry on sage – see 2.785 – so is probably taken from a separate ms. Again, the following entry upon nettle follows a previous entry, 2.787.*

## HERE FOLLOW THE VIRTUES OF NETTLE

793. Nettle is a very hot and dry herb. If it is boiled in white wine, and strained carefully through linen, left to cool, and drunk in the morning and night, it will help a man with jaundice.

Take the seed of nettles, make into a powder, and boil well in spring water, goat's milk, good white wine, or strong old mead. This potion is good for an old cough, and colic. It will also strengthen the absorbent and circulating vessels, if salt is added.

Also, take the seed of the nettle, mix with pepper, and temper with wine and honey. Let it be given as a potion, and however untamed the body may be, it will completely subdue it.

## THE VIRTUES OF BLESSED THISTLE*

794. Blessed thistle is an aperient. Being eaten it will benefit headache, and the midriff, and also strengthen the hearing. It strengthens the brain and sight, not only by eating it, but also when the juice is applied to the eye. When juice cannot be obtained, let the powder be taken in water, the juice being dropped into the eye. This is good for the removal of extravasation of blood in the eyes.

This herb is also a strengthener of the intellect and memory. It is also good for vertigo, and bleeding from the nose and mouth. The powder, mixed with honey, will promote the expectoration of phlegm, strengthen the digestion, restore the appetite, ease nausea, and renovate the blood. If the herb is boiled in water and drunk, it will prevent deterioration of the blood, and preserve it in a healthy condition. If it is eaten it will strengthen members that are weakened by paralysis, as well as the spinal marrow and brain. It will expel the cold humor which weakens the power of the mind, and the strength of the body.

It will also ease painful bowels, and boiled or drunk with wine, it will destroy the stone. Whoever will drink it in a male child's urine, will be cured of the plague and dropsy. It will mature carbuncles, cure cancer and hysteria. The powder will cure hysteria in twelve hours, and if applied to a wound, it will heal it painlessly. If the herb is masticated, it will strengthen the breath. It will cure ague if it is boiled in wine, and drunk warm a quarter-of-an-hour before the paroxysm, the patient being covered well with clothes, so that he may perspire. This will also cure intermittent, inflammatory, and rheumatic fevers.

The powder also taken upon warm wine, or some of the distilled water of the herb, will quickly deliver the patient from every poison affecting the nerves. If the decoction, juice or distilled water is drunk, and the patient perspires for three hours subsequently, it will cure the patient. The powder of the herb, eaten or drunk, will ease pain in the sides and chest. These are the virtues of the blessed thistle.

* *Pughe adds*: Carduus Benedictus.

## THE FOLLOWING ARE THE VIRTUES OF CLEAVERS, OR GOOSE GRASS

795. The juice taken in spring and summer, as the only drink, will expel and completely destroy eruptive poison from the blood and humors. This virus is the cause of all eruptions, boils, scalds, scrofula, lepra, cancer, erysipelas, pneumonia, dropsy, rheumatism, gout, strangury, all sorts of fevers, pocks of flesh and skin, all watery diseases of the eye, all phlegm of the head or stomach, all white swellings of joints or other parts, every inflamed condition of the blood and humors, every headache attended with fever, every oppression of the chest and stomach, or sub-mammary region, every swelling of the legs, feet, or other parts of the body, for there is hardly a disease affecting the human body, except what is occasioned by an eruptive poison in the blood and humors.

Their juice is thus obtained. Take the whole herb, leaves, blossoms, and seed included, (as the season may be), and pound them together well. Then put in an unglazed earthenware vessel, and fill it up without pressing them. Then pour upon it as much as it will allow of pure spring water, and let it stand for a night. Some say that it is best that a quarter of it should be sea water, or water salted as much as sea water, for the first week of drinking. Then ceasing from the salt water, it should be taken fresh as the only drink for nine weeks. It is wonderful how strong and healthy you will become in that time.

Gather the herbs in spring and summer, and dry well by the morning sun, turning them about so that the sun may dry them completely. Do this during the day, and bring them under cover at night. If not dry enough, do this another day, and another again, if in consequence of rain and fog they are not dry enough. Take care not to leave them out in foggy, muggy weather, as the whole virtue of the herbs will be destroyed by this. Gather the leaves, flowers, and seed, and dry them separately, keeping them in an oak chest, or a basket of wheaten straw, covered over well. When required, take the leaves, make an infusion thereof, and drink for three weeks. After that make an infusion of the blossoms, and drink for three weeks. Then make an infusion of the seed, and drink for three weeks. Thus

248

you will proceed in God's order, the consistency of nature, and in accord with the constitution and season of the year.

This is the way in which an infusion is made of these herbs. Bruise them* small with your hands, and fill up an unglazed earthenware vessel with them, covering them with running water that has been boiled. Before you do this, cover the herbs with the hair-bottom** of a milk strainer, so that the herbs may not pass over the edge of the vessel when the water is poured upon them. Let the vessel stand well-covered for six hours, and use the infusion as your sole drink. The herbs should be expressed at night under a press, and the decoction received through a strainer into a clean vessel. It should be drunk warm in going to bed. Should there be any sort of eruption, boil, impostume, ringworm, scab, itching, burning, wound, ulcer, or contusion on your body, wash it with a lotion of the herbs, either juice or decoction. If the disease is considerable, apply the bruised herbs to it. This treatment with potions and local applications has healed scrofula, the skin disease called in Latin lepra, and cancer, when it has destroyed the flesh to the bones.

Take also the seed of the herbs when ripe, and dry in an oven after baking two or three times. When dry enough, powder them in a stone mortar, keeping the powder in a well-covered glass bottle. Carry this with you on a journey, and take a spoonful on clear water three times a day. It will preserve you from all kinds of complaints, and will serve instead of food in case of necessity. It is well to do the same with mallow seed, and to use it in the same way.

*Pughe omits the herbs here, replacing a translation of llysiau cochon with 'them'. Llysion cochion could be carrots, raspberries or rhubarb, but must be an old term for cleavers, whose roots give a red dye; ** It appears that a mat of hair could be used to strain liquids. Rhynged may be a derivative of rhawn, animal hair, but does not appear in any dictionaries in this context.

## THE FOLLOWING ARE THE VIRTUES OF MISTLETOE

796. Mistletoe most frequently grows on the apple tree, or the hawthorn, and occasionally on the oak, which should be preferred, although it is a most excellent plant wherever it grows. Its property is to strengthen the body more than any other plant. Gather it at Christmas time, when the berries are quite ripe, and pick the berries from the branches. Pour boiling water upon them, cover the vessel in which they are contained, and set it to stand near the fire, so that it may simmer a night and a day. It should be then strained into a clean vessel, through a hair cloth*. Let the leaves and sprigs of the plant be bruised small, and laid on a hot baking stone, where they should be thoroughly roasted, being stirred about meanwhile so that they may not be burned. When roasted enough, they should be powdered, half being used for that purpose, and the remainder burnt to fine ashes. The powder and the ashes should be carefully preserved in separate glass vials.

In any case of bodily debility, whether in the nerves, joints, back, head or brain, stomach, heart, lungs, or kidneys, take three spoonfuls of the decoction, and mix with boiling water, ale, mead, or milk. Then add to a good draught of this a spoonful of the powder, which should be drunk in the morning while fasting. Half as much should be taken the last thing at night. It is good for any kind of disease of the brain, nerves, back, epilepsy, mania, or mental infirmity of any kind, paralysis, all weakness of joints, sight, hearing, or senses. It will promote fruitfulness, the begetting of children, and restrain seminal flux. The man who takes a spoonful of it daily in his drink will enjoy uninterrupted health, strength of body, and manly vigour. The same result will follow if he takes a spoonful of the decoction in his drink daily.

If a patient is ill of strangury, flatulent dyspepsia, or dropsy, let him take a spoonful of the ashes on drink three times a day, and when practicable let him drink an infusion of the plant, either fresh gathered or dry. It will preserve and cure him. When the plant grows near at hand, he need only gather the berries fresh daily as wanted, for a decoction, and the plant gathered fresh for an infusion. But when it can only be found far off, let it be used as directed, the plants being kept dry in the house all through the year, gathering them summer, winter, and spring, as they can be procured.

The best places to procure mistletoe are Gwent, Somerset, Breconshire, and Shropshire. The best time to gather it is in the depth of winter, from the feast of St. Andrew [30 November] to Candlemas [2 February, the midpoint of win ter]. And it is also well to gather the green herb from the feast of St. James [25 July] to the Calends of November [1 November]. In order to procure its ashes, it is best that mistletoe should be burnt green before it has lost its sap.

* *'Llennen rawn' - the unmutated Welsh rhawn means long, coarse animal hair, usually horsehair. Llennen is probably a derivative of llen, meaning sheet or screen in this context.*

## THE FOLLOWING ARE THE VIRTUES OF OAK.

797. Oak will supply a variety of remedies, for all diseases proceeding from weakness in the nerves, spinal marrow, and brain. Remedies are procured from the oak in a variety of ways.

Take fresh chips of oak, and macerate in running water, until their virtues are extracted. Then take them out and put in some fresh chips, treating them as before. This being done nine times, boil the liquor down to half, put in a pound of honey for each two gallons of the liquor, and ferment. A quantity equal to the honey, or any less quantity of the decoction of the mistletoe, may be added if there is any at hand. But if not, it will be a very excellent drink nevertheless, and is called oak beer. It is the best drink of any to strengthen the body, constitution, nerves, brain, and spinal marrow. It will also cure diseases which proceed from weakness, a good draught being drunk every morning while fasting.

The inner bark of the oak is an excellent tonic. It should be kept, dried and powdered, as well as simply well-dried, so that it may be at hand when needed, in either form. It is excellent when taken in ale, or as a decoction in all cases of debility, in all fevers, whether continued or inflammatory in tertian or quartan intermittents, or when eruptive poison is present in the blood or humors. A decoction of the fresh bark boiled in ale, or in the milk of cows or goats, is very good in the same diseases.

Take ripe acorns, let them be very crisply roasted, and kept in a well-covered oak vessel. Take a spoonful on your drink night and morning. Whenever a man or woman is the subject of functional or seminal weakness, three tablespoonfuls of this powder should be boiled in a good draught of goats' or cows' milk, then drunk mixed with honey night and morning, for it will remove the complaint. It is useful for all the above mentioned diseases, for uterine haemorrhage in women, for eruptions in all manner of men, and for diseased lungs. It is an excellent ordinary diet (mixed with well-baked wheaten bread), for all weak persons, or those subject to affections of the lungs, or bodily or constitutional debility of any kind.

Malt some acorns and make ale therewith. It is the best and healthiest of any, and an excellent tonic in cases of debility, or diseases proceeding from this.

Gather the leaves of the oak in August or September, dry well, and keep covered. If applied to any contused integument, or watery excoriation, they will heal it.

Take roasted acorns, or the inner bark roasted, ground with corn, and make bread. This bread is the best of any to strengthen a man's body, and to remove all complaints resulting from the winter cold or humidity.

## THE FOLLOWING ARE THE VIRTUES OF VERVAIN

798. Should you be affected with scrofula, take a decoction or infusion of vervain, gathering the entire plant when in seed. Roast it well and powder. Keep this very carefully in a well-covered vessel. Mix it with your ordinary drink for habitual use. Boil the entire plant, root and seed included, in ale, mead, goat or cow milk, and let it be your habitual drink. Mix the powder also with your bread, and let it be your habitual diet, with goat's milk (or with a cow's milk, when you have no goat's milk). If one is affected with running sores, the powder should be sprinkled on them. And take the plant, root and all, pound, and boil with fresh butter, and a little wax, strain well, and apply it. Take the juice of the entire plant, and rub it on your chest daily, as long as the plants can be procured. In winter, mix the powder with honey, and anoint in the same way.

The whole plant is good for all diseases proceeding from the poison of scrofula, whether affecting the lungs, liver, kidneys, brain, eyes, or any other part. Gather this, and every other herb in the name of God, and give no heed to those who say that it should be gathered in the name of the devil, as the devil has nothing to do with goodness.

# EXPOSITION OF THE FOUR ELEMENTS OF MAN

## THE FOLLOWING IS AN EXPOSITION OF THE FOUR ELEMENTS OF MAN - FROM WHICH PROCEED THE FOUR CONSTITUTIONS OR TEMPERAMENTS OF MAN: SANGUINEOUS; CHOLERIC; PHLEGMATIC; AND MELANCHOLIC

### TO RECOGNISE PERSONS OF A SANGUINEOUS CONSTITUTION

799. A person of sanguineous constitution will be naturally fat, but he is not simply fat, as that would show a cold nature. For an abundance of flesh indicates a hot nature; and plenty of flesh is the result of an abundance of blood, as Avicenna says*. Every ruddy, red-haired spare man, is of a sanguine temperament, as Galen** says. Sanguineous men will be merry, and fond of listening to tales and merriment, and for the same cause they are incontinent, and apt to give way to their animal propensities. They will also drink wine jovially. A sanguineous man will share his food of the best kind, for sanguineous people will seek that which corresponds mostly with their nature.

A sanguineous man will also be apt to play, for his blood will have merriment. He will also be fair, from the nature of his constitution, eloquent of speech, apt to acquire all knowledge, arts and deep systems. He will be poetically inclined, and will delight in imagination, and ambitious projects. He will not easily be instigated to anger. He will be of a generous disposition, not covetous, amiable, of an affectionate behaviour, and kindly conduct. He will be of ruddy complexion, for as Avicenna observes, a ruddy complexion of the skin indicates an abundance of blood. It should be a clear transparent red, not livid red, as is the case with those whose countenances are florid in consequence of drinking to excess, or subsisting upon a vegetable diet; for such a complexion indicates lepra, scurvy, excess of humor and blood.

He will sing sweetly and amiably with his voice, he will delight in music, and social intercourse with singers, and with the merry and poetical. He will delight in the harp, and all instrumental music. He will be quick and industrious in work, or on errand. He will also be brave and confident from heat of blood, and will be gentlemanly in his deportment from activity of circulation. When uneducated, he will be apt to become conceited of his own parts, as well as cross-grained, impertinent and disagreeable, in consequence of the over-excited state of his blood. He will be more disposed to fix his mind, and act upon the near than the distant. He will also learn from genius rather than study, and will be satirical and curt in what he says or does. He is apt to laugh and be jolly without reason, save the excited and untameable tendency of the sanguineous temperament.

* *The Rev. John Williams ab Ithel added:* Avicenna, or Abou-Ali-Alhussein-Ben-Abdallah-Ebn-Sina, the Prince of Arabian Philosophers and Physicians, was born in the neighbourhood of Bokhara, in 910, and died of intemperance, a.d. 1038, after having experienced the vicissitudes of fortune, and being reduced from the post of Grand Vizier to the Sultan Mahmoud to the condition of a fugitive. He wrote 'Canorum Medicinae'; 'De Medicinais Cordialibus'; 'Cantica'; 'Opera

Philosophica' &c., of which different versions have been made in Hebrew and Latin. Ed. *The most famous of the 450 treatises by this polymath are The Book of Healing and The Canon of Medicine, which were used as medical textbooks in the great universities of Leuven and Montpelier as late as the 1650s; \*\* Aelius Galenus, Galen of Pergamon (129-199/217) was a Greek philosopher, physician, surgeon and medical researcher. His theories dominated Western medicine for nearly two millennia.*

## TO RECOGNISE THE PHLEGMATIC TEMPERAMENT

800. One who is of a phlegmatic temperament will have brown hair, because his constitution is but weak. In the second place, phlegmatic persons will be short and fat, as their natural strength is not such as to permit them to continue growing. They will be also less energetic than persons of the other temperaments, in consequence of their coldness, which will render them more sleepy also. They will be a prudent people. They will also be idle, and that in consequence of cold, for as heat renders a man light and brisk, so cold makes him heavy and idle. Phlegmatic people will also be fat in consequence of bodily impurity. They will also be sluggish in mind, or sleepy, or given to much sleep.

If instructed they will be intelligent, and will acquire what will be expected of them. However, in consequence of their sluggishness, they will come off indifferently in all competitive efforts, and will soon succumb. The memory will be bad, and they will not love, except from selfish motives. They will not seek merriment, song, or jollity, and when possessing knowledge, they will be found wanting in genius. But when there is a mixture of the sanguineous in the constitution, then we may often find him a man wise in knowledge, and of strong genius; being patient, long suffering, and discreet. He will not love contention, mimicry, nor flippancy, because he will not love, except for what is seemly and substantial.

## TO RECOGNISE THE VAPOURISH [*CHOLERIC*] CONSTITUTION, AND THE PERSONS WHO ARE OF THAT TEMPERAMENT

801. He who is of a vapourish or choleric constitution will be impatient, in consequence of a superfluity of heat, disposing him to precipitancy. One of this constitution will be very ambitious of obtaining superiority, dignity, and authority over others, in as much as natural heat disposes the mind of the man to folly.\* Vapourish persons will also have a facility of acquiring learning in consequence of the heat of bile, but they will not retain what they have learnt. They will also be high-spirited, that is, they will not patiently suffer injustice, in consequence of their heat. They will aspire to great eminence, official position, and social elevation. A choleric man will be as voluptuous as a goat, and passion, rather than lore, will direct him in every thing.

He will be a deceiver, and will be soon angry on account of trifles, exhibiting in this the heat of vapour, and sanguineous ebullition about the heart. He will be cunning, quick, and imprudent in his policy and plans; being more distinguished for violence than constancy in what he does and thinks. He will be slender in his limbs, ungracious in his address, and yellow as saffron in his complexion. As Avicenna says, this complexion indicates haughtiness, one of slender body and limbs, and one who sees a fault in others where it does not exist, and is blind to his own imperfections. He will be kind to those who honour him, cold and haughty to those who do not, and revengeful towards those who wrongly and falsely injure him. The phlegmatic character cannot be commingled [combined] with this constitution. If it could, a sanguineous temperament will be unfaithful and capricious. Of the four constitutions of man, this is the least capable of amelioration and improvement. Rhys the Physician has termed this the vapourish temperament, as it is occasioned by cardiac ebullition, and the bitterness of the bile in man.

* This author has suffered under several such managers – 'arrogance is the façade of the charlatan.'

## THE FOLLOWING ARE INSTRUCTIONS FOR THE RECOGNITION OF THE NATURE AND CONSTITUTION OF MELANCHOLY, AND OF THE TEMPERAMENT OF THE PERSONS WHO ARE MELANCHOLIC

802. He who is of a melancholic constitution will be surly and unmanly, as if at war with himself. Most melancholic people will be also sad and unsociable in consequence of their coldness. They will be also be studious, meditative, and thoughtful, as well as disposed to seek solitude. In consequence of the dryness of the brain, their sleep will not be sound, being broken and disturbed with dreams. Of studious minds, their memory will be good. They will be difficult to please, envious, covetous, apt to evil from moral weakness, little able to follow up their good intentions, and consequently bad paymasters and cheats.

A melancholic man will be a great reader, abstemious, fearful, and his complexion will be earth-like, which, if it has a shade of green, will indicate dignity, as the wise Cassius says. All men of this sort will be exposed to extremes in all things. If sad and sorrowful they will be exceedingly so. If joyful, there will be no limit to their jollity. They love singing in solitude, and from a solitary place, to listen to song and harp. They like to say their minds of others, but in no manner to reveal their own internal feelings. They are lovers of song and curious research, but do not much care to show it. They are apt to cultivate the arts and sciences, taking care to understand what they are about, and to be careful as to what they say and do.

If there is a mixture of the sanguineous, they will be found a superior class of men. If choleric be the mixture, they will be bitter, surly, and most disagreeable men. If there is a phlegmatic admixture, there will be a tendency to insanity, and mental strife. This class of men will be slender of body and limbs. Many a poet will be found of this constitution, and often will they exhibit inordinate love, and excessive hate.

## CHARMS AND MEDICAL FEATS
### Here are recorded the following charms and medical feats discovered through the grace of God, and the intelligence of the sages and saints of olden times.

### TO OBLIGE A MAN TO CONFESS WHAT HE HAS DONE
803. Take a frog alive from the water, extract his tongue, and put him again in the water. Lay this same tongue upon the heart of a sleeping man, and he will confess his deeds in his sleep.

### FOR TOOTHACHE - A REMEDY*
804. Saint Mary sat on a stone, the stone being near her hermitage, when the Holy Ghost came to her, she being sad. "Why art thou sad, mother of my Lord, and what pain torments thee!" "My teeth are painful, a worm called megrim** has penetrated them, and I have masticated, and swallowed it." "I adjure thee daffin o negrbina*** by the Father, and the Son, and the Holy Ghost, the Virgin Mary, and God, the munificent Physician, that thou dost not permit any disease, dolour, or molestation to affect this servant of God here present, either in tooth, eye, head, or in the whole of her teeth together. So be it Amen."

*The Welsh is cyferddawn, meaning a medicinal virtue, or remedy, which Pughe translates as a charm; ** This is the same word in Welsh as migraine, meaning a throbbing pain; *** This phrase is both in the Welsh and Pughe's English translation, and daffin may mean 'sweets' but I can find no meaning for negrbina.*

### A CHARM FOR UTERINE DISEASE WHICH WAS GIVEN BY RHIWALLON THE PHYSICIAN TO GWYRFYL, THE DAUGHTER OF RHYS AP GRUFFYDD AP RHYS AP TEWDWR*
805. I adjure thee, thou diseased uterus, by the Father, the Son, and the Holy Ghost, so that thou might not inflict pain, nor have power for evil in me Gwyrfyl, the daughter of Rhys, the servant of God, either in the head, breast, stomach, or any other part of my body. Let God the Father prevail, let God the Son prevail, and let God the Holy Ghost prevail. Even so be it. Amen.

*Pughe mistakenly calls Gwyrfyl the daughter of Gruffydd ap Tewdwr (1090-1137). Rhys ap Gruffydd was the great Lord Rhys of Deheubarth (1132-1197). Gwyrfyl was one of his daughters, perhaps illegitimate, along with the well-known Gwenllian and Angharad. Her brothers were Hywel, Maelgwn, Gruffydd and Rhys Gryg, to whom Rhiwallon was court physician.*

### FOR TOOTHACHE
806. Obtain an iron nail, and engrave the following words upon it: - | - **agla** - | - **Sabaoth** - | - **athanatos** - | - Insert the nail under the affected tooth. Then drive the nail into an oak tree, and while it remains there the toothache will not return. But you should carve the name of the man affected with toothache on the tree, with the same nail, repeating the following. "By the power of the Father and these consecrated words, as you enter into this wood, so let the pain and disease depart from the tooth of the sufferer. Even so be it. Amen."

256

THUS DID RHIWALLON THE PHYSICIAN RESTRAIN A BLEEDING IN THE CASE OF THE KNIGHT LOGRANIUS. SANGUIS THE KNIGHT* PIERCED THE SIDE OF CHRIST, THE SON OF THE VIRGIN MARY, AND IN CONSEQUENCE THERE ISSUED THE BLOOD AND WATER.

-|- Stay thou blood -|- in the name of the Father, stay thou blood -|- in the name of the Son, stay thou blood -|- in the name of the Holy Ghost, rest thou blood -|- in the name of the blessed Trinity, thou wound bleed not -|-.

### UNNITH DEUS PATRIS, UNNITH DEUS FILIUS, UNNITH DEUS SPIRITUS SANCTUS -|- CHRISTI

Amen -|- Amen -|- Amen -|- Amen -|- so be it.

*Longinus is not mentioned in the Gospels, but was later said to be the Roman soldier who pierced the side of Christ with a lance, when Jesus was on the Cross. The legend grew over time and Longinus was later sainted as a martyr.*

### TO PRODUCE SLEEP

807. Take a goat's horn, and carve the name of the seven sleepers* upon it, and make a knife hilt [handle] of it. The writing should begin at the blade, and these are their names, Anaxeimeys, Malchus, Marsianus, Denys, Thon, Serapion and Constantynn. When the names are inscribed, lay the knife under the sick man's head unknown to him, and he will sleep.

*There was persecution and killing of Christians during the reign of Emperor Decius (249-251CE), and Decius travelled to Ephesus in Turkey to enforce his laws against them. Seven young men, named Maximillian, Jamblichos, Martin, John, Dionysios, Exakostodianos, and Antoninos (Gregory of Tours names them as Achillides, Diomedes, Diogenus, Probatus, Stephanus, Sambatus, and Quiriacus) were tried for being Christians. They were given a short time to consider abandoning Christ before Decius returned to sentence them. They gave away their property to the poor, and went into a cave on Mount Anchilos to pray and prepare for death. Decius returned and told his soldiers to fetch them, but as they had heard of his return, they said a last prayer and fell asleep. When found sleeping, Decius told his men to seal the cave and so bury them alive. Their story was inscribed by a Christian on the wall outside the cave. In the time of the Christian Emperor Theodosius, about 150 years later, the cave was opened by a rich landowner to use as a cattle stall. The sleepers awoke, and sent Diomides to Ephesus to buy some food, and he was amazed to see crosses over churches. The sleepers were celebrated as saints, and every year the Feast of the Seven Sleepers is held. A version of the tale is in the Qur'an. In legend St Mary Magdalene is buried in the cave, and for centuries people were buried as close as possible to the site. In Welsh, a late-riser was called a 'saith cysgadur', a 'seven sleeper'.*

### PRO MORBO KADENDO OR EPILEPTIC DISEASE, WHICH CASTS A MAN DOWN IN AN INSENSIBLE STATE

808. Set thy mind upon God, and say these words three times in the patient's ear, ANAMZAPTA, and when he is restored from the seizing fit, administer to him some dog's gall. The gall bladder should be hung in the house where the sick man dwells, for three days, in a place where it may be exposed to the wind. Then it should be boiled in a quart of ale, until it is reduced to a pint, and given to the patient to drink in the intervals of the fit.

The following is a charm which was made by the Lord Jesus Christ Himself, and shown to the three brethren, asking them where they went. We go, said they to the Mount of Olives, to gather herbs to heal wounds and contusions. Then said He, return again and take some oil of olives, the white of eggs, and black wool, applying them to the injured parts, saying thus: "I adjure thee, O wound, by the grace and power of the eight wounds which were in the true God, and true Man, which He received in His most holy body in order to our redemption, by that which Thou, Jesus Christ, didst Thyself desire, by the weariness which Thou didst suffer, and the atonement which Thou didst Thyself make, that this wound shall neither pain, nor smell, nor putrefy, in the name of the Father, the Son, and the Holy Ghost. Let it be so. Amen."

## FOR AGUE; A CHARM

809. Put the following writing on the sick man's stomach, hanging it about his neck. When our Lord Jesus Christ beheld the cross which was prepared for Him, He trembled greatly, and the Jews asked Him thus, "Dost Thou fear this cross, or is it the ague that affects Thee!" Jesus answered them thus, "I fear not this cross, nor am I yet affected with the ague, but I tremble before my Heavenly Father, in contemplating what He prepares for those who shall crucify Me. And for a truth to you I speak, that whatsoever man shall hear the words I say, and shall believe them, and shall do all that I have commanded therein, prostrating himself before his Heavenly Father, he shall never suffer from the ague, nor shall he have any fear." And now, O Lord Jesus Christ, grant that of thy mercy, the ague may not afflict or trouble thy servant, and the servant of God the Father from Heaven, neither now at present, nor at any other time during his life and existence in this world, in the name of the Father, and the Son, and the Holy Ghost. So be it. Ever Amen.

## TO KNOW WHETHER A SICK MAN SHALL LIVE OR DIE

810. Take an egg laid on Thursday, in the house in which the sick man dwells, and write the following upon it: **f.G.O.G.Y.L.G.Y.S.** Place it in a safe place, outside the house. On the following morning break the egg. If blood comes out of it, he will die. If not, he will live.

## FOR THE DROPSY, OR HYDROPS

811. Rub young swallows with saffron, and in a short time the old swallows will bring them a stone. With this stone the patient will be cured of the hydrops.

## HOW TO LET BLOOD, SO AS TO PRESERVE A MAN'S SIGHT

812. Whoever is bled in the right arm on the eighteenth day of March; and in the left arm on the 20th day of April, will never be blind, for it has been often proved.

## FOR WARTS

813. Wash the warts with the water from a font, in which the seventh son of the same man and wife is baptized.

258

## A WAY IN WHICH A THING CAN BE SEEN, WHICH IS INVISIBLE TO OTHERS

814. Take the gall of a cat, and a hen's fat, mixing them together. Put this in your eyes, and you will see things which are invisible to others.

## TO ENABLE A MAN TO HOLD FIRE IN HIS HAND

815. Take marsh mallows*, and the white of two eggs. Anoint your hands with these, mixed together. Then cover your hands with powdered alum**, and you may handle fire without harm, or hold fire and hot iron in your hand without fear.

*Althea officinalis; **Unsurprisingly, this hydrated potassium aluminium sulphate has fire retardant properties.

## A SNAKE'S SKIN.

The following are the twelve characteristics of a snake's skin, which Alphibam testifies of, and states to be true and effectual to those who use it. I have translated them out of the Arabic to Latin, and from Latin to Cymraeg also.

When the moon is in her first increase, under the sign called Aries, or the Ram, which falls about the middle of the month of March, on the third day of the Calends of April, when the first seed under this sign are formed, then burn the skin of a snake, which has been cast in the time of harvest. Take the ashes, and keep them carefully, for they are the most precious application which any human tongue can order. Let the first instance at hand suffice. Whosoever has a fresh wound, let him cover it with a little of this ash, and it will heal it in three days.

## WEIGHTS AND MEASURES

The following exhibits the weights and measures, which every Physician should employ, so that he may know certainly what proportions to use, when necessary.

**Weights and measures of proportion.**
xx grains of wheat make one Scruple.
iii scruples make one dram.
viij drams make one ounce.
xij ounces make one pound.
And thus are they written in the Books of Physicians.*

**A grain thus ꞯ**

**A scruple thus Ə**

**A dram thus ℥**

**An ounce thus ℥**

**A pound thus S**

And thus are they arranged in accordance with these characters.

| | | | |
|---|---|---|---|
| xx | ꞯ | to | Ə |
| iij | Ə | to | ℥ |
| ᴨiij | ℥ | to | ℥ |
| xij | ℥ | to | S |

* *Pughe notes:* Those signs are now thus written: Grain gr. Scruple Ə Dram 3 Ounce ℥ Pound lb

**Fluid or liquid measures are arranged thus.**
Four podfuls make one spoonful.
Four spoonfuls make one eggshellful.
Four eggshellfuls make one cupful.
Four cupfuls make one quart.
Four quarts make one gallon.
Four gallons make one pailful.
Four pailfuls make one grenn.*
Four grenns make one mydd.
Four mydds make one myddi (or hogshead.)
Even so are fluid and liquid measures arranged.
* *Pughe notes:* 'A large earthen vessel' W.O.P.

*The following are other measures noted by Physicians:-*
Two eggshellfull make half a pan.
Two halfpans, a pan.
Two pans, a phioled.
Two phioleds, a cupful.
Two cupfuls, a quart.

All the measures of solids and fluids should be of warranted weight and measure, so that they may afford warranted and just information. This is order that the medicines administered to the sick may neither be ineffective nor poisonous, and that every dose may be of the proportion intended.

## The following are conjectural measures, dependent upon the Physician's judgment

Four grains of wheat, one pea.
Four peas, one acorn.
Four acorns, one pigeon's egg.
Four pigeon's egg, one hen's egg.
Four hen's eggs, one goose's egg.
Four goose's eggs, one swan's egg.

These proportions cannot be warranted further than the Physician's judgment.

## FOUR PRINCIPAL EXCITING CAUSES OF FEVER AND DISEASE

There are four principal exciting causes of fever and disease in the human body:-

i. Fever, excited by an excess of heat or cold.

ii. Eruptive poison in the blood or humors, produced by irregularities in eating and drinking.

iii. Obstructions in the stomach, veins, or other hollow vessels of the body, so that the food, drink, blood or humors, cannot pass on as usual.

iv. A boil, carbuncle, or plague, and they are occasioned by the entrance of poison into the system. From these four proceed all fevers and diseases incident to the human body, and by the aid of active remedies are they cured.

## USEFUL THINGS*

* These have been sorted alphabetically in English.

The following are things useful to be known by every Physician, and also every head of a family:-

**BATH**.* An infusion or decoction in which the patient or his limb is to be put.

* *Pughe notes:* This word (ennaint) is improperly rendered 'ointment' in the Mabinogi of Geraint ab Erbin.

**CONFECTION**. Fluids mixed with powders or other substances capable of being administered as a draught.

**CONSTITUTION**. The disposition which is in a man, or other living being, or herb, or other matter; being their virtue, inherent property, or nature.

**DECOCTION**. Boiling the herbs or ingredients in the water or fluid required.

**ELECTUARY**. Substances incorporated into a dough so as to be eaten.

**ESSENCE**. An amorphous or odoriferous substance, which may be taken in a draught by mouth, or injected into the nostrils, head,* rectum, or other part.

* *Pughe notes:* External ear

**FOMENTATION**. To be applied as a wash to a hurt, whether hot or cold, as may be wanted.

**INFUSION**. Pouring water or other fluid in a boiling state upon herbs, or whatever other ingredient that may be required.

**PILLS**. Incorporated medical substances, formed into small balls so as to be taken at a gulp.

**POTTAGE OR PORRIDGE**. Pouring boiling or cold water, or other fluid such as may be required upon the herbs or other ingredients, leaving them to stand, then straining under a press.

**POTION**. A draught or fluid prepared according to art.

**REGIMEN**. The food and drink as regulated by medical advice.

**SOAKAGE**. Pouring cold or boiling water, or other fluid on any substance capable of being influenced thereby, so as to become incorporated with what is poured thereupon.

# THE ESSENTIALS OF A PHYSICIAN

These things should be in the possession of a Physician: and then follow the characteristics which should distinguish him, which are called the Essentials of a Physician.

i. A lancet to bleed or open an abscess, also a knife somewhat larger.

ii. A steel or silver spatula to spread plaster.

iii. A pipe and bladder in order to inject to the urinary organs or rectum.

iv. His plasters, his ointments, his pills, his powders, his potions, carefully preserved to meet any demand and occasion.

v. A garden of trees and herbs, where such herbs, shrubs, and trees, as do not everywhere grow naturally, may be kept cultivated, and where foreign trees and plants, which require shelter and culture before they will thrive in Wales, may be grown.

vi. He should also have his dry herbs, roots, seeds, and barks kept at hand, so that they may be had in winter, and at other times when they are not to be obtained growing, or above ground.

vii. He should also have at hand, his honey, wax, pitch, rosin, gums, oil, tallow, grease, lard, marble slab, ale, wine, mead, distillations, and other articles as may be required.

viii. He should also have at hand his mortars, strainer, press, stoneware, glassware, wooden vessels, his fire utensils, and vessels for keeping articles, whether of glass, earthen, or silver, with good covers, so that the drugs may not become inert, or poisonous from want of keeping, carelessness, or ignorance.

ix. He should also have weights and balances at hand, either of silver or tin, so that nothing deleterious might get into the drugs. All his liquid or fluid measures should also be made of silver or tin, for the same reason. Likewise his surgical instruments generally, with the exception of lancets, cutting scalpels, and probing needles.

x. All his weights and measures, whether of solids or of liquids, should be of warranted weight and capacity, that he may be certain of the proportions of all ingredients, so that he may neither exceed nor come short of the quantity required, as this would render the remedy either inert or poisonous.

xi. He should also have his warranted Books of Art authorized by a master, so that he may be cunning in the judgment and science of the wise and skilful Physicians who have preceded him, and who have written with authority in the Cymraeg [*Welsh*], the Latin, and the Arabic.

xii. He should be also declared competent to practise, by authority of the wise and learned masters of the art.

xiii. He should be a kind man, gentle, mild, meek, intelligent, wise, and gentlemanly in act and deed, in word and conduct, being careful not to shame those whom he has to examine, particularly when he has to examine women.

xiv. He should be skilled in all professional acquirements, and should know the complexion and sign of every feminine disease. He should be able to examine the

264

sick, whether man, woman, boy or girl, in regard to age, constitution, sex, and in a mild, gentlemanly way, both as to address and voice.

xv. He should carefully keep all professional secrets, nor should he divulge them on any account to any man, nor on any consideration.

xvi. He should most carefully avoid intoxication, tippling, or incontinence in any shape, as there can be no trust or dependence upon those Physicians who are addicted to such evil deeds, nor can that respect, which learning and professional intelligence are entitled to be accorded them.

xvii. He should be a faithful subject, lest he should practice treachery or treason in the exercise of his profession, on native or foreigner, friend or foe. For the office of a Physician is not to slay, but to preserve from what would slay, and to be in accord with God and His peace, and not with the rage and enmity of man to his fellow man.

xviii. He should always have his case of instruments, his emetics and antidotes about him, in case of need.

xix. He should keep about home as much as he can, so that he may be found when wanted.

xx. He should be constitutionally and habitually devotional, so that the blessing of God may be upon him, and what he does, and that he may be conscientious to do what is right and beneficial in the practice of his art.

And these things are called the Essentials of a Physician.*

* *Pughe, or Williams, footnotes:* It will be interesting to compare these wise 'Essentials' with the oath of the Aesculapiadae, in old Greece, being a formula not unlike that in use among the Pythagoreans, and which was in the following words:-

"I swear by Apollo, the Physician, by Aesculapius, by Hygeia, Panacea, and all the gods and goddesses, that, according to my ability and judgment, I will keep this oath and stipulation, to reckon him, who teaches me this art, equally dear to me as my parents, to share my substances with him, and relieve his necessities if required, to look upon his offspring in the same light as my own brothers, and to teach them this art, if they shall wish to learn it, without fee or stipulation ; and that by precept, lecture, and every other mode of instruction. I will impart a knowledge of this art to my own sons, to those of my teachers, and to disciples bound by a stipulation and oath according to the law of medicine, but to none others. I will follow that system of regimen, which, according to my ability and judgment, I consider for the benefit of my patients; and abstain from what is deleterious and mischievous. I will give no deadly medicine to any one if asked, nor suggest any such counsel; and in like manner, I will not give a woman a pessary to produce an abortion.

With purity and with holiness I will pass my life, and practice my art. I will not cut persons labouring under the stone, but will leave this to be done by men who are practitioners of the work. Into whatever houses I enter, I will go into them for the benefit of the sick, and will abstain from every voluntary act of mischief or corruption; and further, from the seduction of males or females, of freemen or slaves. Whatever in connection with my professional practice, or not in connection with it, I see, or hear, I will not divulge, as reckoning that all such should be kept secret While I continue to keep this oath inviolate, may it be

granted me to enjoy life, and the practice of my art, respected by all men at all times. But should I trespass and violate this oath, may the reverse be my lot."
- Adams' Hippocrates, Vol II. p. 799

And thus ends this Book of Medicine, and I, Howel the Physician, the son of Rhys, the son of Llywelyn, the son of Philip the Physician, have selected the same from the authorized old books of the original Physicians of Myddfai, even Rhiwallon the Physician, and his three sons, Cadwgan, Gruffudd, and Einion, and the other Physicians, their sons and descendants who succeeded them.

And I, Howel the Physician, am regularly descended in the male line from the said Einion, the son of Rhiwallon the Physician of Myddfai, being resident in Cilgwryd, in Gower. May the grace and blessing of God attend this Book, and him who studies it as a directory of the art, for the love of God, and the health of the diseased and maimed. Amen. With God's help even so let it be.

I, William Bona* have transcribed this Work from the Book of John Jones, the Physician, of Myddfai, who was the last of the descendants of the Physicians of Myddfai, Anno Christi, 1743.

And I, Iolo Morganwg have rewritten the same carefully from the Book of the above William Bona, now in the possession of Thomas Bona, Physician, of the Parish of Llanfihangel Iorwerth**, in the

County of Carmarthen, in the year 1801; and with old Howel the Physician I say, The grace of God attend it.

I, John Pughe, Fellow of the Royal College of Surgeons, of Penhelyg House, near Aberdovey, Merionethshire, have finished translating the same into English, this 12th day of February, 1861.

*Wiliam (William) Bona was a poet who was responsible for collecting and copying important manuscripts. He is noted as having written the document before 22 May 1766, in the Report on Manuscripts in the Welsh Language, but the National Library of Wales gives a date of 1743.

**This is now Llanfihangel-ar-Arth near Llandysul in Caramarthenshire. Thomas Bona of Llanfihangel Aber Arth (yet another name for the same village) married Ann Howell upon 3 June 1763 at Abergwili Parish Church. A Thomas Bona was recorded as being born on at least seven occacions in South and West Wales between 1856 and 1915, with the Bona surname occurring regulary around Carmarthen town.

# THE THERAPEUTIC ACTION OF HERBS

This is not included in the Myddfai texts, but included to explain some of the definitions in the preceding:

**Alteratives**: Medicines which gradually alter and correct a poisoned condition of the blood stream.

**Anthelmintics**: Remedies for worms, such as vermicides which kill them insode the body, and vermifuges which expel them.

**Anthilithics**: Agents which reduce, suppress or dissolve urinary stones.

**Antiseptics**: Agents for destroying or inhibiting putrefactive or pathogenic bacteria.

**Antispasmodics**: Agents to reduce or prevent involuntary muscular contractions.

**Astringents**: Remedies which contract organic tissue, reducing secretions or discharges.

**Bitter**: Acting on the mucous membranes of the mouth and stomach to increase appetaite and promote digestion.

**Cathartic**: Laxative.

**Cardiac**: A heart stimulant.

**Carminative**: An egent for the dispersal of gas in the intestine, and to counteract side effects of certain laxatives.

**Cholagogue**: A remedy to increase the flow of bile into the intestines.

**Demulcent**: An agent which softens, soothes and reduces irritation of the mucous membranes.

**Diaphoretic**: A remedy to increase perspiration.

**Diuretic**: A remedy to increase the secretion and expulsion of urine.

**Emetic**: An agent causing one to vomit and empty the contents of the stomach.

**Emmenagogue**: A remedy to begin and help menstrual flow.

**Emollient**: Lotions etc. used externally to soften and soothe.

**Expectorants**: Agents to affect the respiratory passages, for the increased secretion and ejection of mucus. It is thought that footballers are addicted to expectorants.

**Febrifuge**: A remedy to reduce temperature in fevers, by enhancing the evaporation of perspiration.

**Galactagogue**: Agents encouraging the secretion of milk.

**Hypnotic**: A remedy to promote sleeping.

**Nervine**: An agent to calm the nerves.

**Oxytocic**: This has the properties of contracting the uterine muscles and assisting or speeding up childbirth.

**Pectoral**: A cure for pulmonary and other chest diseases.

**Sedative**: An agent to reduce nervousness, distress or agitation.

**Stimulant**: A remedy to qucken the activity of physiological processes.

**Tonic**: An agent to invigorate an organ or the entire body.

**Vulnerary**: Any remedy to promote the healing of wounds.

## PART 7

## HERBS AND HAIR REMEDIES

As someone who has white thinning hair and a bald patch, I have over the years shared the angst of many men, and thus noticed the many remedies for hair loss given by the physicians of Myddfai. Indeed, a successful anti-hairloss product would make the patentee a billionaire almost overnight. If any of the readers finds a safe and successful formula from the following, I would wish that they forward any excess profits to a children's hospice such as Tŷ Hafan.

In Book1, amongst the virtues of mustard is that '*It is good for colic, loss of hair, noise in the ears, and dimness of sight, cutaneous eruptions, palsy, and many other things.*' Remedy 249 in Book I also gives a cure for alopecia: '*Take watercress, bruise well and express the juice. Wash your head therewith and scrub it well. The same juice may also be taken internally, and you will be cured.*' Watercress is a traditional cure for hair loss, owing to the presence of biotin (Vitamin B7) and zinc, and therefore is present in many modern shampoos. It also contains iron, silica and pyridoxine (Vitamin B6). The deficiency of any or all of these components can cause alopecia. In Book 2 we read:

### FOR ALOPECIA
249. Take watercress*, bruise well and express the juice. Wash your head therewith and scrub it well. The same juice may also be taken internally, and you will be cured.

* *Watercress is a traditional cure for hair loss, owing to the presence of biotin (Vitamin B7) and zinc, and therefore is present in many modern shampoos. It also contains iron, silica and pyridoxine (Vitamin B6). The deficiency of any or all of these components can cause alopecia.*

### TO CAUSE THE HAIR TO GROW
318. Take barberry (Berberis vulgaris) and fill an iron pot with it. Fill it up with as much water as it will contain, then boil on a slow fire until reduced to half. With this water, wash your head morning and evening. Take care that the wash does not touch any part where hair should not grow.

### ANOTHER TO CAUSE THE HAIR TO GROW
319. Take two spoonfuls of olive oil, two spoonfuls of new honey, and an onion as large as a pigeon's egg. Pound them together in a stone mortar till it becomes an ointment, and anoint your head therewith night and morning. Wear a leather cap until the hair is grown. It is best to pound the onion well before it is added to the ointment.

### TO PROMOTE THE GROWTH OF HAIR
508. Shave the head clean with a razor, and take honey with the juice of onions in equal parts. Anoint and scrub the head well with the same every morning and night. The head should be washed with the distilled water of honey. It is proven.

269

## ANOTHER TO PROMOTE THE GROWTH OF HAIR

509. Shave the head carefully, anoint with honey, and sprinkle the powder of mollipuffs upon it. (Mollipuffs were called by Pughe Lycoperdon Bovista, now known as the Warted Puffball fungus, Bovista officinalis).

In one of my previous books, Breverton's Complete Herbal, there were many other 'cures' for hair loss. Culpeper noted that *'The cotton or down of Quinces boiled and applied to plague sores, heals them up: and laid as a plaster, made up with wax, it brings hair to them that are bald, and keeps it from falling, if it be ready to shed.'* From the Doctrine of Signatures, we can see that the light down on the skin suggested fine hairs and that the fruit will restore hair to the head. Culpeper also wrote: *'If the peach kernels be bruised and boiled in vinegar, until they become thick, and applied to the head, it marvellously procures the hair to grow again upon bald places, or where it is too thin.'* This last point again owes its reference to the Doctrine of Signatures. The furry down on a peach resembles fine-growing hair.

However, the antiseptic and anti-dandruff properties of hops are of use in today's shampoos and it has recently been included in the group of products marketed to enhance hair growth. This cosmetic property has been proved in tests through the inhibition of I-reductase. There are many anti-baldness shampoos featuring hops, often combined with nettles, burdock, pot marigold and rosemary.

Hops can also be incorporated into bath gels because they stimulate the skin's metabolism. In the Middle Ages, the principal use of rosemary oil was as Spiritus Rosmarini, in hair-lotions, for its odour and effect in preventing premature baldness. A cold infusion of the antiseptic plant is one of the best hair rinses, helping prevent scurf and dandruff. Winter Savory oil is even now used in preparations to prevent incipient baldness. Culpeper also wrote of southernwood: *'The ashes mingled with old salad oil, helps those that have hair fallen, and are bald, causing the hair to grow again either on the head or beard.'*

Folk tales tell how yarrow can prevent but not cure baldness. An old-fashioned way of strenghtneing hair and add shine was to make an infusion of nettle tops. Place the young nettle tops in a large cup of boiling water, cover and leave for a few hours. Take out the tops and rinse your hair with the cool liquid after shampooing.

Liquorice is said to help with age-related mental decline, and used in stop smoking remedies and for hair loss. Burdock root oil extract (Bur oil) has traditionally been popular in Europe as a scalp treatment applied to improve hair strength, shine, and body, and to combat hair loss. Indeed, modern studies indicate that burdock root oil extract is rich in phytosterols and essential fatty acids required for healthy scalp and natural hair growth.

Marsh Mallow was used in Persia to reduce inflammation in teething babies, and the Holy Roman Emperor Charlemagne insisted that it be planted in his

270

gardens. Again, the downy 'hair' covering the plant helped promote hair growth. The Greeks believed aloe symbolized beauty, patience, fortune and good health. Hippocrates (460-370 BCE) told us it was good for hair growth,

Basil essential oil is now used in aromatherapy to alleviate tiredness and depression, and also makes an excellent skin tonic and assists hair growth. It reduces inflammation from insect bites. With analgesic, antiseptic and anti-spasmodic properties, Bay is used for treating dandruff, boosting hair growth, rheumatism, sprains, bruises, ulcers and scabies.

Lemon Balm dressed wounds, cured rabid dog bites, toothache, boils and skin eruptions, pregnancy sickness, treated baldness and was a love charm. Aqua Mellis, a decoction of balm was used in the seventeenth century against baldness. A mixture of honey, salt and bruised onion rubbed into a bald patch would encourage hair growth, as would an infusion of rosemary, sage and peppermint tea left on the head.

Gerard recommended spear plume thistle: '... *being stamped before the floure appeareth, and the juice pressed forth, causeth the haire to grow where it is pilled off, if the place be bathed with the juyce'.* Langham was optimistic about beetroot: *'the asches of the root with hony, resoreth haire, and keepeth the rest from falling'.* John Gerard (1545-1612) also noted *'The juice of onions anointed upon a bild or bald head in the Sun, bringeth the haire again very speedily.'*

Nettle juice, combed through the hair to prevent baldness has been a common folk practice. The Wiltshire cure for dandruff was to massage the scalp with a nettle infusion each day. Pliny recommended parsley for baldness as far back as Pliny's time, and in medieval times we were told: *'powder your head with powdered parsley seed three nights every year, and the hair will never fall off'.* A herbalist may suggest a daily intake of rosemary tea or nettle tea.

A manuscript from 1610 claims that *'if thou wash thy head with* [rosemary water] *and let it drye on agayne by itselfe, it causeth hayre to growe if thou be balde'.* The Housekeeper's & Butler's Assistant for 1862 gives us *'a wash to prevent the hair from falling off'* requiring *'a quarter of an ounce of unprepared tobacco leaves, two ounces of rosemary, two ounces of box leaves, boiled in a quart of water in an earthen pipkin with a lid, for twenty minutes'.* Sniffing horseradish juice could also cure baldness. The Anglo-Saxon version of Apuleius recommended watercress *'in case that a man's hair fall off, take juice; put it on the nose; the hair shall wax'.* There is a saying in French that a bald man *'n'a pas de cresson sous le caillou'* i.e. has no watercress on his head. Gypsies traditionally used St. John's wort as a hair dressing.

Because the walnut was associated by the Doctrine of Signatures with the head, it was used for all related illnesses, from madness to baldness. In the 17th century, a distillation of walnut leaves, honey and wine was used *'to make hair spring on bald-heads.'* Hazel leaves could also be used, and also gave a dark hair dye.

Onion juice, anointed on a bald head in sunshine would speed up hair growth, and the tuber of a Jerusalem artichoke, cut in half, with the cut side rubbed on the hair roots, was another old remedy. All other countries had different plants recommended for hair loss. In Palestine, cassia oil was mixed with olive oil to keep the hair dark, and also to prevent baldness. Soapweed (Yucca glauca) was used by Pueblo Indians as a hair wash shampoo as part of the ritual in initiation ceremonies, though the Kiowa claimed it was an effective cure for baldness and dandruff.

Indian tobacco (Lobelia inflata) was used in Indiana, where a bottle was filled with the pulverized herb, equal parts of brandy or whisky added, and olive oil. The instruction was to let it stand for a few days, then bathe the head once a day with the liquid. Early settlers in New Zealand rubbed the juice from cut stems of the Rimu tree over bald heads as an excellent hair restorer. Dacrydium cupressinum was formerly known as red pine.

While finishing this section, I idly googled herbal hair loss remedies, and two caught my eye: 'I once read in a book that eating honey is good for balding. I once had thinning hair but now I have a full head of hair. If you have just dry hair, honey will make it softer and smoother. I put honey in my tea, oatmeal, on bread, etc. I even eat it straight using a spoon. I go through a 48 oz jar in about three days. If you have a lot of hair loss, it will take some time to get a full head of hair. Just keep at it. (Unless you have a disease, in which case I don't know if it will work.) But for most people it should work. Just don't eat too much at once, it will make you feel nauseous.' Even better was the following: 'Pour milk and let the cat lick it. Grows hair like Stalin. Really.'

## PART 8

## MYDDFAI TODAY

### 8.1

#### TOURS IN WALES 1804-1813 – Richard Fenton

*'Mr. Lewis told me that those old Hereditary Physicians lived at the great house in the Village of Myddfai, and that the family of Jones, who lived at Tyissa, were their descendants, and that the family was never without a medical man in it. There was one branch of the Jones's settled at Carreg Vychan, just by Carreg Levan. The elder Branch centres in the House of Lloyd of Llanvallen, in Brecknockshire… Tuesday. - Rode to see a Tumulus about a mile and a half to the Eastward of Pantycendy. It is sodded without, but within it appears to be a mixture of Earth and stone.*

*From its remarkably conspicuous situation, I should think it a Beacon, as it takes in the Sea Coast, and a wide Circuit of inland Country; but it originally might have been sepulchral, and like many of the Tumuli used in after times for a Beacon. Too large to admit of being tried during my short stay. Ride towards the Van, and by Myddfai, Llwyn y Wermwd, Cilgwyn, and Glansevin house. The ascent gradual till we came to the height above the Vale in which Llanddoysant lies. Saw Talysarn lying exactly on the old Roman road, which the present Turnpike pursues, as having the best course possible. Turn to the left and down a considerable Hill.*

*Bad road to Myddfai. On this side of Myddfai lies the House of the family who were the hereditary Physicians of that place, the descendants of whom are buried at the West end of the Church, and retain their partiality to Medicine, there being several of them buried of the name of Jones, and said to be Surgeons. The Church is double, being separated by a row of neat pillars and moderately pointed Arches. A fine marble Tablet lately set up to Williams of Llwyn y wermwd. On a Tombstone without the Communion rails was an inscription to commemorate one Owen, of the family of Glasallt, Bishop of Llandaff in Charles's time. An old house in the Village called Porth y rhyd. Llwyn y wermwd, a charming situation, ground very parkish, ornamented with fine masses of old wood. To the back a noble view of the Mountains, which from hence look like the view of Cader Idris softened and in miniature from Dolgelly. Follow a narrow winding Vale, each side well wooded, with a rippling stream passing through, dammed up into a large Pond under Llwyn y wermwd house, down to Cilgwyn, late .Miss Price's, and now Mr. Holford's. The Ground very parkish and well wooded.*

*Hence to Glansevin. No fine situation. A house of some pretensions as to external], but all round it appearance of squalid neglect. I heard from an old woman, in ascending towards the Mountain, a piece of a curious fable respecting the origin of the Myddfai Physicians that the first of that family, who took to the profession, was fishing in the lake of the Van, and heard a Voice under Water desiring him to bait his hook with bread; and so doing he hooked a female, who came out of the lake followed by 6 cows, all with names, and was married to the Angler Physician. But she said, after having made him the father of children, that she should quit the world, or at least his society, after receiving 3 unnecessary blows. When at a funeral, she being alone merry, her husband tapped her on the shoulder, saying. What means your mirth in the midst of Sorrow? Says she, That is one of the blows. Again being at a wedding, and she alone being sad, her husband tapped her again a second blow. The woman did not know the cause of the third. So she plunged into the Lake, and her Cows, and was never seen more.*

*The Clerk told me something in addition to this Tale of the Lady of the Lake and the Physician, namely, that she came out of the Lake with 14 cows; and said that when she was destined to return, which would be after she had received three unnecessary blows, she should have as many cows back with her as she could name at a Breath; and that her Breath lasting longer than for her to call the 14 Cows by their Names, she was obliged in addition to have the Oxen in the Plough (a bit of a Bull though), Plough and all, with which she returned to the Lake; and the tradition is that there still appears the furrow the Plough made to be traced to the Lake, and very visibly on the edge of it. '*

## 8.2

## MYDDFAI PAST AND PRESENT

A cache of eight Bronze Age axes, dated 500-700bce, was found near Gellyfelen Farm in the parish of Myddfai. Perhaps they were ritual or had been superseded by iron axes. There were also nine or ten cairns, now much despoiled upon Mynydd Bach, the largest being Tomen y Rhos and Carn Pant Meddygon, dating from 2000-1000bce. Pant y Meddygon was where herbs were gathered. Also on Mynydd Bach, under a *'heap of stones'* was found the Myddfai Cauldron, now in Carmarthenshire Museum at Abergwili. Forty-four inches in circumference and a foot high, it is said that it was acquired from a 'wise woman' who used it four pounding herbs and *simples*. *Simples* was the term for medicinal plants or the medicine obtained from them. There were also three standing stones nearby, and possibly a cromlech, on Blaenddôl Farm. There is also a Roman road, a Roman fort at Y Pigwn and Roman marching camps nearby. Just 250 yards from the centre of Myddfai is Castell Waunberllan, a flat-topped mound once surrounded by a ditch. Y Sithfaen (the erect stone), or St Paul's Marble, stood eight feet high on Pentwyn Farm. Pentwyn was formerly named Gellymaen, which means the grove of the great stone. The stone was moved to Cilgwyn Mansion in 1885. It was said that St Paul preached from the stone. In local tradition the stone was dedicated to the great warrior of the Hundred Years War, Owain Lawgoch, assassinated by the English in 1378. Owain ap Thomas ap Rhodri, Owain of the Red Hand was the last surviving member of the House of Gwynedd.

David James recounts that there are even today farms called Esgairllaethdy in the parish of Mydfai, and Blaensawdde in the neighbouring parish of Llanddeusant. The young man who married the Lady of the Lake farmed with his mother at Blaensawdde, and when married went to farm at Esgairllaethdy, a mile from Myddfai. Pant y Meddygon, where the sons of the Lady of the Lake were taught to gather herbs, adjoins Llyn-y-Fan-Fach. Trackways lead from Esgairllaethdy towards Llyn-y-Fan-Fach, and were said to represent the furrow formed by a plough, when the lady took her animals back to enter the lake. Close to one of the trackways, on Tyngarn, the neighbouring farm to Esgairllaethdy, is a stone with what seems to be a hoof mark in it. It is known as *Ôl Troed y Llô* (the mark of the calf's foot). The tradition of the area supplying doctors is shown in the names of the farms of Llwynifanfeddig and Llwynmeredydd Feddig within Myddfai parish. There is also a meadow on Mynydd Bach called Waun Meddygon.

274

We know from Hearth Tax returns that there were 98 households in Myddfai parish in 1563, growing to 111 in 1668 and to 195 in 1708, and the population was around 900 and 1200 between 1801 and 1881, since when it has declined to around 400 today. In 1840, there were 261 houses, which dropped to around 140 today. David B. James's book upon Myddfai gives full details. Local estates owned much of the land and properties, for instance in 1742 around 52% of the 'chief-rent' paid was from the properties of eight families:

| Owner in 1742 | Properties held | Rent paid as % of Parish total |
|---|---|---|
| David Williams, gent. Llwynywormwood | 23 | 13.5 |
| Daniel Williams, Llwynywormwood | 21 | 3.4 |
| Roderick Gwynne, esq., Brynoie | 14 | 10.1 |
| Owen, esq., Glasallt | 8 | 11.2 |
| Mrs Anne Manwaring | 8 | 6.8 |
| James Price, gent. Cilgwyn | 8 | 2.8 |
| Evan Phillips, gent. | 7 | 5.1 |
| Rees Price, gent., Glantowy | 5 | 2.0 |
| Mr Cornwall | 3 | 6.8 |

By 1839, the estate of Cilgwyn had overtaken Llwynywormwood as the main property-holder, and ten families controlled 77.5% of enclosed land in Myddfai:

| Owner in 1839 | Properties held | % of enclosed land in parish |
|---|---|---|
| James Price Gwynne-Holford, Cilgwyn | 32 | 25.0 |
| Rev. Sir E.H. Griffies Williams, Llwynywormwood | 31 | 14.3 |
| Robert Lewis, Glasallt estate | 16 | 11.0 |
| Rice Williams Price, Williamsfield | 26 | 8.7 |
| Edward Jones, Felindre, Llandovery | 6 | 4.4 |
| Stephen Jones, Ystrad | 4 | 3.3 |
| Lewis Lewis, Lletyifanddu | 6 | 3.1 |
| Charles Bishop, Dôlgarreg | 7 | 2.8 |
| Edward Pryse Lloyd, Glansevin | 5 | 2.5 |
| Walter Rice, Llwynybrain | 4 | 2.4 |

The Glasallt house and estate date from at least 1644, and Cilgwyn from at least 1699. Glasallt Fawr is now a home for adults with learning difficulties. (The Celtic-British name of Glasallt, green hillside or green woodlands, is replicated in Scotland). Cilgwyn Manor became a care home, built around 1800, but behind it stands the original Cefn Cilgywn. Cilgwyn, a grade II listed country manor with 37 bedrooms, has been recently put on the market at a knock-down £450,000. Llwynywormwood (Lwynywermod) is also seventeenth century, but the mansion house has gone and Prince Charles bought the farmhouse and cottages as his only property in Wales. The estate owners were usually absentee landlords, leasing out their mansions.

Rhyblid Farm was said to be a home of a descendant of the Myddfai physicians. Likewise the farms of Llwynmerdydd Feddyg and Llwynifan Feddyg, also still in existence today. There was a St David's church situated at Dôl Hywel, mentioned in a 1324 inventory for Talley Abbey. Any remains are probably now covered by the Usk Reservoir. There is a field named Waun Capel on what used to by Tycryd Farm, which could have been the site.

Esgair Llaethdy (the ridge of the dairy) where the Lady of the Lake lived with her sons, and Blaensawdde, both mentioned in the text, still exist. Blaensawdde Farm near Llanddeusant is early post-Medieval at least, and was the home of the mother of Rhiwallon. Llanddeusant is now dedicated to Simon and Jude but this is possibly a Norman rededication, as Teilo and David were supposed to have met there.

The present church of Llanfihangel ym Myddfai is said to have a stoup taken from St David's church at Dôl Hywel. Llanfihangel, the church of St Michael, dates from before 1284, when Edward I appropriated the right to appoint a clergyman. It is possibly upon a Celtic site, and may have been rededicated from an early Welsh saint, an extremely common Norman occurrence across Wales.

Nearby Glansevin was formerly called Llansevin, which attests to an early church, dedicated to an unknown saint, Sevin. (Perhaps St Savin of France?) It is thought that there has been a building on the site of Plas Glansevin for over a thousand years. There is a Welsh legend that Saint Marchell, mother of Brychan Brycheiniog, the 6th century king of Brycheiniog (Brecon), while on a journey to Ireland with an escort of 300 men, rested for one night at 'Llansevin'. From the 16th century until after World War II, Plas Glansevin was the seat of the Lloyd family, one of the oldest surviving families from the early peoples of Wales, dating back to Tewdwr Mawr (Tudor the Great). It is now a small hotel.

# THE MYDDFAI INITIATIVE

Myddfai is a hamlet rather than a village, three miles from Llandovery and surrounded by hills. Three streams meet here, as do six lanes, and there used to be a great horsefair. There were three pubs but none remain. There have been many incomers, mainly from England, so the Welsh language is no longer ubiquitous except among the older inhabitants. No less than 90% of the population growth in Wales comes from in-migration, so despite some incomers learning the language, it is slowly dying out as a first tongue all over Wales. Welsh culture is atrophying, and Welsh history is not taught in schools or colleges. Michael Gove's new initiative to teach history in schools is going to start with the Anglo-Saxons, pagan invaders who drove the Christian British back into Wales, ignoring hundreds of years of the history of the original British people. A vibrant culture and promotion of Welsh heritage can regenerate tourism and revitalise a decaying economy, which is failing in all socio-economic indicators against the rest of Britain and Europe.

In my *The Book of Welsh Saints* of 2000, I put forward a template of each community in Wales celebrating its local saint's day with a festival, and have been strongly involved with trying to put Glyndŵr Day on the map across Wales, without any political support whatever. I also organised a huge Celtic International Festival (CICFEST) in Cardiff Bay with Mike Johnston of the Coal Exchange and Derek Smith of Mabon. Additionally, with Richard Booth, the 'King' of Hay-on-Wye and President of the International Booktowns Association, I made a presentation to Barri councillors and committee people to make it the world's first international 'bookport'. There was little enthusiasm, and it seems that there is little impetus for change across Wales. Much of any economic dynamism comes from incomers. However, Myddfai has been, is, and can be an examplar of village regeneration for other rural communities and towns to follow.

Over fifty years ago, the Tŷ Talcen Charity was founded '*for the purposes of physical and mental training, recreation, social, moral and intellectual development or otherwise as may be found expedient to the inhabitants of the Parish of Myddfai.*' It has since expressed these aims as being for the whole of Wales, and developments over the past two years have focused attention of social and economic regeneration, especially through the Tŷ Talcen Project. With three chapels and a church serving a tiny and shrinking population, there are no longer any shops and many properties are second or holiday homes. The village successfully applied for the BIG Lottery Fund and Sarah Beeny's Village SOS BBC TV programme was filmed in Myddfai. The old village hall was demolished and a new one built, with a café/tearoom and interpretation centre, shop, auditorium, meeting room, toilets and kitchen. This acts as a community hub, holding talks, dances, exercise classes, exhibitions and the like. A recent event was organised by Dr Don Williams, on 2 July 2011, with talks upon the physicians and their descendants. Local craftspeople sell their wares in the shop, which stocks the full range of Myddfai Trading Company products. The Tŷ Talcen charity runs the new premises, staffed by local volunteers, and the Myddfai Trading Company was launched in 2010 with over eighty different projects sold under the Myddfai brand. Myddfai products include greetings cards, cosmetics, herbs, glassware, woodware, art, toiletries, pottery, etc. Prince Charles, who has a home in nearby Llwynywermod, has been extremely supportive, saying that *The aspirations of the Charity and Trading Company to develop a sustainable economic and social future have been put on a sound footing and I wish the entire community of Myddfai every success as it continues with this important development*'.

Myddfai Community Hall and Visitor Centre is opposite the church, and profits go to the Tŷ Talcen Charity (No.534022). Opening hours are March to October 10.30-5 Tuesday-Sunday; November-February 11-4 Wednesday-Saturday. It is closed upon Mondays except all Bank Holidays, apart from Christmas and New Year. The website is myddfai.com. The trading arm will help sustain the community hall & is now selling to over 90 outlets in Wales; some are fairly large such as The National Trust and CADW points. The community arm of the project is the hall, which has been built very sustainably. It has been designed to be the heart of the community, acting as a venue for all the community events. The community has taken its destination and localism as a brand, and the promotion of the traditions and stories sell both Myddfai products and the destination for tourism.

The point is that the project is keeping up its impetus. As Hugh Davies, project director, states, the Myddfai Project will always be '*built on the past, set in the present, but for the future*'. People are even more enthusiastic now that most of the hard work has been accomplished. A workshop in January 2010 promoted the vision of '*a vibrant community with reasons for families and young people to come and live locally.*' The local community is dedicated to ongoing progress towards this goal, and some of the ideas for development are: workspaces for starter businesses; the village being a hub of activity; more tourists and visitors (there have been 80,000 visitors to the new hall in around 18 months); a pub; affordable housing; working telephone box; more organised activities such as walks and guided tours; tennis court and playground area; provision for younger community members; outlet for farmers' produce; rural life museum; regular social events such as Myddfai Physicians' Festival; credit union; landscaping e.g. flower beds, hanging baskets; faster broadband.

There is a Carmarthenshire 'East tourism cluster' which includes the areas around Myddfai, Llanddeusant, Llandovery, Llandeilo and Llangathen. Llandeilo and Llandovery are excellent shopping centres with delicatessens, hotels, pubs etc. Llandeilo has Dinefwr Castle, Newton House and an exhibition on the Book of Teilo, now in Lichfield Cathedral, and Llandovery has the iconic stainless steel statue of Llywelyn ap Gruffydd Fychan outside its castle. It would be easy to make a guide for a week's touring, sightseeing, walking and shopping in such a historic and attractive area. The excellent Castle Hotel next to Llandovery's castle combines a sheep and cider festival with music from Wales at the end of September, and more such festivals are needed featuring local food, crafts, music and the like.

The Myddfai website tells us: *The Myddfai physicians practised medicine based on observation and aligned with Hippocratic principles. They believed that the patient was responsible for her own health and emphasized moderation and good sense with food, work, and sleeping habits. They utilized simple preparations (mostly poultices and infusions), preferred working with simples, and mainly used the plants growing around their home. It was peasant green pharmacy at its finest. They focused on the whole body rather than symptoms and conditions. As in many places, the knowledge and the herbal traditions of Myddfai are in jeopardy, threatened to be lost in historical obscurity. Luckily there's The Red Book of Hergest which has some documentation of their methods and practices. But even more exciting is that Welsh herbalist Lara Bernays is compiling an oral history of the native plant medicines of Myddfai (her hometown) in a series of community films called Myddfai Memories.'*

**8.4**

## MYDDFAI TRADING COMPANY

Its aim is to support economic activity and rural regeneration through its trading activity and is set up as a 'Social Enterprise' in 2010. It sells the products of local craftspeople, and was established with support from the Big Lottery Village SOS Fund. It works alongside its sister charity, Myddfai Tŷ Talcen, to raise awareness of the unique heritage and history of Myddfai, and of the impact that social enterprise can have for individuals, business and communities. Its products are sold in the village hall, the National Botanic Garden and in displays across Wales. It sells a range and gift packs of organic herbs, and tea towels, bone china mugs and aprons featuring Myddfai and its plants. There are also natural cosmetics, toiletries, silk art cards based upon the *Mabinogion*, cards based upon Welsh folk sayings and Myddfai, and Welsh and bilingual language greetings cards. There is also a range of herbal teas, beautifully packaged in traditional tin. Myddfai Trading Company won the top award of best Rural Enterprise 2010 in Wales. See myddfai.com for more details.

**8.5**

## VILLAGE SOS 2010/2011

HRH Prince Charles has written a foreword to the booklet *The Myddfai Story* praising its efforts *'to develop a sustainable economic and social future'*. The booklet relates: *'The village nestles in the foothills on the edge of the Brecon Beacons National Park. A traditional community with three chapels and a church serving a tiny population, Myddfai was in terminal decline with no shops, school or pub and a shrinking population, with many houses in the village becoming second or holiday homes. The only secular meeting place, the village hall, was no longer fit for purpose.'* Over ninety per cent of Welsh population growth in the last three decades has come from outside Wales. This, combined with the increase in holiday and second homes, has severely endangered the Welsh language (despite what politicians claim), and has been the greatest influx of incomers, possibly in the world. It is affecting the nature and character of Wales and Welshness. Against this background, villagers, many not native to the area, decided that community action was needed.

In May 2010, Hugh Davies, Les Griffith and business expert Jo Gideon presented a vision of a regenerated Myddfai to national heads of the Biog Lottery. BBC television filmed the progress of their creation of plans for a new community building, and the presenter Sarah Beeny interviewed residents.

Myddfai was successful in its application and received a £10,000 development grant and assistance with a detailed business plan. In July 2010 the Myddfai Trading Company was launched, and promoted sales of its product to the trade at Birmingham's International Autumn Fair. Volunteers assisted throughout the process. In September 2010, there was a special evening of memories and music in the old community hall before it was demolished. The new community centre, café and gift shop, designed by Huw Griffiths Architects and built by Doel and Rowlands has been a huge success, with a main auditorium seating 200 people. It was opened by Prince Charles and the Duchess of Cornwall on 30 June 2011.

The gift shop features products from local craftspeople, predominantly with a Welsh or local theme. The artist and printmaker responsible for the cover illustration, Judith Stroud, sells a range of postcards based upon the herbal remedies of the Physicians of Myddfai. She is inspired by Welsh heritage, producing prints of the wild flowers and landscapes of Wales, among other works. Some of her works, linocuts and details of her gallery can be found on the website www.judithstroud.co.uk.

## 8.6

## THE NATURAL HEALTHCARE CENTRE AND HERBAL DISPENSARY

In 2007 Lara Bean (née Lara Bernays) wrote the bilingual *Myddfai's Memories: Recipes & Remembered Remedies – A Guide to Myddfai's Living Heritage*. The booklet was produced as part of the oral history project *Milltir Sgwâr*, - 'a sense of belonging'. There is an accompanying DVD, and Lara's purpose was to examine what remained of Myddfai's herbal heritage and to get the people of Myddfai to share '*their memories of plants, people and places, allowing us to experience Myddfai through the eyes of the past and keep our unique heritage and valuable legacy alive.*' This is incredibly important work, which is being carried out in cultures across the world but less so here on our doorstep in Britain. Villagers not only remember local herbs being gathered and used, recommended by their forefathers, but continue to gather and use herbs as home remedies today. This is all part of the Myddfai tradition.

As a Celtic country Wales has a rich herbal heritage, Lara now collects remembered remedies across south west Wales, from the times when people collected what was on the land to cure themselves and their families. All the remedies collected are added to the *Remembered Remedies* archive at Kew Gardens as part of the project *Ethnomedica*. Lara leads walks, talks and workshops, sharing her knowledge of the names and discussing both traditional and modern uses. By sharing such information, Lara's aim is to keep this valuable knowledge alive, which is such an important part of our Welsh culture.

Growing up in Myddfai, herbs were an integral and '*incredible part*' of the local culture. She remembers when growing up that schoolchildren with a bad chest were given a teaspoon of blackcurrant juice and ground ivy, comfrey poultices were applied to sprains and nettles were part of the spring diet said to '*cleanse the blood*'. Inspired by this culture of using herbs, and fascinated by the modern scientific understanding and clinical application of this ancient art of medicinal plants, Lara went on to follow in the footsteps of The Physicians of

Myddfai and become a Medical Herbalist. Lara studied a science degree in Herbal Medicine at University of Westminster and is a Member of the National Institute of Medical Herbalists.

Lara says that Pant y Meddygon used to host more plants, but with grazing and a forestry plantation the landscape has taken its toll. Dôl Hywel, where the Usk Reservoir now lies, had rich red soil and a far greater variety of plants, but even more of the landscape has been lost to the Forestry Commission. She wishes to keep the Myddfai tradition alive, not to just archive material, so she practises herbal medicine and shares her knowledge, based upon a scientific education. Lara has travelled to China and America in search of herbal best practice, and now runs The Natural Healthcare Centre and Herbal Dispensary in the coastal village of Newport, Pembrokeshire. It is a group of fully qualified complementary healthcare professionals, offering a wide spectrum of therapies, with a holistic approach to improving health. With her family home in Myddfai Lara's roots remain in this magical village and she continues to return and work in Myddfai leading walks, talks and workshops.

## 8.7

## MYDDFAI HERBS

Myddfai Herbs was founded in Llandeilo thirty-five years ago by the Stella Byrne who has both Welsh and Irish ancestry. In 2001 she was joined by her husband Dylan Warren-Davis in the practice at Llandeilo. Stella has a BSc in microbiology and both are qualified members of the National Institute of Medical Herbalists, which was founded in 1864. Stella has been promoting herbal medicine and a holistic approach to illness across South Wales, teaching many current practitioners in the area through her workshops. She called the practice Myddfai Herbs to promote awareness of the use of medical plants and the rich herbal heritage of the medieval Physicians of Myddfai in the area.

While many drugs today are made from plant sources, it is medical herbalists who carry on the living tradition of the Physicians and often use the same herbs daily as those recorded in their writings.

She believes that the practice of taking and synthesising the active ingredient by withdrawing it from a plant ignores the effect of the whole plant, or how it works in combinations with other plants. The more a compound is refined, the more toxic it can become, because counter-balancing compounds in the same plant are discarded. Thus side-effects may be avoided by using the whole plant. For example Aspirin, used by many as an anti-inflammatory drug, can cause internal bleeding from the stomach. By contrast meadowsweet (*Filipendula ulmaria*), one of the original source herbs for the chemical used to make aspirin, has anti-inflammatory properties without causing this bleeding. In fact one of the principal uses of meadowsweet is for healing gastric ulceration and bleeding. In other words, the herb heals the very side-effect that the isolated drug causes. Herbalists are well trained in chemical structures and pharmacology of plant constituents.

Stella and Dylan believe, like this author, that the cartel of multinational pharmaceutical companies is mainly interested in patenting a particular compound's value in medicine to make windfall profits. Having worked in multinational companies, I can easily agree with this. Large companies exist to make profits, not to exist for consumer benefits. If, say, eating daffodil flowers halted the progress of senile dementia, this would receive no publicity. Instead, the active ingredient galantamine will be synthesised, patented and sold globally at artificially inflated prices until the patent expires. The 'dangers' of eating daffodil flowers would at the same time be sold into the media by PR campaigns with the promise of heavy advertising revenues.

There has recently been announcement by the MHRA against the use of Echinacea in children under 12 year olds. In response a survey conducted by members of the NIMH demonstrated that there have only been three cases of tentative minor side effects in 20,006 case histories, which suggests that the MHRA announcement is unfounded. Echinacea is known to be an active anti-viral plant, whereas synthetic drugs cannot be developed to adequately fight new and existing viruses.

The principal problem in health provision may be that many doctors are not holistic physicians, and are subject to constant lobbying from the pharmaceutical industry and its representatives. Many GPs are under severe time constraints, preventing them from being able to fully listen to and care for the needs of their patients. Local herbalists were greatly used and valued members of the community when doctors were charging fees. Only in the 1950s when the National Health Service provided free visits to doctors, did the practice of herbal medicine begin dying out in Wales, but it has seen a major revival over the last decade. Many GPs are now actively combining mainstream medicine with an alternative and complementary approach.

When Stella came to the area, many of her patients still remembered Dr Yemm of Ammanford, and Dr. Walters of Swansea who practised urine analysis. They were qualified doctors but throughout the Great Depression and after, gave free medical and herbal medicine services. Herbalists charged a penny a week for families when they were well and employed, but gave free treatment to the unemployed. Dr Yemm was particularly loved because there was no-one else in the Amman valley that would help working-class people for no fees. Aneurin Bevan is supposed to have had the idea for a National Health Service from such men.

In response to the EU Traditional Herbal Medicinal Products Directive which has sought to remove access to herbal products throughout Europe. Following massive public support for herbal medicine, the Department of Health announced forthcoming statutory recognition of medical herbalists, ensuring the public's continued access to herbal medicine in the UK. This legal recognition will do much to restore the public's confidence in the profession and the value of herbal medicine again after a decade of denigration before the Directive came into force. The legislation is due to be in place by April 2013.

Stella also makes the point that the environmental situation of the plant will affect its efficiency. Thus Welsh herbs have a specific signature dependent upon the soil, weather conditions, climate and the place where they are growing. The more healthy and abundant a plant grows in a particular area, the stronger its medicinal properties will be. Effectiveness is not just about genomes, but other factors as well. Stella and Dylan make the point that there are diminishing ecosystems across the world, leading to the loss of plant diversity. In Wales we have lost pristine deciduous forests, uplands, river valleys and peat bogs, much in the name of progress. In Culpeper's time, the mid-seventeenth century, as can be seen in his herbal, the parasitic broomrape was widespread, but has now almost totally disappeared because of modern farming methods. The diversity of plants is falling constantly because of intensive farming methods; in the past they assisted the immunity of animals. Cattle and sheep had a diverse diet of wild flowers, instead of just feeding on grass or artificial feeds. The repeated monoculture of grass (and other crops) causes the breakdown of soil structure and loss of its fertility. To compensate for loss of yields ever increasing amounts of chemical fertilisers are needed, which accentuates the depletion of minerals from the soil.

When livestock had wild herbs to feed on they would have built up their immune systems generally; however when they are sick they instinctively know which plants to feed upon them if they have access to them. The absence of wild herbs in the pasture is likely to be the main factor as to why infectious diseases such as TB and blue-tongue are increasing in farm animals. Because of this, cattle may be giving the TB to the badgers rather than the other way around. As a result badgers could be being made the scapegoats for the shortcomings of modern agricultural practices, and their slaughter is unlikely to solve this problem. The loss of the biodiversity, including plant, fungi, animal and insect species, in British meadows parallels the importance of loss of the biodiversity in tropical rainforests.

Stella and Dylan are also involved in an experimental project reintroducing 'weeds' such as eyebright and yellow rattle to a farm, to investigate whether this leads to an improvement in the health of livestock by reducing the monoculture of rye grass and allowing other species to become established.

The use of organo-phosphates (OP's) in insecticides upon nearly all farms does have profound health implications, not just to workers exposed to the chemicals. Organo-phosphates do not break down in the soil. As animals graze on the grass they ingest these compounds. In cattle they end up in the mammary tissue, and in turn enter our food chain through the milk and dairy products. Inside the body OP's mimic the action of oestrogen. One molecule of these xeno-oestrogens acts like 20 molecules of normal oestrogen. It is thought that the recent dramatic increase of breast cancers in women and prostate cancers in men are caused by oestrogen mimics derived from OP's in the food chain. 'Run-off' from the land washes OP's into the river systems, where they poison aquatic life and contribute to loss of fish habitat.

In 2010 Stella and Dylan using their combined 60 years experience of using herbs, formulated the recipes and developed the herbal teas range, made by the Myddfai Trading Company, which includes such blends as Physician's Treasure, Bardic Bliss, Llyn-y-Fantastic Tea, Ceredwen's Brew and Myddfai Magic. The names of the teas were intentionally chosen to pay homage to the Physicians of Myddfai. They continue to practise herbal medicine in Llandeilo. Myddfai Herbs has produced a superb interactive CD, *A Welsh Herbal: A Herbal Journey through he Culture and Places of Wales*, and *An English Herbal* is also in progress. Both will be available in book and electronic form in the future. See myddfaiherbs.co.uk for more information.

## 8.8

### THE NATIONAL BOTANIC GARDEN OF WALES

There is a herb garden of native plants at Llanarthne, just below the science centre, which was designed to contain many of the plants used by the Myddfai Physicians. The Apothecaries Garden has twelve named beds: Greco-Roman Medicine, Pharmacy, Herbal Medicine, Homeopathy, Aromatics, Culinary, Economics, Physicians of Myddfai, Doctrine of Signatures, Superstition & Symbolism, World Medicine and Strewing Herbs. Apothecaries across Wales and beyond would have used these plants to treat all manner of illnesses. The landscaped park and gardens of the original 18th-century Middleton Hall estate are the setting for national botanic garden which opened to the public in 2000 amid great public acclamation. Near the entrance to the garden is a '*Welsh landscape*' with native meadows and woodlands. Then comes the Broadwalk, over 700 feet long, with a rill which runs down through a geological display of Welsh rocks. The garden's collection of herbaceous plants is planted along its edges, with narrow paths leading into the plantings to facilitate access. There is also a Japanese garden and a herb garden, named after the Physicians of Myddfai, with an ethnobotanical collection of native pharmacological Welsh plants. It is the Great Glasshouse which has received most of the adulation, because it is a stunning piece of architecture - the largest single-span glasshouse in the world. It concentrates upon the Mediterranean floras of the world - cheaper to maintain than tropical floras - including Chile, California, south-west Australia, South Africa, the Mediterranean basin and the Canary Isles.

The wonderful Walled Garden is also interesting as it is a '*phylogeny garden*', which reflects evolutionary time. The earliest flowering plants appeared before dinosaurs became extinct 65 million years ago. Thus as you walk out from the centre, you move from the earliest plant families such as water lilies in pools, magnolias and buttercups, to the families that have more recently evolved – legumes, daisies and grasses. Plant lineages are traceable through their DNA, and the garden is designed to be 'a snapshot in evolutionary time'. Research is being carried out into the rare plants of Wales, such as the spreading bellfower, whorled caraway, meadow thistle and Ley's whitebeam, in order to ensure their survival in certain locations

Dr. Natasha de Vere is leading research at the National Botanic Garden on plant sciences, including their medical properties. Wales is the first nation in the world to have DNA barcoded all of its native flowering plants and conifers, opening up huge potential for research into biodiversity conservation and human health. The Welsh flora DNA barcodes are freely available on the Barcode of Life Database for use by researchers around the world. We can now identify any plant species in Wales from the tiniest fragment of leaf, seed or pollen grain, using DNA barcoding as a unique identifier for that species. There are many potential applications, for example: to understand why pollinators are endangered; to find out what plants bees have visited to make honey; to help to monitor the effects of hay fever by being able to identify exactly what pollen is in the atmosphere; to improve animal health by analysing the exact composition of the diet of livestock in pastures; and to provide quality control for plant-based products such as herbal medicines by identifying the constituent components. All the 1143 species of native flowers in Wales have been placed upon a DNA database, and Wales is the first country in the world to DNA barcode its native flora. It is part of the international effort to DNA barcode all living things.

The International Barcode of Life Project is the largest biodiversity genomics initiative ever undertaken, with more than 25 nations working together throughout the world. Cardiff University's School of Pharmacy has been analysing honey sent in from across the UK, checking for honey with the potential to counter hospital acquired infections MRSA and Clostridium Difficile. Then the National Botanic Garden in Llanarthne, Carmarthenshire, profiled the DNA of the most powerful honeys, checking for the plants which contributed. The scientists have found that honey from one source is better than others at treating infections. By DNA testing it was found that the bees at hives near Tywyn produced this superior honey, and that their main source of pollen was bluebells and galium. Thus scientists are now trying to isolate the active ingredient for treating MRSA.

A previous study found that daffodils were useful in the treatment of dementia, but only grown in certain soils and a certain height above sea level. Daffodils began to be grown and cropped around Myddfai, but the active ingredient is now being processed from chemicals. Trained herbalists would say that this is for the pharmaceutical companies to obtain patents and charge high prices, and that isolating a substance leads to side effects. They would affirm that the whole plant is better at treating an illness. For visitors to Wales, the nearby restored Aberglasney Gardens are a delight, and for those nearer to Cardiff, the walled Cowbridge Physic Garden, set into the medieval town walls, is a superb attraction. It would be wonderful if Myddfai would establish a walled herb garden to attract visitors, and reinstitute the annual June Horse Fair.

# REFERENCES

Breverton, Terry *Breverton's Complete Herbal* Quercus 2011

Byrne, Stella and Warren-Davis, Dylan *A Welsh Herbal* interactive CD-Rom, published by Myddfai Herbs

Cule, John editor *Wales and Medicine* The British Society for the History of Medicine 1973

Cule, John *The Court Mediciner in the Welsh Laws*, Journal of the History of Medicine 21 (1966)

Fenton, Richard Tours in Wales 1804-1813

*Geiriadur Prifysgol Cymru* [Welsh Dictionary] online from Aberystwyth University

Griffiths, P. Rhys, BS, MB *Abstract of a Paper on Early Welsh Medicine*, The British Medical Journal 27 October 1888

Henderson, Heather M., *The Physicians of Myddfai: the Welsh Herbal Tradition*, Botanical Journal of Scotland 46.4 (1994), 623-7

James, David B., *Myddfai, its Land and Peoples*, Aberystwyth 1991

Kenward, James. *Ab Ithel: an account of the life and writings of the Rev. John Williams Ab Ithel, M.A., late Rector of Llanymowddwy, Merioneth*. Tenby: London: R. Mason; W. Kent & Co., 1871. The greater portion of this work (to page 192) was originally published in the form of editorial articles in the *Cambrian Journal* of 1862-3-4

Lewis, Gwyneth *Edward Willams and Eighteenth Century Forgeries* – unpublished thesis Oxford University 1990

Owen, Morfydd E., Meddygion Myddfai: a Preliminary Survey of Some Medieval Medical Writing in Welsh, Studia Celtica 10/11 (1975-6), )

Owen, Morfydd E., The Medical Books of Medieval Wales and the Physicians of Myddfai, The Carmarthenshire Antiquary 1995

Owen, Morfydd E., *Meddygon Myddfai: who were they and what did they know?* The Carmarthenshire Antiquary xlviii 2011

Pughe, John translator and Rev. John Williams ab Ithel editor, The Physicians of Myddvai; Meddygon Myddfai, or the medical practice of the celebrated Rhiwallon and the sons, of Myddvai, in Caermarthenshire, Physicians to Rhys Gryg, Lord of Dynevor and Ystrad Towy, about the middle of the thirteenth century. From ancient mss. in the libraries of Jesus College, Oxford, Llanover, and Tonn; with an English translation; and the Legend of the Lady of Llyn y Van. The Welsh MSS. Society, D.J. Roderic, Llandovery; Longman & Co. London 1860-61

Turner, I. and T.D.,*Ymarfer Fferylliaeth Meddygon Myddfai (The Pharmacy of the Physicians of Myddfai)*. Welsh School of Pharmacy 1995

Williams, Dr. Donald *Meddygon Myddfai: a modern cohort*, The Carmarthenshire Antiquary xlviii 2011

Withey, Alan *Medicine and Mortality in Early Modern Monmouthshire: The Commonplace Book of John Gwin of Llangwm*, Welsh History Review June 2008

# OTHER BOOKS BY TERRY BREVERTON

1. 'AN A-Z of WALES and the WELSH' (300 pages) March 2000 ISBN 0715407341 - published Christopher Davies – *'the first encyclopaedia of Wales'*; *'a comprehensive anthology'*

2. 'THE SECRET VALE OF GLAMORGAN' (230 pages) June 2000 ISBN 190352900X supported by a Millennium Commission grant for local parishes *'a historian's delight'*

3. 'THE BOOK OF WELSH SAINTS' (606 pages) September 2000 ISBN 1903529018 hardback – 'this book is a really extraordinary achievement: a compilation of tradition, topography and literary detective work that can have few rivals. I have enjoyed browsing it immensely, and have picked up all sorts of new lines to follow up' – Archbishop Rowan Williams; 'an enormous work of research'

4. '100 GREAT WELSHMEN' (376 pages) May 2001 ISBN 1903529034 Welsh Books Council **Welsh Book of the Month** *'painstaking research'*; *'a fascinating compendium'* (New Edition 2005)

5. '100 GREAT WELSH WOMEN' (304 pages) ISBN 1903529042 September 2001 *'an absolute must for all those who value their Welsh heritage'*

6. 'THE PATH TO INEXPERIENCE' (158 pages) ISBN 1003529077 March 2002 *'magnificent, compassionate and moving'*

7. 'THE WELSH ALMANAC' (320 pages) ISBN 1903529107 WBC **Welsh Book of the Month** July 2002 hardback 'a tremendous undertaking'; 'it will take its place on the bookshelf with other important works of reference'

8. 'THE BOOK OF WELSH PIRATES AND BUCCANEERS' (388 pages) ISBN 1903529093 WBC **Welsh Book of the Month** April 2003 *'exemplary'*; *'an immense work of great scholarship'; effectively a study of the whole genre of piracy'*

9. 'GLAMORGAN SEASCAPE PATHWAYS' (144 pages) ISBN 1903529115 June 2003 supported by a Millennium Commission WCVA Arwain grant. **Fellow of the Millennium Award** (FMA) *'fascinating'*

10/11. 'BLACK BART ROBERTS – THE GREATEST PIRATE OF THEM ALL' (254 pages) ISBN 1903529123 March 2004 (published abridged as BLACK BART ROBERTS – THE GREATEST PIRATE OF THEM ALL by Pelican Publishing USA [166 pages] ISBN 1-58980-233) *'a must read for anyone interested in pirates'*

12/13. 'THE PIRATE HANDBOOK' (290 pages) ISBN 1903529131 Autumn 2004 (published abridged in USA by Pelican Publishing 2004 as THE PIRATE DICTIONARY [192 Pages] ISBN 9781589802438) - WBC **Welsh Book of the Month** *'this wonderful sourcebook is an absolute must'; 'a vitally important addition to the canon of naval literature'*

14. Introduction and 3 major poems in 600th anniversary commemorative book on Owain Glyn Dŵr, (98 pages) ISBN 0862437385 published by Y Lolfa June 2004.

15/16. 'SIR HENRY MORGAN – THE GREATEST BUCCANEER OF THEM ALL' (174 pages) ISBN 1903529174 Spring 2005 – WBC **Welsh Book of the Month** (published abridged by Pelican USA as ADMIRAL SIR HENRY

MORGAN – KING OF THE BUCCANEERS [120 pages] ISBN 9781589802773

17. '100 GREAT WELSHMEN' (NEW EDITION) (432 pages) ISBN 1903529034 2005 'a veritable goldmine of a book'; '*a massive treasure chest of facts and figures which no collector of books on Wales can overlook.*' 2006

18. 'WELSH SAILORS OF WORLD WAR II' (with Phil Carradice) (448 pages) ISBN 9781903529195 March 1st, 2007 - WH Smith **Welsh Book of the Month** '*an account worthy of the pen of Xenophon*'

19/20. 'THE FIRST AMERICAN NOVEL: THE JOURNAL OF PENROSE, SEAMAN BY WILLIAM WILLIAMS, & THE BOOK, THE AUTHOR AND THE LETTERS IN THE LILLY LIBRARY BY TERRY BREVERTON' (446 pages) ISBN 9781903529201 August 30th 2007. This is '*The Journal of Lewellin Penrose – Seaman*', and an autobiography of William Williams - **Everett Helm Visiting Fellowship Award** of Indiana University. To be published by Quercus, London

21. Introduction and Annotated Edition of Exquemelin's 'THE BUCCANEERS OF AMERICA' (192 pages) August 2008 – commissioned July 2007 for Quarto Publishing. Consultant editor and writer: 'THE ILLUSTRATED PIRATE DIARIES: A REMARKABLE EYEWITNESS ACCOUNT OF CAPTAIN MORGAN AND THE BUCCANEERS", for worldwide distribution by Apple Press (UK 9781845433000), New Holland (Australia) and Collins (USA 0061584487 and 9780061584480). *Das Piraten-Tagebuch* (trans. Karen Schuler & Henning Dedekind; *Dzienniki Piratow* etc.

22. IMMORTAL WORDS: HISTORY'S MOST MEMORABLE QUOTATIONS AND THE STORIES BEHIND THEM 384pp Quercus History/Borders – August 2009 (978-1-84866-0045) - the USA version sold 25,000 copies in 2 weeks, and it is being sold internationally

23. OWAIN GLYNDŴR – THE STORY OF THE LAST PRINCE OF WALES (978-1-84868-3280) – 192pp July 2009 Amberley

24. WALES - A HISTORICAL COMPANION (978-1-84848-326-4) — 360pp November 2009 Amberley Publishing

25/26. BREVERTON'S NAUTICAL CURIOSITIES – A BOOK OF THE SEA 384pp April 2010 (978-1-84724-766-6) Quercus UK and BREVERTON'S NAUTICAL COMPENDIUM Globe Pequot USA 2010

27. IMMORTAL LAST WORDS – HISTORY'S MOST MEMORABLE DYING REMARKS, DEATHBED DECLARATIONS AND FINAL FAREWELLS 384pp Quercus/Borders (978-1-84916-478-8) September 2010 (published in Holland as Onsterfelikje Laatste Woorden)

28. 1000 WELSH HERITAGE SITES 324pp (978-1-84868-991-6) – Amberley Publishing – October 2010

29. BREVERTON'S PHANTASMAGORIA – A COMPENDIUM OF MONSTERS, MYTHS AND LEGENDS 384pp (978-0-85738-337-2) Quercus 7 July 2011

30. BREVERTON'S COMPLETE HERBAL – A BOOK OF REMARKABLE PLANTS AND THEIR USES – BASED ON NICOLAS CULPEPER'S THE ENGLISH PHYSITIAN OF 1652 AND COMPLEAT HERBALL OF 1653 (978-0-85738-336-5) – 384pp Quercus 29 September 2011

31. I HAVE A DREAM – INSPIRING WORDS AND THOUGHTS FROM THE WORLD'S GREATEST LEADERS (978-1-84866-134-9) 384pp Quercus January 2012

32. BIRD WATCHING: A PRACTICAL GUIDE WITH PHOTOS AND FACTS (978-1-4454-8868-4) Parragon USA – the largest non-fiction illustrated book publisher in the world 2012

33. BACKYARD BIRDS Parragon USA 2012

34. BREVERTON'S ENCYCLOPEDIA OF INVENTIONS – a compendium of technological leaps, groundbreaking discoveries and scientific breakthroughs that changed the world 384pp (978-1-78087-239-1) Quercus May 2012

35. THE WELSH – THE BIOGRAPHY Amberley – November 2012

36. THE PHYSICIANS OF MYDDFAI – Cambria Books November 2012

37. THE JOURNAL OF PENROSE, SEAMAN – Cambria Books 2012

38. THE WHITE INDIANS – 2013

39. THE ORIGINS OF THE CELTS - 2013

Four childrens' pop-up books – Here Comes Tow Truck, Here Comes Bulldozer, Here Comes Dump Truck, Here Comes Fire Truck, Grosset & Dunlap USA 1992

Lightning Source UK Ltd.
Milton Keynes UK
UKOW051340261112

202783UK00001B/6/P

9 780957 245990